S0-AEF-943

SOLUTIONS MANUAL FOR

GENERAL CHEMISTRY

PRINCIPLES AND STRUCTURES 4/E

James Brady
Gerard Humiston

Larry Peck
Texas A&M University

JOHN WILEY & SONS
NEW YORK CHICHESTER BRISBANE TORONTO SINGAPORE

ISBN 0 471 80680 3
Printed in the United States of America

10 9 8 7 6 5 4

PREFACE

This Solutions Manual has been prepared as a supplement to GENERAL CHEMISTRY - PRINCIPLES AND STRUCTURE, FOURTH EDITION by James Brady and Gerard Humiston. The textbook is an excellent introduction to modern general chemistry. A thorough understanding of general chemistry should also include the ability to work problems and answer questions related to the principles and concepts presented. For many students the most difficult part of science is the development of the ability to utilize knowledge in new situations.

Through the use of the textbook and this solutions manual, this author hopes that students will improve their problem-solving skills while learning a considerable amount of chemistry. Knowledge gained and problem-solving skills acquired in a general chemistry course should prove valuable in subsequent science and technical courses as well as assisting in preparing students for a wide variety of professions.

Many of the problems can be answered (solved) in more than one way. I encourage students to develop solutions that they understand. For consistency I have striven to follow the methods used by the authors of the textbook (Brady and Humiston). Where practical, I have striven to include dimensions and to show only the correct number of significant figures (In some problems an extra digit is carried in intermediate steps). I believe that students will find this book beneficial during their study of general chemistry. To gain the most benefit from this book, one should view it as a learning resource and not just as a place to go for answers. Students should always strive to solve each question first without using this book. Then, when the solution given in this book is referred to, the student should develop not only a better understanding of the chemistry associated with the question, but also increase skills in recalling and applying scientific facts.

I wish to thank Drs. Frank Kolar and Kuniyasu Tatsumoto for their tremendous assistance in proofreading and checking this manual and my family (Sandra, Molly and Marci) for their typing and support during the production of this manual.

Larry Peck
Chemistry Department
Texas A&M University

CONTENTS

1 INTRODUCTION

1.1 A law is a generalized statement of facts that has been obtained by experiment. Theories attempt to explain how nature behaves in the operation of laws.

1.2 A doctor uses the results of lab tests and a patient's symptoms (observation) to diagnose the patient's disease (hypothesis). Treatment with various medications is then used to test the diagnosis.

1.3 Quantitative observations result in numerical data while qualitative observations do not have numbers associated with them. Quantitative measurements are more useful because they provide more information.

1.4 Data are the bits of information obtained from experiments and may be classified as either qualitative or quantitative.

1.5 Significant figures indicate the reliability of measurements.

1.6 Precision refers to how closely two measurements of the same quantity come to each other while accuracy refers to how close an experimental observation lies to the actual value.

1.7

Number (measured)	Number of significant figures
1.0370	**5**
0.000417	**3**
0.00309	**3**
100.1	**4**
9.0010	**5**

1.8 (a) Speed = $\frac{346.2 \text{ miles}}{6.27 \text{ hr}}$ = **55.215311 miles /hr.**

(b) The maximum uncertainty in the distance traveled is **± 0.1 miles.**

(c) The maximum uncertainty in the time is **± 0.01 hr.**

(d) If the distance is 346.3, the calculated speed would be 55.231. This shows a difference in the second decimal place. If the time is 6.26, the calculated speed would be 55.127. This shows a difference in the first decimal place. Either error is possible; therefore, the uncertainty of the calculated speed cannot be less than ±0.1.

1.9 (a) 1,250 = **1.25×10^3** (b) 13,000,000 = **1.3×10^7**

(c) 60,230,000,000,000,000,000,000 = **6.023×10^{22}**

(d) **2.1457×10^5** (e) **3.147×10**

1.10 (a) **4.0×10^{-4}** (b) **3×10^{-10}** (c) **2.146×10^{-3}**

(d) **3.28×10^{-5}** (e) **9.1×10^{-13}**

1.11 (a) 3×10^{10} = **30,000,000,000** (b) 2.54×10^{-5} = **0.0000254**

(c) 122×10^{-2} = **1.22** (d) 3.4×10^{-7} = **0.00000034**

(e) 0.0325×10^6 = **32,500**

1.12 (a) **3.0×10^3 m** (b) **3.00×10^3 m**

(c) 3,000 m x 100 cm /m = 300,000 cm or **3.0×10^5 cm** (to 2 sign. figures)

1.13 (a) 2.41 (3 signicant figures) x 3.2 (2 signicant figures) = **7.7** (2 sign. figures)

(b) 4.025 x 18.5 = 7.33 x 10 or **73.3** (c) **0.785** (d) **3.478** (e) **81.4**

1.14 (a) **1.638×10^9** (b) **2.16×10^9** (c) **4.1970×10^6** (d) **8.5×10**

(e) **1.00**

1.15 (a) $(341.7 - 22) + (0.00224 \times 814005) = (320) + (1.82 \times 10^3) =$ **$\underline{2.14 \times 10^3}$**

(b) **$\underline{1.21 \times 10^4}$** (c) $(3.53 \div 0.084) - (14.8 \times 0.046) = 42 - 0.68 =$ **$\underline{41}$**

(d) **$\underline{5.9}$** (e) $(4.15 + 82.3) \times (0.024 + 3.000) = 86.4 \times 3.024 =$ **$\underline{261}$**

(f) $0.2510 \times (15.50 - 12.75) = 0.2510 \times 2.75 =$ **$\underline{0.690}$**

1.16 (a) $(3.42 \times 10^8) \times (2.14 \times 10^6) =$ **$\underline{7.32 \times 10^{14}}$**

(b) $(1.025 \times 10^6) \times (14.8 \times 10^{-3}) =$ **$\underline{1.52 \times 10^4}$**

(c) $(143.7) \times (84.7 \times 10^{16}) =$ **$\underline{1.22 \times 10^{20}}$**

(d) $(5274) \times (0.33 \times 10^{-7}) =$ **$\underline{1.7 \times 10^{-4}}$**

(e) $(8.42 \times 10^{-7}) \times (3.211 \times 10^{-19}) =$ **$\underline{2.70 \times 10^{-25}}$**

1.17 (a) $(12.45 \times 10^6) \div (2.24 \times 10^3) =$ **$\underline{5.56 \times 10^3}$**

(b) $822 \div 0.028 =$ **$\underline{2.9 \times 10^4}$**

(c) $(635.4 \times 10^{-5}) \div (42.7 \times 10^{-14}) =$ **$\underline{1.49 \times 10^{10}}$**

(d) $(31.3 \times 10^{-12}) \div (8.3 \times 10^{-6}) =$ **$\underline{3.8 \times 10^{-6}}$**

(e) $(0.74 \times 10^{-9}) \div (825.3 \times 10^{18}) =$ **$\underline{9.0 \times 10^{-31}}$**

1.18 (a) $(8.3 \times 10^{-6}) \times (4.13 \times 10^{-7}) \div (5.411 \times 10^{-12}) =$ **$\underline{6.3 \times 10^{-1}}$**

(b) $[(3.125 \times 10^{-6}) + (5.127 \times 10^{-5})] \times (6.72 \times 10^8) = (5.440 \times 10^{-5}) \times$

$(6.72 \times 10^8) =$ **$\underline{3.66 \times 10^4}$**

(c) $[14.39 + (2.43 \times 10^1)] \div 1275 = 38.7 \div 1275 =$ **$\underline{3.04 \times 10^{-2}}$**

(d) $[(1.583 \times 10^{-4}) - (0.00255)] \times [(142.3) + (0.257 \times 10^2)] =$

$(-2.39 \times 10^{-3}) \times (1.680 \times 10^2) =$ **$\underline{-4.02 \times 10^{-1}}$**

(e) $(0.0000425) \div [0.0008137 + (2.65 \times 10^{-5})] =$ **$\underline{5.06 \times 10^{-2}}$**

1.19 There is an **infinite number** of significant figures in each of the numbers. They are called exact numbers.

1.20 The units grams and milliliters are more appropriate in the laboratory because of the size (small) of the quantities used.

1.21 (a) $1.40 \text{ m} \times \frac{100 \text{ cm}}{1 \text{ m}} = \mathbf{1.40 \times 10^2 \text{ cm}}$

(b) $2800 \text{ mm} \times \frac{1 \text{ m}}{1{,}000 \text{ mm}} = \mathbf{2.8 \text{ m}}$ (if 2800 has only two signicant figures)

(c) $185 \text{ mL} \times \frac{1 \text{ L}}{1{,}000 \text{ mL}} = \mathbf{0.185 \text{ L}}$ (d) $18 \text{ g} \times \frac{1 \text{ kg}}{1{,}000 \text{ g}} = \mathbf{0.018 \text{ kg}}$

(e) $10 \text{ yd}^2 \times (3 \text{ ft /yd})^2 \times (12 \text{ in. /ft})^2 \times (1 \text{ m /39.37 in.})^2 = \mathbf{8.4 \text{ m}^2}$
(10 yd^2 is assumed to have 2 sign. figures)

(f) $100 \text{ miles} \times \frac{5280 \text{ ft}}{\text{mi}} \times \frac{12 \text{ in.}}{\text{ft}} = \mathbf{6.34 \times 10^6 \text{ in}}$. (if 100 miles is assumed to be 3 sign. figures)

(g) $\frac{20 \text{ ft}}{\text{s}} \times \frac{1 \text{ mi}}{5280 \text{ ft}} \times \frac{60 \text{ s}}{\text{min}} \times \frac{60 \text{ min}}{\text{hr}} = \mathbf{14 \text{ mi /hr}}$ (20 ft /s is assumed to be 2 sign. figures)

(h) $1 \text{ mi}^3 \times (5280 \text{ ft /mi})^3 \times (12 \text{ in. /ft})^3 \times (1 \text{ m /39.37 in.})^3 = \mathbf{4 \times 10^9 \text{ m}^3}$

(i) $\frac{40 \text{ mi}}{\text{hr}} \times \frac{5280 \text{ ft}}{\text{mi}} \times \frac{12 \text{ in.}}{\text{ft}} \times \frac{1 \text{ m}}{39.37 \text{ in.}} \times \frac{100 \text{ cm}}{\text{m}} \times \frac{1 \text{ hr}}{60 \text{ min}} \times \frac{1 \text{ min}}{60 \text{ s}} = \mathbf{1.8 \times 10^3 \text{ cm /s}}$

(j) $25 \text{ L} \times 1000 \text{ cm}^3 \text{ /L} \times (1 \text{ dm /10 cm})^3 = \mathbf{25 \text{ dm}^3}$

1.22

	prefix	power of ten	symbol
(a)	pico	10^{-12}	p
(b)	mega	10^{6}	M
(c)	centi	10^{-2}	c
(d)	nano	10^{-9}	n
(e)	kilo	10^{3}	k

1.23 The freezing point and boiling point of water are chosen as the reference temperatures for practical experimental reasons. In each case water can exist as a mixture of two phases and will maintain a constant temperature while heat is added or removed until one of the phases is converted into the other. This allows time to accurately mark the thermometer immersed in the mixture.

1.24 (a) **nm** (b) **mm** (c) **mg** (d) **cm** (e) **μL** (f) **L** or **dm^3**

1.25 F = m x a, therefore, **$N = kg \times m \times s^{-2}$**

1.26 **For the Pferdburper:** 10 km /1 L x 1 L /1.057 qt x 4 qt /gal x 1000 m /km x 39.37 in. /m x 1 ft /12 in. x 1 mile /5280 ft = **24 miles /gal**. **Therefore, the Pferdburper is better than the Smokebelcher and its 21 miles /gal.**

1.27 35 miles /hr x (5280 ft /mile) x (12 in./ft) x (1 m /39.37 in.) x (1km /1000 m) = **56 km /hr**

1.28 4.3 miles x (5280 ft /mile) x 12 in./ft x 1 m /39.37 in.x 1 km /1000 m = **6.9 km**

1.29 142 thrubs /wk x 1 /14 x 1 lb potatoes /2 thrubs x 52 wk /yr = **260 lb potatoes / year**

1.30 [30°C x (9 /5)] + 32 = **86°F** [1983°C x (9 /5)] + 32 = **3601°F**

1.31 (5 /9) x (6152°F - 32) = **3400°C** 3400°C + 273 = **3673 K**

1.32 [(9 /5) x (-78°C)] + 32 = **-108°F** -78°C + 273 = **195 K**

1.33 (5 /9) x (98.6°F - 32) = **37.0°C** [(9 /5) x (39°C)] + 32 = **102°F**

1.34 One can derive the formula **°N=(°C - 80) x (100°N /138°C)**. Using this formula, the f.p. of water (0°C) would be equal to (0 - 80) x (100 /138) or **-58°N** and the b.p.of water (100°C) would be equal to (100 - 80) x (100 /138) or **14°N**.

1.35 The normal oral body temperature is 98.6°F. Such a thermometer could only be used to determine a temperature with a minimum uncertainty of ±1°F.

1.36 An <u>extensive property</u> is one that depends on the size of the sample used. An <u>intensive property</u> is one that is independent of the size of the sample used.

Extensive Properties	Intensive Properties
Force (weight), length, number of atoms	Freezing point, color, specific heat

1.37 Some properties that differ for a copper penny and a piece of window glass are density, color, luster, transparency, electrical conductivity, malleability, reactivity with sulfur and reactivity with nitric acid. Both have the property of retaining a constant volume and are incompressible. Although both may seem to be solids, glass is actually a liquid which flows very slowly requiring years at common temperatures to show a change in shape.

1.38 The <u>mass</u> of an object is a measure of its resistance to a change in velocity and is a measure of the amount of matter in that object. <u>Weight</u> is the force with which an object of a certain mass is attracted by gravity to the earth (or to some other body such as the moon).The mass of an object does not vary from place to place; it is the same regardless of where it is measured.

1.39 **(a)** Physical property of heptane: a liquid, forms a heterogeneous mixture with water and floats on water. **(b)** Chemical property of heptane: flammable, vapors burn explosively when mixed with air (oxygen) and a spark is applied.

1.40 Density is the ratio of an object's mass to its volume. Specific gravity is the ratio of the object's density to the density of water. Units for density are g /mL; specific gravity has no units.

1.41 Density = 14.3 g /8.46 cm^3 = **1.69 g /cm^3**

1.42 D = mass /vol. = 50.8 g /(36.2 mL - 25.0 mL) = **4.54 g /mL**

1.43 Vol. of cyl. = area x length = π x r^2 x length = 3.14 x $(1.24 \text{ cm})^2$ x 4.75 cm = 22.9 cm^3 Therefore, density = 104.2 g /22.9 cm^3 = **4.55 g /cm^3**

1.44 **(a)** 11.35 g /cm^3 = ? g /12.0 cm^3 Therefore, mass = **136 g**

(b) 11.35 g /cm^3 = 155 g / ? cm^3 Therefore, volume = **13.7 cm^3**

1.45 **(a)** 1.492 g /mL = 10.00 g /? mL Therefore, vol. = **6.702 mL**

(b) 1.492 g /mL = ? g /10.00 mL Therefore, mass = **14.92 g**

1.46 **(a)** Mass of water in the pycnometer is 34.914 g - 25.296 g = 9.618 g. Therefore, the vol. of the pycnometer can be calculated from the mass of water and its density. D = mass /volume

0.9970 g /mL = 9.618 g /? mL Volume = **9.647 mL**

(b) Density of unknown = (33.485 g - 25.296 g) ÷ 9.647 mL= **0.8489 g /mL**

1.47 **(a)** **500 numerical values** **(b)** **105 numerical values**

1.48 **(a)** Sp. grav. of X = density of X ÷ density of water

Sp. grav. of isopropyl alcohol = 6.56 lb /gal ÷ 8.34 lb /gal = **0.787**

(b) Sp. grav. of X times density of water = density of X

0.787 x 1.00 g /mL = **0.787 g /mL**

1.49 Sp. grav. of propylene glycol times the density of water = the density of propylene glycol. Density of propylene glycol = 1.04 x 8.34 lb /gal = 8.67 lb /gal. The weight of 10,000 gal. of propylene glycol would be 8.67 lb /gal x 10,000 gal = **8.67×10^4 lb**

1.50 The density of each is: #1= 275 g÷ 275 mL =1.00 g /mL, #2= 389 g÷ 245 mL = 1.59 g /mL and #3 =299 g÷ 265 mL = 1.13. Since the density of the contents of the first beaker is the closest to that of water, the secret agent should have selected the **first beaker**.

1.51 Potential energy is the energy due to position of particles that either attract or repel each other. Kinetic energy is the energy due to motion; K.E. = $1/2\ mv^2$.

1.52 An endothermic process absorbs heat (energy) as it proceeds. An exothermic process emits heat (energy) as it proceeds.

1.53 Repulsive

1.54 Heat is a form of energy, whereas the measure of the intensity of heat is known as temperature.

1.55 cal /g °C or J /g °C. For water, sp. ht. = 1.000 cal /g °C or 4.184 J /g °C. Water has the largest specific heat of any common substance. During the winter the water loses some of its heat and prevents the surrounding land masses from becoming too cold. During the summer, the water can absorb large amounts of heat and prevent surrounding land masses from becoming too hot.

1.56 Kinetic energy (K.E.) = (1/2) mv^2

K.E. = (1/2) x 4500 kg x $(1.79\ m/s)^2$ = 7.21 x 10^3 kg m^2/s^2

Since one joule (J) = 1 kg m^2/s^2, 7.21 x 10^3 kg m^2/s^2 = **7.21 x 10^3 J**

1 cal = 4.184 J; therefore, 7.21 x 10^3J x 1 cal ÷ 4.184J = **1.72 x 10^3 cal**

1.57 K.E. = (1/2) mv^2= (1/2) x145 lb x $(15.3\ mi/hr)^2$ x $(5280\ ft/mi)^2$ x

$(12\ in./ft)^2$ x $(1\ m/39.37\ in.)^2$ x $(1\ hr/60\ min)^2$ x $(1\ min/60\ sec)^2$ x

454 g /1 lb x 1 kg /10^3g = 1.5398 x 10^3 kg m^2/s^2 = **1.54 x 10^3 J** or **1.54 kJ**

1.58 K.E. = (1/2) mv^2 = (1/2) x 255 kg x $(80.0 \times 10^3\ m/3600\ sec)^2$ =

6.30 x 10^4 J or **63.0 kJ**

1.59 K.E. = (1/2) x 2.4 ton x 2000 lb /ton x 0.454 kg /lb x (35 mi /hr x 5280 ft /mi x

12 in. /ft x 1 m /39.37 in. x 1 hr /3600 $sec)^2$ = (1/2) x 2179 kg x $(15.65\ m\ s^{-1})^2$

= **2.7 x 10^5 J** 2.7 x 10^5 J x 1 cal ÷ 4.184 J = 6.4 x 10^4 cal

6.4 x 10^4 cal x 1 g H_2O x 1°C /cal x 1 /10°C = **6.4 x 10^3 g H_2O**

1.60 K.E. = (1/2) mv^2

K.E.=(1/2) x1500 kg x $(60\ m/s)^2$ x (1J /kg m^2/s^2) x (1 cal /4.184J) =

6.5 x 10^5 cal

1.61 Work = force x distance (510 kg m /s^2) x 40 m x (J x s^2 /kg m^2) =

2.0 x 10^4 J

1.62 Specific heat of water is 1.00 cal /(g x °C) or 4.184 J /(g x °C). The change in temperature of 150 g of H_2O when 35.0 cal are removed will be: [35.0 cal x (1 g x °C /cal)] x (1 /150 g) = 0.233°C. Since energy is being removed, the

(1.62 continued)

temperature will decrease or, stated another way, the temperature change will be <u>**-0.233°C**</u>. The change in temperature when 40.0 J are added will be:

40.0 J x (g x °C /4.184 J) x (1 /150 g) = <u>0.0637°C</u>.

1.63 (4.184 J / g °C) x 500 g x 24°C = <u>5.0×10^4 J</u>

(1.00 cal /g °C) x 500 g x 24°C = <u>1.2×10^4 cal</u>

1.64 Energy lost by the Cu = energy gained by the water. Sp. heat x mass x change in temp. x (-1) = sp. heat x mass x change in temp. (The negative one is needed since the sign of heat lost is the opposite of that of heat gained.)

(0.385 J /g °C) x 3.14 g x (X °C -100°C) x (-1) = (4.184 J /g °C) x 10.00 g x (X°C - 25.0°C); (121°C - 1.21 X°C) = (41.8 X°C - 1046°C)

X°C = <u>27.1°C</u>.

1.65 <u>Elements</u> are the simplest forms of matter that can exist under ordinary chemical conditions. <u>Compounds</u> consist of two or more elements which are always present in the same proportions. <u>Mixtures</u> consist of two or more compounds that do not react chemically and differ from elements and compounds in that they may be of variable composition and do not undergo phase changes at constant temperature.

1.66 A physical change does not alter the chemical composition of the substances involved while a chemical change always produces one or more new substances with a different chemical composition from the original substances.

1.67 A <u>solution</u> is a homogeneous mixture and has uniform properties throughout. It consists of one phase.

1.68 Compound because of the constant composition between the two samples.

This can be shown by the calculation of the percentage silicon in each sample.

Sample #1 [3.44 g silicon ÷ (3.44 g + 3.91 g total)] x 100 = 46.8% silicon

Sample #2 [6.42 g silicon ÷ (6.42 g + 7.30 g total)] x 100 = 46.8% silicon

1.69

Homogeneous	Heterogeneous
sea water	smog
air	smoke
black coffee	club soda (with bubbles)
	ham sandwich

1.70 There are four phases: copper pan, iron nails, glass marbles, water.

1.71 Chromatography separates mixtures into their components by using the different tendencies of substances to be adsorbed onto the surface of certain solids. A spot of a solution of a mixture is placed at one end of the surface of such a solid. A suitable solvent is then allowed to flow over the surface. The solvent lifts the components from the surface and carries them along at different rates with the more strongly adsorbed components moving more slowly. This results in a separation of the components if the strength of their adsorptions are different.

1.72 A magnet could be used to separate the iron filings from the other two components. The salt and copper powder can be added to water. The salt dissolves and the copper powder can be filtered from the solution. The salt can be recovered by evaporating off the water.

1.73 1. Matter is composed of indivisible particles called atoms.

2. All atoms of a given element have the same properties which differ from the properties of all other elements.

(continued)

(1.73 continued)

3. A chemical reaction consists of a reshuffling of atoms from one set of combinations to another with the individual atoms remaining intact.

1.74 Dalton's theory explained the law of conservation of mass and the law of definite proportions. It predicted the law of multiple proportions.

1.75 Atomic mass.

1.76 Atoms are the fundamental particles of all matter that cannot be further subdivided by ordinary chemical means. A molecule is a group of atoms bound tightly enough together that they behave as one.

1.77 The amu is one-twelfth of the mass of an atom of carbon-12. It is sometimes referred to as a dalton.

1.78

$$\frac{1\ \text{amu}'}{\text{F atom}} \times \frac{1\ \text{F atom}}{18.998\ \text{amu}} \times \frac{12.011\ \text{amu}}{\text{C atom}} = \underline{0.63222\ \text{amu}'/\text{C atom}}$$

$$\frac{1\ \text{amu}'}{\text{F atom}} \times \frac{1\ \text{F atom}}{18.998\ \text{amu}} \times \frac{1.0079\ \text{amu}}{\text{H atom}} = \underline{0.053053\ \text{amu}'/\text{H atom}}$$

1.79 No! Not unless the ratio of the atoms is known (its empirical formula).

1.80 If the formula of a compound is CX_4, a hypothetical equation for the formation of CX_4 would be: $C + 4X \longrightarrow CX_4$. From this knowledge and the values given in the problem, one can solve this problem by one of several different approaches. One method is to divide the mass of X by the mass of C to obtain the mass of X compared to C. (6.92 /0.584 = 11.8) The mass of X is 11.8 times the mass of C. If 4 atoms of X are combined with one atom of C, the 4

(1.80 continued)

atoms of X weigh 11.8 times the mass of 1 atom of C. Since 1 atom of C is 12.00 amu's, 4 atoms of X are 11.8 x 12.0 or 142 amu's. Therfore, 1 atom of X = 142 /4 or **35.5 amu**

1.81 **(a)** During a chemical reaction, mass is neither created nor destroyed.

(b) In any pure chemical substance, the same elements are always combined in the same proportions, by mass.

(c) When two elements combine to from more than one compound, the masses of one of the elements that are combined with the same mass of the other in the various compounds are in ratios of small whole numbers.

1.82 24 g H x (6.0 g C /1.0 g H) = $\underline{\mathbf{1.4 \times 10^2\ g\ C}}$

1.83 The law of definite composition can be demonstrated by more than one method. One method is to show that the percentage composition does not change from one sample to the next. Another method is to show a constant ratio of elements. This problem has been solved using the percentage method. Problem 1.84 has been solved using the ratio method. Students with more chemical knowledge than has been presented thus far in the textbook may select a third method.

Sample #1 %X = [(4.31 g X) ÷ (4.31 g +7.69 g total)] x 100 = 35.9% X

Sample #2 %X = 35.9% X

Sample #3 %X = (0.718 g ÷ 2.00 g sample) x 100 = 35.9% X

Each sample is 35.9% X and 64.1% Y.

1.84 (See discussion at the beginning of the solution to problem 1.83) In this solution we will compare the ratio of weights of the elements present.

For sample #1: 1.00 g C /6.33 g F = 0.158 g C / 1 g F

1.00 g C /11.67 g Cl = 0.0857 g C / 1 g Cl

6.33 g F /11.67 g Cl = 0.542 g F /1 g Cl

For sample #2: 2.00 g C /12.66 g F = 0.158 g C /1 g F

2.00 g C /23.34 g Cl = 0.0857 g C /1 g Cl

12.66 g F /23.34 g Cl = 0.542 g F /1 g Cl

For both samples the ratio of mass of carbon to mass of fluorine is 0.158. The ratio of carbon to chlorine is 0.0857 and the ratio of fluorine to chlorine is 0.542 in both samples. These data support the law of definite composition.

1.85 For sample #1: 1.26 g oxygen /10.0 g copper

For sample #2: 2.52 g oxygen /10.0 g copper

The ratio of the two masses of oxygen is 1.26 to 2.52 or 1 to 2. These data illustrate the law of multiple proportions.

1.86 First, for each sample, calculate the amount of one of the elements per gram of the other element. Then compare the results. Grams of phosphorus per gram of oxygen will be calculated. It would be equally correct to calculate the grams of oxygen per gram of phosphorus and to compare those results.

For sample #1: 0.845 g P /(1.50 g sample - 0.845 g P) = 1.29 g P /1 g of O

(continued)

(1.86 continued)

For sample #2: 1.09 g P /(2.50 g sample - 1.09 g P) = 0.773 g P/1 g of O

This gives 1.29 g P (#1) to 0.773 g P (#2) or when each is divided by the smallest they become 1.67 to 1.00, multiplying by 3 the ratio becomes 5-to-3.

1.87 The ratio of N's is 4:1 with the first compound being N_2O. Therefore, the second one must contain 1/4th as much N. The formula of the second compound would be $N_{1/2}O$. The correct way to write the formula of $N_{1/2}O$ is to double the numbers so that fractional atoms will not be needed, thus, NO_2.

1.88 The first statement of the question shows that in MnO there are 4.00 g of O combined with 13.7 g of Mn. In MnO_2 there will be twice as much O combined with the same amount of Mn. The ratio would be: $\frac{13.7\text{ g Mn}}{2 \times 4.00\text{ g O}}$.

Using this ratio one can solve for the number of grams of oxygen that would be combined with 7.85 g of manganese in the compound MnO_2.

$$\frac{13.7\text{ g Mn}}{2\times 4.00\text{ g O}} = \frac{7.85\text{ g Mn}}{?\text{ g O}} \qquad ?\text{ g O} = \underline{4.58\text{ g oxygen}}$$

1.89 **(a)** Fe **(b)** Na **(c)** K **(d)** P **(e)** Br **(f)** Ca **(g)** N **(h)** Ne **(i)** Mn **(j)** Mg

1.90 **(a)** silver **(b)** copper **(c)** sulfur **(d)** chlorine **(e)** aluminum **(f)** gold **(g)** chromium **(h)** tungsten **(i)** nickel **(j)** mercury

1.91 **(a)** Potassiun = **2 atoms**, Sulfur = **1 atom**

(b) Sodium = **2 atoms**, Carbon = **1 atom**, Oxygen = **3 atoms**

(c) Potassium = **4 atoms**, Iron = **1 atom**, Carbon and Nitrogen = **6 atoms each**

(1.91 continued)

(d) N = <u>3 atoms</u>, H = <u>12 atoms</u>, Phosphorus = <u>1 atom</u>, O = <u>4 atoms</u>

(e) Sodium = <u>3 atoms</u>, Silver = <u>1 atom</u>, Sulfur = <u>4 atoms</u>, Oxygen = <u>6 atoms</u>

1.92 $CaSO_4 \cdot 2H_2O$

1.93 Aluminum = **<u>1 atom</u>** Hydrogen = **<u>24 atoms</u>** Oxygen = **<u>20 atoms</u>**

Potassium = **<u>1 atom</u>** Sulfur = **<u>2 atoms</u>**

1.94 **a and c**

2 STOICHIOMETRY: CHEMICAL ARITHMETIC

2.1 All three represent a set number of objects; the mole is 6.022×10^{23} things, the dozen is 12 things and the gross means 144 things. There are 6.022×10^{23} things in a mole.

2.2 **6.022×10^{23} atoms of carbon or 12.011 grams of carbon**

2.3 **1-to-2**

2.4 (a) **1-to-1** (b) **1-to-1** (c) **1-to-3** (d) **1-to-1** (e) **1-to-3** (f) **1-to-3**

2.5 (a) **2-to-5** (b) **12.0** (c) **2.50** (d) **0.240** (e) **0.750**

2.6 (a) **2.00** (b) **0.720** (c) **6.00** (d) **3.00**

2.7 (a) **$(SiO_2)_x$** (b) **50** (c) **50**

(d) **4.50 moles of Si and 9.00 moles of O**

2.8 $As_2S_3 \longrightarrow 2As + 3S$; $1.00 \text{ mol } As_2S_3 \times \frac{3 \text{ mol S}}{1 \text{ mol } As_2S_3} = \mathbf{3.00 \text{ mol S}}$

2.9 $1.50 \text{ mol } Cr_2O_3 \times \frac{3 \text{ mol O}}{1 \text{ mol } Cr_2O_3} = \mathbf{4.50 \text{ mol O}}$

2.10 $CaCO_3 \longrightarrow CaO + CO_2$

$$1.00 \text{ mol } CaCO_3 \times \frac{1 \text{ mol } CO_2}{1 \text{ mol } CaCO_3} = \mathbf{1.00 \text{ mol } CO_2}$$

2.11 Using $Al_2(SO_4)_3$ + 3Ba? —> 3 $BaSO_4$ + ?X, one can calculate the moles of $BaSO_4$ from 1.25 moles of aluminum sulfate by:

$$1.25 \text{ mol } Al_2(SO_4)_3 \times \frac{3 \text{ mol } BaSO_4}{1 \text{ mol } Al_2(SO_4)_3} = \underline{3.75 \text{ mol } BaSO_4}.$$

2.12 (a) Mg 1 mol = <u>24.3 g</u> (b) C 1 mol = <u>12.0 g</u> (c) Fe 1 mol = <u>55.8 g</u>

(d) Cl 1 mol = <u>35.5 g</u> (e) S 1 mol = <u>32.1 g</u> (f) Sr 1 mol = <u>87.6 g</u>

2.13 (a) $50.0 \text{ g Na} \times \frac{1 \text{ mol Na}}{23.0 \text{ g Na}} = \underline{2.17 \text{ mol Na}}$

(b) <u>0.668 mol As</u> (c) <u>0.962 mol Cr</u> (d) <u>1.85 mol Al</u>

(e) <u>1.28 mol K</u> (f) <u>0.463 mol Ag</u>

2.14 Formula weights are preferred in compounds where formula units are used to describe a neutral aggregate of ions, e.g. NaCl.

2.15 (a) <u>40.304</u> (b) <u>110.99</u> (c) <u>208.239</u> (d) <u>135.03</u> (e) <u>163.9407</u>

2.16 (a) <u>60.0843</u> (b) <u>58.320</u> (c) <u>246.47</u> (d) <u>812.37</u> (e) <u>176.126</u>

(f) <u>342.299</u>

2.17 $\frac{194.193 \text{ g}}{1 \text{ mol}} \times 1.35 \text{ mol} = \underline{262 \text{ g of Caffeine}}$

2.18 $\frac{334.39 \text{ g}}{1 \text{ mol}} \times 2.33 \text{ mol} = \underline{779 \text{ g of Penicillin}}$

2.19 $\frac{303.26 \text{ g}}{1 \text{ mol}} \times 6.30 \text{ mol} = 1910 \text{ g or } \underline{1.91 \times 10^3 \text{ g of } PbSO_4}.$

2.20 $\frac{79.90 \text{ g}}{1 \text{ mol}} \times 0.144 \text{ mol} = \underline{11.5 \text{ g of } TiO_2}.$

2.21 $242\ g \times \frac{1\ mol}{84.01\ g} = $ **2.88 mol $NaHCO_3$.**

2.22 $1.40 \times 10^3\ g \times \frac{1\ mol}{58.12\ g} = $ **24.1 mol C_4H_{10}.**

2.23 $\frac{85.3\ g\ H_2SO_4}{98.02\ g\ /mol} = $ **0.870 mol H_2SO_4.**

2.24 $25.0\ g \times \frac{1\ mol}{347.1\ g} = $ **0.0720 mol $PbHAsO_4$.**

2.25 125 g KCl x 1 mol K /74.55 g KCl = **1.68 mol K**

2.26 $632\ g\ FeS_2 \times \frac{1\ mol\ FeS_2}{120.0\ g\ FeS_2} \times \frac{2\ mol\ S}{1\ mol\ FeS_2} = $ **10.5 mol S**

2.27 $1.00 \times 10^3\ g\ SO_2 \times \frac{1\ mol\ SO_2}{64.06\ g\ SO_2} \times \frac{1\ mol\ FeS_2}{2\ mol\ SO_2} = $ **7.81 mol FeS_2**

2.28 For Fe; $\frac{55.847\ g}{mol} \times \frac{1\ mol}{6.022 \times 10^{23}\ atoms} = $ **9.274×10^{-23} g /atom**

For SO_2; $\frac{64.06\ g}{mol} \times \frac{1\ mol}{6.022 \times 10^{23}\ molecules} = $ **1.064×10^{-22} g /molecule**

2.29 $3.50 \times 10^{17}\ atoms\ C \times \frac{4\ atoms\ H}{2\ atoms\ C} = $ **7.00×10^{17} atoms H**

$3.50 \times 10^{17}\ atoms\ C \times \frac{1\ mol\ C}{6.022 \times 10^{23}\ atoms\ C} \times \frac{12.01\ g\ C}{1\ mol\ C} =$

6.98×10^{-6} g C

$7.00 \times 10^{17}\ atoms\ H \times \frac{1\ mol\ H}{6.022 \times 10^{23}\ atoms} \times \frac{1.008\ g\ H}{mol\ H} =$

1.17×10^{-6} g of H

2.30 $\frac{342.30 \text{ g}}{\text{mol}} \times \frac{1 \text{ mol}}{6.022 \times 10^{23} \text{ molecules}} = \underline{\mathbf{5.684 \times 10^{-22} \text{ g /molecule}}}$

$\frac{5.684 \times 10^{-22} \text{ g /molecule}}{12.011 \text{ g /mol}} \times \frac{6.022 \times 10^{23} \text{ molecules}}{\text{mol}} = \underline{\mathbf{28.50 \text{ times heavier}}}$

(Note: this is a ratio and like all ratios it is unitless.)

$25.0 \text{ g suc.} \times \frac{1 \text{ mol}}{342.30 \text{ g}} \times \frac{6.022 \times 10^{23} \text{ molecules}}{\text{mol}} = \underline{\mathbf{4.40 \times 10^{22} \text{ molecules}}}$

$25.0 \text{ g suc.} \times \frac{1 \text{ mol}}{342.30 \text{ g}} \times \frac{6.022 \times 10^{23} \text{ molecules}}{\text{mol}} \times \frac{45 \text{ atoms}}{\text{molec.}} =$

$\underline{\mathbf{1.98 \times 10^{24} \text{ atoms}}}$

2.31 $4.00 \times 10^{-8} \text{ g of } C_3H_8 \times \frac{1 \text{ mol}}{44.10 \text{ g}} \times \frac{6.022 \times 10^{23} \text{ molecules}}{\text{mol}} \times$

$\frac{3 \text{ atoms C}}{\text{molecule}} = \underline{\mathbf{1.64 \times 10^{15} \text{ atoms C}}}$

2.32 $3.0 \text{ cm} \times \frac{1 \text{ atom}}{1.5 \times 10^{-8} \text{ cm}} \times \frac{1 \text{ mol}}{6.022 \times 10^{23} \text{ atom}} \times \frac{12.0 \text{ g}}{\text{mol}} =$

$\underline{\mathbf{4.0 \times 10^{-15} \text{ g C}}}$

2.33 $5.00 \times 10^{20} \text{ molecules } S_8 \times \frac{8 \text{ atom S}}{\text{molecule } S_8} \times \frac{2 \text{ atoms Cu}}{\text{atom S}} \times$

$\frac{1 \text{ mol Cu}}{6.022 \times 10^{23} \text{ atoms}} \times \frac{63.5 \text{ g Cu}}{\text{mol Cu}} = \underline{\mathbf{0.844 \text{ g Cu}}}$

2.34 **(a)** % Fe in $FeCl_3$ = 55.85 /[55.85 + (3 x 35.45)] x 100 = **<u>34.43% Fe</u>**

<u>65.57% Cl</u>

(b) Na_3PO_4 **<u>42.07% Na</u>**, **<u>18.89% P</u>**, **<u>39.04% O</u>**

(2.34 continued)

(c) $KHSO_4$ **28.71% K, 0.74% H, 23.55% S, 47.00% O**

(d) $(NH_4)_2HPO_4$ **21.21% N, 6.87% H, 23.46% P, 48.46% O**

(e) Hg_2Cl_2 **84.98% Hg, 15.02% Cl**

2.35 (a) C_6H_6 **92.26% C, 7.74% H**

(b) C_2H_5OH **52.14% C, 13.13% H, 34.73% O**

(c) $K_2Cr_2O_7$ **26.58% K, 35.35% Cr, 38.07% O**

(d) XeF_4 **63.34% Xe, 36.66% F**

(e) $CaCO_3$ **40.04% Ca, 12.00% C, 47.96% O**

2.36 $$30.0\text{ g gly} \times \frac{1\text{ mol gly}}{75.07\text{ g gly}} \times \frac{1\text{ mol N}}{\text{mol gly}} \times \frac{14.01\text{ g N}}{\text{mol N}} = \underline{5.60\text{ g N}}$$

2.37 $$12.0\text{ g }NH_3 \times \frac{1\text{ mol }NH_3}{17.03\text{ g }NH_3} \times \frac{3\text{ mol H}}{\text{mol }NH_3} \times \frac{1.008\text{ g H}}{\text{mol H}} = \underline{2.13\text{ g H}}$$

2.38 **56.3% P, 43.7% S**

2.39 (a) $$9.34\text{ g }CO_2 \times \frac{1\text{ mol }CO_2}{44.01\text{ g }CO_2} \times \frac{1\text{ mol C}}{\text{mol }CO_2} \times \frac{12.01\text{ g C}}{\text{mol C}} = \underline{2.55\text{ g C}}$$

$$5.09\text{ g }H_2O \times \frac{1\text{ mol }H_2O}{18.02\text{ g}} \times \frac{2\text{ mol H}}{\text{mol }H_2O} \times \frac{1.008\text{ g H}}{\text{mol H}} = \underline{0.569\text{ g H}}$$

(b) 4.25 - 2.55 - 0.569 = **1.13 g O**

(c) (2.55 g C /4.25 g sample) x 100 = **60.0% C, 13.4% H, 26.6% O**

2.40 Structural formulas represent the way the atoms in a molecule are linked together. Molecular formulas specify the actual number of each kind of atom found in a molecule. Empirical formulas give the relative number of atoms of each element present in a molecule.

2.41 (a) $\underline{NH_4SO_4}$ (b) $\underline{Fe_2O_3}$ (c) $\underline{AlCl_3}$ (d) $\underline{CH}$ (e) $\underline{C_3H_8O_3}$

(f) $\underline{CH_2O}$ (g) $\underline{Hg_2SO_4}$

2.42 $\underline{C_2H_6O_2}$ and $\underline{CH_3O}$

2.43 A simplest formula is calculated from experimentally observed or measured data obtained by a chemical analysis of the compound. Webster's defines empirical as "Pertaining to, or founded upon, experiment or experience."

2.44 $S_?O_?$ $S = \dfrac{1.40\text{ g}}{32.06\text{ g / mol}} = 0.0437\text{ mol}$ $O = \dfrac{2.10}{15.999} = 0.131\text{ mol}$

$S_{0.0437}O_{0.131}$ or $\dfrac{S_{0.0437}}{0.0437}\,\dfrac{O_{0.131}}{0.0437} = \underline{S_1O_3}$ or $\underline{SO_3}$

2.45 moles C = 0.423 g /12.011 g /mol = 0.0352 mol C

moles Cl = 2.50 g /35.45 g /mol = 0.0705 mol Cl

moles F = 1.34 g /18.998 g /mol = 0.0705 mol F

$C_{0.0352}Cl_{0.0705}F_{0.0705} = \underline{CCl_2F_2}$

2.46 $\dfrac{7.04\text{ g P}}{30.97\text{ g P /mol P}} = 0.227\text{ mol P}$ $\dfrac{5.46\text{ g S}}{32.06\text{ g S /mol S}} = 0.170\text{ mol S}$

$P_{0.227}S_{0.170}$ or $P_{0.227/0.170}S_{0.170/0.170}$ or $P_{1.34}S_{1.00}$ or $\underline{P_4S_3}$

2.47 $\frac{2.55 \text{ g C}}{12.01 \text{ g C /mol C}} = 0.212 \text{ mol C}$

$\frac{0.569 \text{ g H}}{1.008 \text{ g H / mol H}} = 0.564 \text{ mol H}$

$\frac{1.13 \text{ g O}}{15.999 \text{ g O /mol O}} = 0.0706 \text{ mol O}$

$C_{0.212/0.0706}H_{0.564/0.0706}O_{0.0706/0.0706} = \underline{C_3H_8O}$

2.48 (Assume a 100 g sample). $14.5 \text{ g C} \times \frac{1 \text{ mol C}}{12.01 \text{ g C}} = 1.21 \text{ mole}$

$85.5 \text{ g Cl} \times \frac{1 \text{ mol Cl}}{35.45 \text{ g Cl}} = 2.41 \text{ mol Cl}$

$C_{\frac{1.21}{1.21}}Cl_{\frac{2.41}{1.21}}$ or $\underline{CCl_2}$.

2.49 $\frac{75.7 \text{ g As}}{74.9 \text{ g /mol}} = 1.01 \text{ mol As}$ $\frac{24.3 \text{ g O}}{16.0 \text{ g /mol}} = 1.52 \text{ mol O}$

$As_{\frac{1.01}{1.01}}O_{\frac{1.52}{1.01}} = As_{1.00}O_{1.50} = \underline{As_2O_3}$.

2.50 1.31 g S and 4.22 - 1.31 g Cl = 2.91 g Cl

$\frac{1.31 \text{ g S}}{32.06 \text{ g /mol}} = 0.0409 \text{ mol S}$ $\frac{2.91 \text{ g Cl}}{35.5 \text{ g /mol}} = 0.0820 \text{ mol Cl}$

$S_{0.0409/0.0409}Cl_{0.0820/0.0409} = \underline{SCl_2}$.

2.51 $\frac{60.8 \text{ g Na}}{23.0 \text{ g /mol}} = 2.64 \text{ mol Na}$ $\frac{28.5 \text{ g B}}{10.8 \text{ g /mol}} = 2.64 \text{ mol B}$

$\frac{10.5 \text{ g H}}{1.01 \text{ g H}} = 10.4 \text{ mol}$ $\underline{NaBH_4}$.

2.52 $\frac{63.2 \text{ g C}}{12.0 \text{ g/mol}} = 5.27 \text{ mol C}$ $\frac{5.26 \text{ g H}}{1.01 \text{ g/mol}} = 5.21 \text{ mol H}$

$\frac{31.6 \text{ g O}}{16.0 \text{ g/mol}} = 1.98 \text{ mol O}$ $C_{5.27/1.98}H_{5.21/1.98}O_{1.98/1.98}$

$C_{2.66}H_{2.63}O_{1.00}$ times 3 = $\underline{C_8H_8O_3}$.

2.53 $C_?H_?O_? + ?O_2 \longrightarrow CO_2 + H_2O$

From the mass of CO_2 one can calculate the mass of C in the sample. From the mass of H_2O one can calculate the mass of H in the sample. From the mass of the sample and masses of C and H, one can obtain the mass of O in the sample. From these masses, the moles of each and the empirical formula can be calculated.

$$1.030 \text{ g } CO_2 \times \frac{1 \text{ mol } CO_2}{44.01 \text{ g } CO_2} \times \frac{1 \text{ mol C}}{\text{mol } CO_2} \times \frac{12.01 \text{ g C}}{\text{mol C}} = 0.2811 \text{ g C}$$

$$0.632 \text{ g } H_2O \times \frac{1 \text{ mol } H_2O}{18.02 \text{ g } H_2O} \times \frac{2 \text{ mol H}}{\text{mol } H_2O} \times \frac{1.008 \text{ g H}}{\text{mol H}} = 0.0707 \text{ g H}$$

$$0.537 - 0.2811 - 0.0\,707 = 0.185 \text{ g O}$$

$$0.2811 \text{ g C} \times \frac{1 \text{ mol}}{12.01 \text{ g}} = \underline{0.02341 \text{ mol C}}$$

$$0.0707 \text{ g H} \times \frac{1 \text{ mol H}}{1.008 \text{ g}} = \underline{0.0701 \text{ mol H}}$$

$$0.185 \text{ g O} \times \frac{1 \text{ mol O}}{16.0 \text{ g}} = \underline{0.0116 \text{ mol O}}$$

$$C_{0.02341/0.0116}H_{0.0701/0.0116}O_{0.0116/0.0116} = \underline{C_2H_6O}$$

2.54 From the amount of H_2O and CO_2 produced from the 1.35-g sample, one can calculate the % H and % C. From the amount of NH_3 produced from the 0.735-g sample, one can obtain the % N. From the difference, one can obtain % O. Once the % composition is known, the problem becomes a problem very much like Problems 2.48, 2.49, 2.51, and 2.52.

$$\%\text{ H: } 0.810\text{ g } H_2O \times \frac{1\text{ mol } H_2O}{18.02\text{ g } H_2O} \times \frac{2\text{ mol H}}{\text{mol } H_2O} \times \frac{1.01\text{ g H}}{\text{mol H}} = 0.0908\text{ g}$$

$$\frac{0.0908\text{ g H}}{1.35\text{ g sample}} \times 100 = \underline{6.73\%\text{ H}}$$

$$\%\text{ C: } 1.32\text{ g } CO_2 \times \frac{1\text{ mol } CO_2}{44.01\text{ g } CO_2} \times \frac{1\text{ mol C}}{\text{mol } CO_2} \times \frac{12.01\text{ g C}}{\text{mol C}} = 0.360\text{ g C}$$

$$\frac{0.360\text{ g C}}{1.35\text{ g sample}} \times 100 = \underline{26.7\%\text{ C}}$$

$$\%\text{ N: } 0.284\text{ g } NH_3 \times \frac{1\text{ mol } NH_3}{17.03\text{ g } NH_3} \times \frac{1\text{ mol N}}{\text{mol } NH_3} \times \frac{14.01\text{ g N}}{\text{mol } NH_3} = 0.234\text{ g N}$$

$$\frac{0.234\text{ g N}}{0.735\text{ g sample}} \times 100 = \underline{31.8\%\text{ N}}$$

0.735

$$\%\text{ O: } 100.0 - 6.73 - 26.7 - 31.8 = \underline{34.8\%\text{ O}}$$

Empirical Formula: $C_{26.7/12.01}H_{6.73/1.01}N_{31.8/14.01}O_{34.8/16.0}$

or $C_{2.22}H_{6.66}N_{2.27}O_{2.18}$ or $\underline{CH_3NO}$

2.55 (See the discussion for Problem 2.54.) This problem has the adde

(a) % C: 0.138 g CO_2 x $\frac{1\text{ mol } CO_2}{44.01\text{ g } CO_2}$ x $\frac{1\text{ mol C}}{\text{mol } CO_2}$ x 12.01

(2.55 continued)

$$\frac{0.377 \text{ g C}}{0.150 \text{ g sample}} \times 100 = \underline{\mathbf{25.1\% \ C}}$$

$$\% \text{ H: } 0.0566 \text{ g } H_2O \times \frac{1 \text{ mol } H_2O}{18.02 \text{ g } H_2O} \times \frac{2 \text{ mol H}}{\text{mol } H_2O} \times \frac{1.01 \text{ g H}}{\text{mol H}} = 0.00634 \text{ g}$$

$$\frac{0.00634 \text{ g H}}{0.150 \text{ g sample}} \times 100 = \underline{\mathbf{4.23\% \ H}}$$

$$\% \text{ N: } 0.0238 \text{ g } NH_3 \times \frac{1 \text{ mol } NH_3}{17.03 \text{ g } NH_3} \times \frac{1 \text{ mol N}}{\text{mol } NH_3} \times \frac{14.01 \text{ g N}}{\text{mol N}} = 0.0196 \text{ g N}$$

$$\frac{0.0196 \text{ g N}}{0.200 \text{ g sample}} \times 100 = \underline{\mathbf{9.79\% \ N}}$$

$$\% \text{ Cl: } 0.251 \text{ g AgCl} \times \frac{1 \text{ mol AgCl}}{143.3 \text{ g AgCl}} \times \frac{1 \text{ mol Cl}}{\text{mol AgCl}} \times \frac{35.45 \text{ g Cl}}{\text{mol Cl}} = 0.0621 \text{ g Cl}$$

$$\frac{0.0621 \text{ g Cl}}{0.125 \text{ g sample}} \times 100 = \underline{\mathbf{49.7\% \ Cl}}$$

% O: 100.0 - 25.1 - 4.23 - 9.79 - 49.7 = $\underline{\mathbf{11.2\% \ O}}$

(b) Emp. F = $C_{25.1/12.01}H_{4.23/1.01}N_{9.79/14.01}Cl_{49.7/35.45}O_{11.2/16.0}$

= $C_{2.09}H_{4.19}N_{0.70}Cl_{1.40}O_{0.70}$ = $\underline{\mathbf{C_3H_6NCl_2O}}$

2.56 **(a)** Empirical weight = 135.1, therefore $\underline{\mathbf{Na_2S_4O_6}}$.

(b) Empirical weight = 73.5, therefore $\underline{\mathbf{C_6H_4Cl_2}}$.

(c) Empirical weight = 60.5, therefore $\underline{\mathbf{C_6H_3Cl_3}}$.

(d) Empirical weight = 122.1, therefore $\underline{\mathbf{Na_{12}Si_6O_{18}}}$.

(e) Empirical weight = 102.0, therefore $\underline{\mathbf{Na_3P_3O_9}}$.

2.57 % C $0.6871\ g\ CO_2 \times \frac{1\ mol\ CO_2}{44.01\ g\ CO_2} \times \frac{1\ mol\ C}{mol\ CO_2} \times \frac{12.01\ g\ C}{mol\ C} = 0.1875\ g\ C$

$\frac{0.1875\ g\ C}{0.5000\ g\ sample} \times 100.0 =$ **37.50% C**

% H $0.1874\ g\ H_2O \times \frac{1\ mol\ H_2O}{18.02\ g\ H_2O} \times \frac{2\ mol\ H}{mol\ H_2O} \times \frac{1.008\ g\ H}{mol\ H} = 0.02097\ g\ H$

$\frac{0.02097\ g\ H}{0.500\ g\ sample} \times 100.0 =$ **4.194% H**

% O = 100.00 - 37.50 - 4.194 = **58.31% O**

Empirical Formula $C_{37.50/12.01}H_{4.194/1.008}O_{58.31/16.00}$

$C_{3.122}H_{4.161}O_{3.644}$ or $C_{1.000}H_{1.333}O_{1.167}$ Multiply by 6.

$\underline{C_6H_8O_7}$

Molecular Formula

Empirical formula weight = 192. MW = empirical formula weight.

Therefore, the molecular formula is $\underline{C_6H_8O_7}$.

2.58 The formula weight of the C_8H_8 unit is 104.

$\frac{MW}{FW\ C_8H_8} = \frac{10^6}{104} = 1 \times 10^4$ **Therefore, n = 1×10^4 styrene units.**

2.59 The law of conservation of mass.

2.60 Coefficients are: (a) **1, 2, 1, 1** (b) **2, 1, 1, 1** (c) **8, 3, 4, 9**

(d)1, 1, 2 (e) **2, 1, 2, 1**

2.61 Coefficients are: (a) **2, 3, 1, 6** (b) **2, 1, 1, 2, 2** (c) **3, 2, 1, 6**

(d) **1, 3, 1, 3, 3** (e) **1, 1, 1, 1, 2**

2.62 Coefficients are: **(a) 2, 13, 8, 10 (1, 13/2, 4, 5)**

(b) 2, 17, 14, 6 (1, 17/2, 7,3) (c) 1, 6, 4

(d) 4, 11, 2, 8 (2, 11/2, 1, 4) (e) 4, 5, 4, 6 (2, 5/2, 2, 3)

2.63 Coefficients are: **(a) 1, 2, 1, 1 (b) 1, 4, 2, 1, 1 (c) 1, 3, 1, 3**

(d) 3, 1, 1, 2 (e) 2, 9, 4, 6, 2

2.64 (a) $2.50 \text{ mol CaC}_2 \times \frac{1 \text{ mol C}_2\text{H}_2}{\text{mol CaC}_2} = \mathbf{2.50 \text{ mol C}_2\text{H}_2}$

(b) $0.500 \text{ mol CaC}_2 \times \frac{1 \text{ mol C}_2\text{H}_2}{\text{mol CaC}_2} \times \frac{26.0 \text{ g C}_2\text{H}_2}{\text{mol C}_2\text{H}_2} = \mathbf{13.0 \text{ g C}_2\text{H}_2}$

(c) $(3.20 \text{ mol C}_2\text{H}_2)(2 \text{ mol H}_2\text{O} / \text{mol C}_2\text{H}_2) = \mathbf{6.40 \text{ mol H}_2\text{O}}$

(d) $28.0 \text{ g C}_2\text{H}_2 \times \frac{1 \text{ mol C}_2\text{H}_2}{26.0 \text{ g C}_2\text{H}_2} \times \frac{1 \text{ mol Ca(OH)}_2}{\text{mol C}_2\text{H}_2} \times \frac{74.1 \text{ g Ca(OH)}_2}{\text{mol Ca(OH)}_2} =$

$\mathbf{79.8 \text{ g Ca(OH)}_2}$

2.65 (a) $14.3 \text{ g ClO}_2 \times \frac{1 \text{ mol ClO}_2}{67.45 \text{ g ClO}_2} \times \frac{5 \text{ mol HClO}_3}{6 \text{ mol ClO}_2} = \mathbf{0.177 \text{ mol HClO}_3}$

(b) $5.74 \text{ g HCl} \times \frac{1 \text{ mol HCl}}{36.46 \text{ g HCl}} \times \frac{3 \text{ mol H}_2\text{O}}{\text{mol HCl}} \times \frac{18.02 \text{ g H}_2\text{O}}{\text{mol H}_2\text{O}} = \mathbf{8.51 \text{ g H}_2\text{O}}$

(c) $4.25 \text{ g ClO}_2 \times \frac{1 \text{ mol ClO}_2}{67.45 \text{ g ClO}_2} \times \frac{5 \text{ mol HClO}_3}{6 \text{ mol ClO}_2} \times \frac{84.46 \text{ g HClO}_3}{\text{mol HClO}_3}$

$= 4.43 \text{ g HClO}_3$

or $0.853 \text{ g H}_2\text{O} \times \frac{1 \text{ mol H}_2\text{O}}{18.02 \text{ g H}_2\text{O}} \times \frac{5 \text{ mol HClO}_3}{3 \text{ mol H}_2\text{O}} \times \frac{84.46 \text{ g HClO}_3}{\text{mol HClO}_3}$

(continued)

(2.65 continued)

$= 6.66 \text{ g } HClO_3$ Since 4.25 g of ClO_2 will produce less $HClO_3$ than will 0.853 g of H_2O, the ClO_2 is the limiting reagent and will determine the mass of $HClO_3$ produced. Answer = **$\underline{4.43 \text{ g } HClO_3}$**

2.66 (a) **$\underline{P_4 + 5O_2 \longrightarrow P_4O_{10}}$**

(b) **$\underline{0.100 \text{ mol } P_4O_{10}}$**

(c) $$50.0 \text{ g } P_4O_{10} \times \frac{1 \text{ mole } P_4O_{10}}{283.9 \text{ g } P_4O_{10}} \times \frac{1 \text{ mole } P_4}{\text{mole } P_4O_{10}} \times \frac{123.9 \text{ g } P_4}{\text{mol } P_4} = \underline{\mathbf{21.8 \text{ g } P_4}}$$

(d) $$25.0 \text{ g } O_2 \times \frac{1 \text{ mole } O_2}{32.0 \text{ g } O_2} \times \frac{1 \text{ mol } P_4}{5 \text{ mol } O_2} \times \frac{123.9 \text{ g } P_4}{\text{mol } P_4} = \underline{\mathbf{19.4 \text{ g } P_4}}$$

2.67 (a) $$0.0250 \text{ mol } N_2H_4 \times \frac{2 \text{ mol } HNO_3}{\text{mol } N_2H_4} = \underline{\mathbf{0.0500 \text{ mol } HNO_3}}$$

(b) $$1.35 \text{ mol } H_2O \times \frac{7 \text{ mol } H_2O_2}{8 \text{ mol } H_2O} = \underline{\mathbf{1.18 \text{ mol } H_2O_2}}$$

(c) $$1.87 \text{ mol } HNO_3 \times \frac{8 \text{ mol } H_2O}{2 \text{ mol } HNO_3} = \underline{\mathbf{7.48 \text{ } H_2O}}$$

(d) $$22.0 \text{ g } N_2H_4 \times \frac{1 \text{ mol } N_2H_4}{32.05 \text{ g } N_2H_4} \times \frac{7 \text{ mol } H_2O_2}{\text{mol } N_2H_4} = \underline{\mathbf{4.80 \text{ mol } H_2O_2}}$$

(e) $$45.8 \text{ g } HNO_3 \times \frac{1 \text{ mol } HNO_3}{63.02 \text{ g } HNO_3} \times \frac{7 \text{ mol } H_2O_2}{2 \text{ mol } HNO_3} \times \frac{34.02 \text{ g } H_2O_2}{\text{mol } H_2O_2}$$

$$= \underline{\mathbf{86.5 \text{ g } H_2O_2}}$$

2.68 (a) $$35.0 \text{ mol Fe} \times \frac{3 \text{ mol CO}}{2 \text{ mol Fe}} = \underline{\mathbf{52.5 \text{ mol CO}}}$$

(2.68 continued)

(b) $4.50 \text{ mol } CO_2 \times \frac{1 \text{ mol } Fe_2O_3}{3 \text{ mol } CO_2} = \underline{\mathbf{1.50 \text{ mol } Fe_2O_3}}$

(c) $0.570 \text{ mol Fe} \times \frac{1 \text{ mol } Fe_2O_3}{2 \text{ mol Fe}} \times \frac{159.7 \text{ g } Fe_2O_3}{\text{mol } Fe_2O_3} = \underline{\mathbf{45.5 \text{ g } Fe_2O_3}}$

(d) $48.5 \text{ g } Fe_2O_3 \times \frac{1 \text{ mol } Fe_2O_3}{159.7 \text{ g } Fe_2O_3} \times \frac{3 \text{ mol CO}}{\text{mol } Fe_2O_3} = \underline{\mathbf{0.911 \text{ mol CO}}}$

(e) $18.6 \text{ g CO} \times \frac{1 \text{ mol CO}}{28.0 \text{ g CO}} \times \frac{2 \text{ mol Fe}}{3 \text{ mol CO}} \times \frac{55.85 \text{ g Fe}}{\text{mol Fe}} = \underline{\mathbf{24.7 \text{ g Fe}}}$

2.69 (a) $6.50 \text{ mol } TiCl_4 \times \frac{2 \text{ mol } H_2O}{\text{mol } TiCl_4} = \underline{\mathbf{13.0 \text{ mol } H_2O}}$

(b) $8.44 \text{ mol } TiCl_4 \times \frac{4 \text{ mol HCl}}{\text{mol } TiCl_4} = \underline{\mathbf{33.8 \text{ mol HCl}}}$

(c) $14.4 \text{ mol } TiCl_4 \times \frac{1 \text{ mol } TiO_2}{\text{mol } TiCl_4} \times \frac{79.9 \text{ g } TiO_2}{\text{mol } TiO_2} = \underline{\mathbf{1.15 \times 10^3 \text{ g } TiO_2}}$

(d) $85.0 \text{ g } TiCl_4 \times \frac{1 \text{ mol } TiCl_4}{189.7 \text{ g } TiCl_4} \times \frac{4 \text{ mol HCl}}{\text{mol } TiCl_4} \times \frac{36.46 \text{ g HCl}}{\text{mol HCl}} = \underline{\mathbf{65.3 \text{ g HCl}}}$

2.70 $1{,}000 \text{ kg } C_6H_5Cl \times \frac{1 \text{ kmol } C_6H_5Cl}{112.6 \text{ kg } C_6H_5Cl} \times \frac{1 \text{ kmol DDT}}{2 \text{ kmol } C_6H_5Cl} \times \frac{354.5 \text{ kg DDT}}{\text{kmol DDT}}$

$= \underline{\mathbf{1.574 \times 10^3 \text{ kg DDT}}}$

2.71 $\frac{5 \text{ grains}}{\text{tablet}} \times 2 \text{ tablets} \times \frac{1 \text{ g}}{15.4 \text{ grains}} \times \frac{1 \text{ mol aspirin}}{180.2 \text{ g}} \times \frac{1 \text{ mol } C_7H_6O_3}{\text{mol aspirin}}$

$\times \frac{138.1 \text{ g } C_7H_6O_3}{\text{mol } C_7H_6O_3} = \underline{\mathbf{0.5 \text{ g } C_7H_6O_3}}$

2.72 (a) $\underline{(CH_3)_2NNH_2 + 2N_2O_4 \longrightarrow 4H_2O + 2CO_2 + 3N_2}$

(b) $50.0\ kg\ (CH_3)_2NNH_2 \times \frac{1\ kmol\ (CH_3)_2NNH_2}{60.10\ kg} \times \frac{2\ kmol\ N_2O_4}{kmol\ (CH_3)_2NNH_2}$

$\times \frac{92.02\ kg\ N_2O_4}{kmol\ N_2O_4} = \underline{\mathbf{153\ kg\ N_2O_4}}$

2.73 $500\ g\ sugar \times \frac{1\ mol\ sugar}{180.2\ g} \times \frac{2\ mol\ C_2H_5OH}{mol\ sugar} \times \frac{46.08\ g\ C_2H_5OH}{mol\ C_2H_5OH}$

$= \underline{\mathbf{256\ g\ C_2H_5OH}}$

2.74 (a) $20.0\ g\ Pb \times \frac{1\ mol\ Pb}{207.2\ g\ Pb} \times \frac{1\ mol\ wh.\ lead}{6\ mol\ Pb} \times \frac{775.6\ g\ wh.\ lead}{mol\ wh.\ lead}$

= **12.5 g white lead**

(b) $14.0\ g\ O_2 \times \frac{1\ mol\ O_2}{32.0\ g\ O_2} \times \frac{2\ mol\ CO_2}{3\ mol\ O_2} \times \frac{44.01\ g\ CO_2}{mol\ CO_2} = \underline{\mathbf{12.8\ g\ CO_2}}$

2.75 (a) **16.0 pounds** (b) **23.0 pounds** (c) **160 pounds**

(d) **46.0 pounds** (e) **55.8 pounds**

2.76 $2.40\ ton\text{-}mol\ CaCl_2 \times \frac{1\ ton\text{-}mole\ Ca}{1\ ton\text{-}mol\ CaCl_2} \times \frac{40.08\ tons\ Ca}{1\ ton\text{-}mole\ Ca} = \underline{\mathbf{96.2\ tons\ Ca}}$

2.77 $25.0\ tons\ Ca_3(PO_4)_2 \times \frac{1\ ton\text{-}mol\ Ca_3(PO_4)_2}{310.2\ tons\ Ca_3(PO_4)_2} \times \frac{2\ ton\text{-}mol\ H_2SO_4}{ton\text{-}mol\ Ca_3(PO_4)_2} \times$

$\frac{98.08\ tons\ H_2SO_4}{ton\text{-}mol\ H_2SO_4} = \underline{\mathbf{15.8\ tons\ H_2SO_4}}$

2.78 $650\ lb\ H_2 \times \frac{1\ lb\text{-}mol\ H_2}{2.02\ lb\ H_2} \times \frac{2\ lb\text{-}mol\ NH_3}{3\ lb\text{-}mol\ H_2} \times \frac{17.04\ lb\ NH_3}{lb\text{-}mol\ NH_3}$

$= \underline{\mathbf{3.66 \times 10^3\ lb\ NH_3}}$

2.79 That reactant that is completely consumed before any of the remaining reactants are used up is the limiting reactant. First calculate the number of moles of each reactant present. Then compare their ratios with that for the balanced chemical equation. From this deduce which reactant will be depleted first.

2.80 (a) $0.40 \text{ mol Fe} \times \frac{2 \text{ mol HCl}}{\text{mol Fe}} = 0.80$ mol HCl required to react with 0.40 mol Fe.

Since only 0.75 mol HCl is available, HCl is the limiting reactant.

(b) $0.75 \text{ mol HCl} \times \frac{1 \text{ mol } H_2}{2 \text{ mol HCl}} =$ **0.38 mol H_2**

(c) Moles of Fe required to react with 0.75 mole of HCl is:

$$0.75 \text{ mol HCl} \times \frac{1 \text{ mol Fe}}{2 \text{ mol HCl}} = 0.38 \text{ mol Fe}$$

There is 0.40 mol of Fe present. Therefore, at least 0.40 - 0.38 or **0.02 mol of Fe will remain after the reaction has stopped.**

2.81 (a) Limiting reactant? Moles Al? $20.0 \text{ g Al} \times \frac{1 \text{ mol}}{26.98 \text{ g}} = 0.741 \text{ mol Al}$

Mole H_2SO_4? $115 \text{ g } H_2SO_4 \times \frac{1 \text{ mol}}{98.08 \text{ g}} = 1.17 \text{ mol } H_2SO_4$

Select either reactant as the limiting reagent and determine if a sufficient quantity of the other is present. Let's select the H_2SO_4. How many moles of Al are needed to react with it ? $1.17 \text{ mol } H_2SO_4 \times \frac{2 \text{ mol Al}}{3 \text{ mol } H_2SO_4} = 0.780 \text{ mole Al}$

The Al present is less than that required to react with all the H_2SO_4.

Therefore, **Al is the limiting reactant.**

(2.81 continued)

(b) $0.741 \text{ mol Al} \times \frac{3 \text{ mol } H_2}{2 \text{ mol Al}} = \underline{1.11 \text{ mol } H_2}$

(c) $0.741 \text{ mol Al} \times \frac{1 \text{ mol } Al_2(SO_4)_3}{2 \text{ mol Al}} \times \frac{342.1 \text{ g } Al_2(SO_4)_3}{\text{mol } Al_2(SO_4)_3}$

$= \underline{127 \text{ g } Al_2(SO_4)_3}$

(d) $0.741 \text{ mol Al} \times \frac{3 \text{ mol } H_2SO_4}{2 \text{ mol Al}} \times \frac{98.08 \text{ g } H_2SO_4}{\text{mol } H_2SO_4} = 109 \text{ g } H_2SO_4$ needed

Excess = 115 g - 109 g = $\underline{6 \text{ g } H_2SO_4}$

2.82 (a) $35.0 \text{ g } C_2H_2 \times \frac{1 \text{mol } C_2H_2}{26.04 \text{ g } C_2H_2} = 1.34 \text{ mol } C_2H_2$

$51.0 \text{ g HCl} \times \frac{1 \text{ mol HCl}}{36.46 \text{ g HCl}} = 1.40 \text{ mol HCl}$

Since they react in a 1:1 mole ratio, **the C_2H_2 is the limiting reactant**.

(b) $1.34 \text{ mol } C_2H_2 \times \frac{1 \text{ mol } C_2H_3Cl}{\text{mol } C_2H_2} \times \frac{62.50 \text{ g } C_2H_3Cl}{\text{mol } C_2H_3Cl} = \underline{83.8 \text{ g } C_2H_3Cl}$

(c) 1.40 - 1.34 = 0.06 mole of excess HCl

$0.06 \text{ mole HCl} \times \frac{36.46 \text{ g HCl}}{\text{mol HCl}} = \underline{2 \text{ g HCl}}$

2.83 First find the limiting reactant. $150 \text{ g } CCl_4 \times \frac{1 \text{ mol } CCl_4}{153.8 \text{ g } CCl_4} = 0.975 \text{ mol } CCl_4$

$100 \text{ g } SbF_3 \times \frac{1 \text{ mol } SbF_3}{178.8 \text{ g } SbF_3} = 0.559 \text{ mol } SbF_3$

The needed mol ratio is 3 mol CCl_4 to 2 mol SbF_3. Is 0.975 mol of CCl_4 to

(2.83 continued)

0.559 mol of SbF_3 larger or smaller than the needed 3:2 ratio? $\frac{0.975}{0.559} = 1.74$

Larger! Therefore, the **<u>SbF_3 is the limiting reactant</u>.**

(a) $0.559 \text{ mol SbF}_3 \times \frac{3 \text{ mol CCl}_2\text{F}_2}{2 \text{ mol SbF}_3} \times \frac{120.9 \text{ g CCl}_2\text{F}_2}{\text{mol CCl}_2\text{F}_2} = \mathbf{101 \text{ g CCl}_2\text{F}_2}$

(b) Moles of CCl_4 needed to react with 0.559 mole of SbF_3 is:

$$0.559 \text{ mol SbF}_3 \times \frac{3 \text{ mol CCl}_4}{2 \text{ mol SbF}_3} = 0.838 \text{ mol CCl}_4$$

$$(0.975 \text{ mol CCl}_4 - 0.838 \text{ mol CCl}_4) \times \frac{153.8 \text{ g CCl}_4}{\text{mol CCl}_4}$$

= **<u>21.1 g CCl_4 excess</u>**

2.84 Calculate the limiting reactant first.

$$0.950 \text{ g Ag} \times \frac{1 \text{ mol Ag}}{107.9 \text{ g Ag}} = 8.80 \times 10^{-3} \text{ mol Ag}$$

$$0.140 \text{ g H}_2\text{S} \times \frac{1 \text{ mol H}_2\text{S}}{34.08 \text{ g H}_2\text{S}} = 4.11 \times 10^{-3} \text{ mol H}_2\text{S}$$

$$0.0800 \text{ g O}_2 \times \frac{1 \text{ mol O}_2}{32.00 \text{ g O}_2} = 2.50 \times 10^{-3} \text{ mol O}_2$$

Needed mole ratio is 4:2:1. If H_2S is the limiting reactant, 8.22×10^{-3} mol of Ag and 2.06×10^{-3} mol of O_2 are needed. Therefore, we see that H_2S is the limiting reactant and that Ag and O_2 are present in excess. From this one can calculate the maximum mass of Ag_2S that can be obtained.

$$4.11 \times 10^{-3} \text{ mol H}_2\text{S} \times \frac{2 \text{ mol Ag}_2\text{S}}{2 \text{ mol H}_2\text{S}} \times \frac{247.8 \text{ g Ag}_2\text{S}}{\text{mol Ag}_2\text{S}} = \mathbf{1.02 \text{ g Ag}_2\text{S}}$$

2.85 (a) $0.430 \text{ mol } COCl_2 \times \frac{2 \text{ mol HCl}}{1 \text{ mol } COCl_2} = \underline{\textbf{0.860 mol HCl}}$

(b) $11.0 \text{ g } CO_2 \times \frac{1 \text{ mol } CO_2}{44.01 \text{ g } CO_2} \times \frac{2 \text{ mol HCl}}{\text{mol } CO_2} \times \frac{36.45 \text{ g HCl}}{\text{mol HCl}} = \underline{\textbf{18.2 g HCl}}$

(c) Needed mole ratio is 1:1. Therefore, the $COCl_2$ is the limiting reactant.

$$0.200 \text{ mol } COCl_2 \times \frac{2 \text{ mol HCl}}{\text{mol } COCl_2} = \underline{\textbf{0.400 mol HCl}}$$

2.86 What is present after the first reaction and before any of the second takes place?

$5.00 \text{ g } C_2H_2 \times \frac{1 \text{ mol } C_2H_2}{26.04 \text{ g } C_2H_2} = 0.192 \text{ mol } C_2H_2$ to start with.

$1.92 \text{ mol } C_2H_2 \times \frac{1 \text{ mol } C_2H_2Br_2}{\text{mol } C_2H_2} = 0.192 \text{ mol } C_2H_2Br_2$ after the first rxn.

$40.0 \text{ g } Br_2 \times \frac{1 \text{ mol } Br_2}{159.8 \text{ g } Br_2} = 0.250 \text{ mol } Br_2$ before the first reaction.

Excess Br_2 after first reaction is: 0.250 - 0.192 = 0.058 mol Br_2

Therefore, after the first reaction, there are 0.192 mol $C_2H_2Br_2$ and 0.058 mol Br_2. The Br_2 will be the limiting reactant for the second reaction. The maximum mass of $C_2H_2Br_4$ that can be produced is:

$$0.058 \text{ mol } Br_2 \times \frac{1 \text{ mol } C_2H_2Br_4}{\text{mol } Br_2} \times \frac{345.6 \text{ g } C_2H_2Br_4}{\text{mol } C_2H_2Br_4} = \underline{\textbf{20. g } C_2H_2Br_4}$$

The mass of unreacted $C_2H_2Br_2$ is:

$$(0.192 \text{ mol} - 0.058 \text{ mol}) \times \frac{185.8 \text{ g } C_2H_2Br_2}{\text{mol } C_2H_2Br_2} = \underline{\textbf{24.9 g } C_2H_2Br_2}$$

2.87 The theoretical yield is the maximum amount of product that could be produced from a given quantity of reactant regardless of any other products. The percent yield is a comparison of the theoretical yield to the yield that is actually obtained; it is the efficiency of the reaction. The actual yield is the amount of product that you actually obtain in a given experiment when the reaction is carried out.

2.88 (a) $15.0\ g\ C_6H_6 \times \frac{1\ mol\ C_6H_5Br}{78.12\ g\ C_6H_6} \times \frac{157.0\ g\ C_6H_5Br}{mol\ C_6H_5Br} = \underline{30.1\ g\ C_6H_5Br}$

(b) $2.50\ g\ C_6H_4Br_2 \times \frac{1\ mol\ C_6H_4Br_2}{235.9\ g\ C_6H_4Br_2} \times \frac{1\ mol\ C_6H_6}{mol\ C_6H_4Br_2} \times \frac{78.12\ g\ C_6H_6}{mol\ C_6H_6}$

$= \underline{0.828\ g\ C_6H_6}$

(c) $(15.0\ g\ C_6H_6 - 0.828\ g\ C_6H_6) \times \frac{1\ mol\ C_6H_6}{78.12\ g\ C_6H_6} \times \frac{1\ mol\ C_6H_5Br}{mol\ C_6H_6} \times$

$\frac{157.0\ g\ C_6H_5Br}{mol\ C_6H_5Br} = \underline{28.5\ g\ C_6H_5Br}$

(d) $\text{Percentage yield} = \frac{\text{actual yield}}{\text{theoretical yield}} \times 100$

$\%\ \text{yield} = \frac{28.5}{30.1} \times 100 = \underline{94.7\%}$

2.89 (a) Mol CH_3Cl + mol CH_2Cl_2 + mol $CHCl_3$ + mol CCL_4 must equal mol of CH_4 at the start if the total amount of C is to be maintained.

mol CH_4 ? $\frac{20.8\ g\ CH_4}{16.04\ g\ /mol} = 1.30\ mol\ CH_4$

mol CH_3Cl ? $\frac{5.0\ g\ CH_3Cl}{50.5\ g\ /mol} = 0.099\ mol\ CH_3Cl$

(continued)

(2.89 continued)

mol CH_2Cl_2 ? $\frac{25.5 \text{ g } CH_2Cl_2}{84.93 \text{ g /mol}}$ = 0.300 mol CH_2Cl_2

mol $CHCl_3$? $\frac{59.0 \text{ g } CHCl_3}{119.37 \text{ g /mol}}$ = 0.494 mol $CHCl_3$

mol CCl_4 ? 1.30 - 0.099 - 0.30 - 0.494 = 0.41 mol CCl_4

mass CCl_4 ? 0.41 mol CCl_4 x 153.8 g /mol = <u>63 g CCl_4</u>

(b) If all the available CH_4 had been converted to CCl_4, the theoretical yield would be:

$$1.30 \text{ mol } CH_4 \times \frac{1 \text{ mol } CCl_4}{\text{mol } CH_4} \times \frac{153.8 \text{ g } CCl_4}{\text{mol } CCl_4} = \underline{2.00 \times 10^2 \text{ g } CCl_4}$$

(c) $\frac{63}{200} \times 100 = \underline{32\%}$

(d) $CH_4 + Cl_2 \longrightarrow CH_3Cl + HCl$, $CH_4 + 2Cl_2 \longrightarrow CH_2Cl_2 + 2HCl$

$CH_4 + 3Cl_2 \longrightarrow CHCl_3 + 3HCl$, $CH_4 + 4Cl_2 \longrightarrow CCl_4 + 4HCl$

(0.099 mol CH_3Cl x 1) + (0.300 mol CH_2Cl_2 x 2) + (0.494 mol $CHCl_3$ x 3) + (0.41 mol CCl_4 x 4) = 3.82 mol Cl_2

3.82 mol Cl_2 x 70.91 g /mol = <u>271 g Cl_2</u>

2.90 $\frac{30.0 \text{ g}}{80.0 \text{ g /mol}}$ = 0.375 mol starting material

Step # 1 0.375 x 50% = 0.188 mol

Step # 2 0.188 x 50% = 0.0940 mol

Step # 3 0.0940 x 50% = 0.0470 mol

(2.90 continued)

Step # 4 0.0470 x 50% = 0.0235 mol

Step # 5 0.0235 x 50% = 0.0118 mol

Step # 6 0.0118 x 50% = 0.00590 mol

0.00590 mol x 100 g /mol = **0.590 g** (assuming that 50% has more than 2 significant figures)

If 30.0 g yield 0.590, then how much would be required to produce 10.0 g?

10.0 g product x 30.0 g reactant /0.590 g product = **508 g reactant**

2.91 (a) A solution is a homogeneous mixture that has uniform properties throughout.

(b) The solvent is the component whose physical state doesn't change when the solution is formed. It is usually the major component.

(c) Solute(s) is(are) the substance(s) that is(are) dissolved in the solvent to form a solution.

(d) Concentration is the term used to describe the relative amounts of solute and solvent.

(e) A dilute solution has a relatively low concentration of solute.

(f) A concentrated solution has a relatively high concentration of solute.

2.92 Molar concentration = no. of moles of solute /total volume of the solution in liters

2.93 Place 180 g of $C_6H_{12}O_6$ in a 1.00-liter volumetric flask. Dissolve the sugar in some water; then dilute to a total volume of 1.00 liter.

2.94 0.20 M Na_3PO_4 means; $\frac{0.20 \text{ mol } Na_3PO_4}{1{,}000 \text{ mL solution}}$ and /or $\frac{1{,}000 \text{ mL solution}}{0.20 \text{ mol } Na_3PO_4}$

2.95 (a) 0.250 mol /0.400 L soln. = 0.625 mol /L soln. = **0.625 M NaCl**

(b) 1.45 mol /0.345 L = **4.20 M sucrose**

(c) $\frac{195 \text{ g } H_2SO_4}{0.875 \text{ L soln.}} \times \frac{1 \text{ mol}}{98.08 \text{ g}}$ = **2.27 M H_2SO_4**

(d) $\frac{80.0 \text{ g KOH}}{0.200 \text{ L}} \times \frac{1 \text{ mol}}{56.1 \text{ g}}$ = **7.13 M KOH**

2.96 (a) 1.35 mol NH_4Cl /2.45 L soln. = 0.551 mol /L soln. = **0.551 M NH_4Cl**

(b) 0.422 mol $AgNO_3$ /0.742 L soln. = **0.569 M $AgNO_3$**

(c) 3.00×10^{-3} mol KCl /0.0100 L soln. = **0.300 M KCl**

(d) $\frac{4.80 \times 10^{-2} \text{ g } NaHCO_3}{0.0250 \text{ L}} \times \frac{1 \text{ mol}}{84.01 \text{ g}}$ = 0.0229 mol $NaHCO_3$ /L soln. =

0.0229 M $NaHCO_3$

2.97 (a) $\frac{0.250 \text{ mmol}}{\text{mL}} \times \frac{10^{-3} \text{ mol}}{\text{mmol}} \times \frac{10^{3} \text{ mL}}{\text{L}}$ = **0.250 mol /L**

(b) **0.250 M** (c) **M = mol /L = mmol /mL**

2.98 (a) $\frac{0.150 \text{ mol}}{\text{L}} \times 0.250 \text{ L}$ = **0.0375 mol Li_2CO_3**

(b) $\frac{0.150 \text{ mol } Li_2CO_3}{\text{L}} \times 0.630 \text{ L soln.} \times \frac{73.89 \text{ g } Li_2CO_3}{\text{mol } Li_2CO_3}$ =

6.98 g Li_2CO_3

(c) $\frac{0.0100 \text{ mol } Li_2CO_3}{0.150 \text{ mol } Li_2CO_3 \text{ /L soln.}}$ = 0.0667 L = **66.7 mL solution**

(2.98 continued)

(d) $0.0800\ g\ Li_2CO_3 \times \frac{1\ mol\ Li_2CO_3}{73.89\ g\ Li_2CO_3} \times \frac{1\ L}{0.150\ mol\ Li_2CO_3}$

$\times \frac{10^3\ mL}{L} = \underline{7.22\ mL\ solution}$

2.99 (a) $0.100\ mol\ KOH \times \frac{1\ L\ soln.}{0.375\ mol\ KOH} \times \frac{10^3\ mL}{L} = \underline{267\ mL\ soln.}$

(b) $45.0\ mL\ soln. \times \frac{0.375\ mol\ KOH}{L\ soln.} \times \frac{1\ L}{10^3\ mL} = \underline{0.0169\ mol\ KOH}$

(c) $10.0g\ KOH \times \frac{1\ mol\ KOH}{56.11\ g\ KOH} \times \frac{1\ L\ soln.}{0.375\ mol\ KOH} \times \frac{10^3\ mL}{L} =$

$\underline{475\ mL\ soln.}$

(d) $1\ mL\ soln. \times \frac{1\ L}{10^3\ mL} \times \frac{0.375\ mol\ KOH}{L\ soln.} \times \frac{56.11\ g\ KOH}{1\ mol\ KOH} =$

$\underline{0.0210\ g\ KOH}$

2.100 $\frac{0.250\ mol}{L} \times \frac{2.00\ L}{1} \times \frac{158.2\ g\ Ca(C_2H_3O_2)_2}{mol} = \underline{79.1\ g\ Ca(C_2H_3O_2)_2}$

2.101 $250.0\ mL \times \frac{3.00 \times 10^{-2}\ mmol}{mL} \times \frac{10^{-3}\ mol}{mmol} \times \frac{101.11\ g\ KNO_3}{mol} =$

$\underline{0.758\ g\ KNO_3}$

2.102 $\frac{0.150\ mol\ MgSO_4}{L} \times 0.500\ L \times \frac{246.5\ g\ MgSO_4{\cdot}7H_2O}{mol\ MgSO_4} =$

$\underline{18.5\ g\ MgSO_4{\cdot}7H_2O}$

2.103 The number of moles of solute in soln. does not change as a solution is diluted.

2.104 Add the more dense, concentrated reagent slowly to the water.

2.105 $M_iV_i = M_fV_f$ (V_i = initial vol. in mL)

$(18.0 \text{ M}) V_i = (5.0 \text{ M})(V_i + 100)$ $18.0\, V_i = 5.0\, V_i + 500$

$13.0\, V_i = 500$ $V_i = 38.5$ or **38 mL** (2 significant figures)

2.106 Concentrated NH_3 is 15 **M** (Table 2.2) $15 \text{ M} \times V_i = 0.500 \text{ M} \times 250 \text{ mL}$

$$V_i = \frac{0.500 \text{ M} \times 250 \text{ mL}}{15 \text{ M}} \qquad V_i = \mathbf{8.3\ mL}$$

2.107 Concentrated H_2SO_4 is 18 **M** (Table 2.2)

$$18 \text{ M} \times V_i = 3.0 \text{ M} \times 400 \text{ mL} \qquad V_i = \frac{3.0 \text{ M} \times 400 \text{ mL}}{18 \text{ M}} = \mathbf{67\ mL}$$

2.108 $0.500 \text{ M} \times 100 \text{ mL} = 0.200 \text{ M} \times V_f$

$$V_f = \frac{0.500 \text{ M} \times 100 \text{ mL}}{0.200 \text{ M}} = \mathbf{2.50 \times 10^2\ mL}$$

2.109 $1.00 \text{ M} \times 85.0 \text{ mL} = 0.650 \text{ M} \times V_f$

$$V_f = \frac{1.00 \text{ M} \times 85.0 \text{ mL}}{0.650 \text{ M}} \qquad V_f = 131 \text{ mL}$$

V of H_2O added is 131 mL - 85.0 mL = **46 mL**

2.110 $$15.0 \text{ mL NaOH} \times \frac{0.750 \text{ mol NaOH}}{\text{L}} \times \frac{1 \text{ L}}{1000 \text{ mL}} = \mathbf{0.01125\ mol\ NaOH}$$

$$0.01125 \text{ mol NaOH} \times \frac{1 \text{ mol } H_2SO_4}{2 \text{ mol NaOH}} = 5.625 \times 10^{-3} \text{ mol } H_2SO_4$$

$$\frac{5.625 \times 10^{-3} \text{ mol } H_2SO_4}{0.0250 \text{ L}} = 0.225 \text{ M } H_2SO_4 \text{ used in reaction}$$

(2.110 continued)

$1.40\ \mathbf{M} \times 250\ \text{mL} = 0.225\ \mathbf{M} \times V_f \qquad V_f = \dfrac{1.40\ \mathbf{M} \times 250\ \text{mL}}{0.225\ \mathbf{M}}$

$= 1.56 \times 10^3\ \text{mL or } \underline{\mathbf{1.56\ L}}$

2.111 Known values: **M** = moles /L or **M** x L = moles

Let ? = L of 1.00 **M** HCl added

$0.600\ \mathbf{M} = \dfrac{(0.500\ \mathbf{M} \times 0.0500\ \text{L}) + (1.00\ \mathbf{M} \times ?\ \text{L})}{(0.0500\ \text{L} + ?\ \text{L})}$

0.0300 + 0.600 ? = 0.0250 + ?

0.400 ? = 0.0050 ? = 0.0125 L or **12 mL**

2.112 (a) $3.50\ \text{g Al} \times \dfrac{1\ \text{mol Al}}{26.98\ \text{g Al}} \times \dfrac{3\ \text{mol}\ H_2SO_4}{2\ \text{mol Al}} \times \dfrac{1\ \text{L soln.}}{0.200\ \text{mol}\ H_2SO_4} \times$

$\dfrac{10^3\ \text{mL}}{\text{L}} = \underline{\mathbf{973\ mL}}$

(b) $\dfrac{0.200\ \text{mol}\ H_2SO_4}{\text{L}} \times 0.400\ \text{L} \times \dfrac{3\ \text{mol}\ H_2}{3\ \text{mol}\ H_2SO_4} = \underline{\mathbf{8.00 \times 10^{-2}\ mol\ H_2}}$

2.113 (a) $\dfrac{0.250\ \text{mol NaBr}}{\text{L}} \times 0.300\ \text{L} = 0.0750\ \text{mol NaBr}$

$0.400\ \text{mol}\ AgNO_3\ /\text{L} \times 0.200\ \text{L} = 0.0800\ \text{mol}\ AgNO_3$

Since they react in a 1:1 mole ratio, the **NaBr is the limiting reactant.**

(b) $0.0750\ \text{mol NaBr} \times \dfrac{1\ \text{mol AgBr}}{\text{mol NaBr}} \times \dfrac{187.8\ \text{g AgBr}}{\text{mol AgBr}} = \underline{\mathbf{14.1\ g\ AgBr}}$

2.114 (a) $\dfrac{0.400\ \text{mol NaOH}}{\text{L}} \times 0.0250\ \text{L} = 0.0100\ \text{mol NaOH}$

(continued)

(2.114 continued)

$$0.0100 \text{ mol NaOH} \times \frac{1 \text{ mol } H_2SO_4}{2 \text{ mol NaOH}} = 0.00500 \text{ mol } H_2SO_4$$

Use $\quad \mathbf{M} = \frac{\text{moles}}{\text{L}} \qquad 0.200\ \mathbf{M} = \frac{0.00500 \text{ mol}}{?\ \text{L}}$

$$?\ \text{L} = 0.00500\ /0.200 = 0.0250\ \text{L} = \underline{\mathbf{25.0\ mL}}$$

(b) $\frac{0.270 \text{ mol } H_2SO_4}{\text{L}} \times 0.0500 \text{ L} = 0.0135 \text{ mol } H_2SO_4$

$$0.0135 \text{ mol } H_2SO_4 \times \frac{2 \text{ mol NaOH}}{\text{mol } H_2SO_4} = 0.0270 \text{ mol NaOH}$$

$0.100\ \mathbf{M} = \frac{0.0270 \text{ mol}}{?\ \text{L}} \qquad ?\ \text{L} = 0.0270\ /0.100 = 0.270\ \text{L} = \underline{\mathbf{270\ mL}}$

(c) 0.300 mol NaOH /L x 0.0400 L = 0.0120 mol NaOH

0.350 mol H_2SO_4 /L x 0.015 L = 0.00525 mol H_2SO_4

Needed mole ratio is 2:1. Therefore, the limiting reactant is H_2SO_4.

$$0.00525 \text{ mol } H_2SO_4 \times \frac{1 \text{ mol } Na_2SO_4}{\text{mol } H_2SO_4} = \underline{\mathbf{0.00525\ mol\ Na_2SO_4}}$$

2.115 Let's use the definition of molarity as mmol solute divided by mL solution as a working equation. $\quad \mathbf{M} = \frac{\text{mmol}}{\text{mL}}$ can be substituted into as needed.

(a) $\frac{0.200 \text{ mmol } MgCl_2}{\text{mL}} \times 75.0 \text{ mL} = 15.0 \text{ mmol } MgCl_2$

$$15.0 \text{ mmol } MgCl_2 \times \frac{2 \text{ mmol NaOH}}{\text{mmol } MgCl_2} = 30.0 \text{ mmol NaOH}$$

(2.115 continued)

$$0.300\ M = \frac{30.0\ mmol}{?\ mL} \qquad ?\ mL = 30.0/0.300 = \mathbf{100\ mL}$$

(b) $\frac{0.600\ mmol\ MgCl_2}{mL} \times 50.0\ mL = 30.0\ mmol\ MgCl_2$

$$30.0\ mmol\ MgCl_2 \times \frac{1\ mmol\ Mg(OH)_2}{mmol\ MgCl_2} = 30.0\ mmol\ Mg(OH)_2$$

$$30.0\ mmol\ Mg(OH)_2 \times \frac{1\ mol}{10^3\ mmol} \times \frac{58.33\ g\ Mg(OH)_2}{mol\ Mg(OH)_2} = \underline{1.75\ g}$$

(c) $\frac{0.200\ mmol\ MgCl_2}{mL} \times 30.0\ mL = 6.00\ mmol\ MgCl_2$

$$\frac{0.140\ mmol\ NaOH}{mL} \times 100\ mL = 14.0\ mmol\ NaOH$$

The needed mole- or mmol- ratio is 1 of $MgCl_2$ to 2 of NaOH. In this reaction the $MgCl_2$ is the limiting reagent.

$$6.00\ mmol\ MgCl_2 \times \frac{1\ mmol\ Mg(OH)_2}{mmol\ MgCl_2} \times \frac{10^{-3}\ mol}{mmol} \times \frac{58.33\ g\ Mg(OH)_2}{mol\ Mg(OH)_2} =$$

$\underline{0.350\ g\ Mg(OH)_2}$

2.116 $0.2867\ g\ AgCl \times \frac{1\ mol\ AgCl}{143.32\ g\ AgCl} \times \frac{1\ mol\ AgNO_3}{mol\ AgCl} = 2.000 \times 10^{-3}\ mol\ AgNO_3$

$$M = \frac{2.000 \times 10^{-3}\ mol\ AgNO_3}{0.02000\ L} = \underline{0.1000\ M\ AgNO_3}$$

3 THE PERIODIC TABLE AND THE MAKEUP OF ATOMS

3.1 The ability to deform when hammered is called malleability. A blacksmith relies on the malleability of iron when forging a horseshoe.

3.2 Ductility is the ability of a metal to stretch when pulled from opposite directions. This property is used in the manufacture of wire.

3.3 Three properties, other than malleability and ductility, of metals are: (1) metallic luster, (2) good conductors of heat and (3) good conductors of electricity.

3.4 Sodium reacts avidly with air and moisture. Iron reacts slowly with air and moisture. Gold does not react with air and moisture. Iron is not used to make jewelry because it reacts with air and moisture, also known as tarnishing or rusting.

3.5 $2Na + 2H_2O \longrightarrow 2NaOH + H_2$

3.6 Gold and Copper

3.7 Since they are good conductors of heat, metals feel hot when left in the sun. As your hand absorbs heat from the metal heat travels quickly from the neighboring parts of the objects to replace the heat your hand absorbed.

3.8 The plating of electrical contacts

3.9 Tungsten has the highest melting point of any element, which accounts for its use as the filament in electrical light bulbs. Mercury has the lowest melting point of any metal. Mercury is the fluid used in some thermometers.

3.10 Oxygen (O_2), nitrogen (N_2), hydrogen (H_2), fluorine (F_2), chlorine (Cl_2), bromine (Br_2), and iodine (I_2)

O_2, N_2, H_2, F_2 and Cl_2 are gases.

Br_2 is a liquid. I_2 is a solid.

3.11 Graphite and diamond. Both are made up of carbon. Both lack luster, are nonmalleable and nonductile. Graphite is soft and opaque while diamond is transparent and very hard.

3.12 Yes. Copper has luster which sulfur lacks.

3.13 Oxygen and nitrogen

3.14 Fluorine

3.15 Metalloids look like metals but are darker in color. They conduct electricity but not nearly as well as metals. Metalloids are much more like nonmetals than metals.

3.16 Elements arranged in order of increasing atomic weights. Elements with similar properties placed in columns.

3.17 To leave room for yet undiscovered elements.

3.18 Because in Mendeleev's Table, elements in any particular column had to have similar properties.

3.19 Atomic weight = 71, Melting point = 409°C, Boiling point = 2233°C,

Formula of chloride, $GaCl_3$; Formula of oxide, Ga_2O_3

Melting point of chloride, 388°C

Atomic weight and formulas agree very well. Boiling point is high, as expected. Other properties do not agree very well.

3.20 Co and Ni, Th and Pa, and U and Np

3.21 The Noble Gases were missing because none of them had been discovered.

3.22

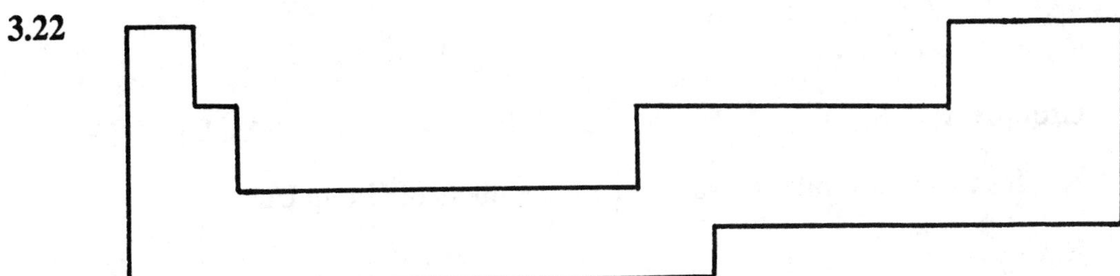

3.23 The vertical columns in the periodic table are called groups. The rows in the periodic table are called periods.

3.24 When the elements are arranged in order of increasing atomic number, there occurs a periodic repetition of similar chemical and physical properties.

3.25 Mg, Se and Br

3.26 Ru, W and Ag

3.27 Elements 58 through 71 and 90 through 103

3.28 F

3.29 F_2, Cl_2, Br_2 and I_2

3.30 K

3.31 Ba

3.32 Ta, Nd and Cs

3.33 B, Al, Si, Ge, As, Sb, Te, Po and At

3.34 The metallic character of the elements decreases from left to right across a period of the periodic table, from metals to metalloid, to nonmetals. From the top to the bottom of Group VA the elements change from nonmetals (N and P) to metalloids (As and Sb) to the metal, Bi.

3.35

	Metals	Nonmetal	Metalloids
Period 4	K, Ca, Sc, Ti, V, Cr, Mn, Fe, Co, Ni, Cu, Zn, Ga	Se, Br, Kr	Ge, As
Group VA	Bi	N, P	As, Sb

3.36 K. It should be similar to Na; both are members of Group IA.

3.37 $RaCl_2$

3.38 (b) iron (c) chromium (d) copper (f) silver and (g) gold are transition metals

3.39 Michael Faraday discovered in 1834 that chemical changes could be caused by the passage of electricity through water solutions of chemical compounds. These experiments demonstrated that matter is electrical in nature.

3.40 See Figure 3.10

3.41 Cathode rays travel in straight lines, cast shadows, turn pinwheels, heat metal foil, and can be bent by an electric or magnetic field.

3.42 The negatively charged particles in the cathode rays are called fundamental particles and are, in fact, electrons. Since cathode rays are always the same

(continued)

(3.42 continued)

regardless of the components used, it was concluded that they are fundamental particles of matter, i.e., particles that cannot be broken into something simpler and are the building blocks of all substances.

3.43 Like charges repel and unlike charges attract. The greater the magnitude of the charge, the greater the effect. If the charged particle is moving, the effect of attraction or repulsion will be a curved path. The greater the mass, the more difficult it will be for the path of the charged particle to curve. Therefore, the deflection will be proportional to the charge and inversely proportional to the mass.

3.44 (a) One coulomb is equal to the amount of charge that moves past a given point in a wire when an electric current of 1 ampere flows for 1 second.

$\underline{1\text{ C} = 1\text{ A} \times 1\text{ s}}$

(b) $\dfrac{1.60 \times 10^{-19}\text{ C}}{e^-} \times \dfrac{6.022 \times 10^{23}\ e^-}{\text{mol } e^-} = \dfrac{\mathbf{9.64 \times 10^{4}\ C}}{\textbf{mol } \mathbf{e^-}} = \dfrac{\text{the charge on a}}{\text{mol of electrons}}$

3.45 (a) $\dfrac{9.11 \times 10^{-28}\text{ g}}{e^-} \times \dfrac{6.022 \times 10^{23}\ e^-}{\text{mol } e^-} = \underline{5.49 \times 10^{-4}\text{ g /mol } e^-}$

(b) $\dfrac{5.49 \times 10^{-4}\text{ g /mol } e^-}{1.0079\text{ g /mol H}} \times 100 = \underline{5.44 \times 10^{-2}\%}$

3.46 Since each charge must be equal to the charge of the electron or a multiple of that charge, look first at the smallest number. Are the other numbers a multiple of that charge? No. Next, look at the differences between the various values. The

(3.46 continued) smallest difference is 0.8×10^{-19}.

Are all the charges a multiple of 0.8×10^{-19}? Yes. Is it the largest possible number that can be divided into all the values? Yes. Therefore, **you would predict, based upon these data, that -0.80×10^{-19} or -8.0×10^{-20} coulombs would be the charge on the electron**.

3.47 Electrons (cathode rays) passing through the gas knock electrons off neutral molecules, which leaves positively charged particles behind.

3.48 Canal rays are rays of positive particles that pass through a perforated cathode.

3.49 Hydrogen is the lightest of all elements and has the largest e /m ratio for any positive ion. Proton.

3.50 The path of the particles is guided by a magnetic field which deflects them in curved paths. The degree of curvature of these paths is determined by the charge-to-mass ratio of the ions and the strength of the magnetic field.

3.51 (a) Charge-to-mass ratio of the proton =

$$\frac{+1.602 \times 10^{-19}\text{ coulombs}}{1.67 \times 10^{-24}\text{ g}} = \mathbf{9.59 \times 10^{4}\ C/g}$$

(b) Charge-to-mass ratio of the electron = 1.76×10^{8} C /g

(Note: the sign of the charge has been dropped for this consideration.)

$$\frac{\text{Charge-to-mass ratio of the proton}}{\text{Charge-to-mass ratio of the electron}} = \frac{9.59 \times 10^{4}\ C/g}{1.76 \times 10^{8}\ C/g} = \mathbf{5.45 \times 10^{-4}}$$

Since the mass of a proton is much greater than the mass of an electron, one should expect the charge-to-mass ratio of a proton to be less than that of an electron. This answer verifies just what one would expect.

3.52 The number of protons in the atom's nucleus

3.53 A different number of protons in their nuclei, 7 for N and 8 for O.

3.54 $\frac{+4.8 \times 10^{-19}\ C}{1.6 \times 10^{-19}\ C /\ e^- \text{ lost}} = +3$ or $\underline{Al^{3+}}$

3.55 $-3.2 \times 10^{-19}\ C / 1.6 \times 10^{-19}\ C / e^-$ gained $= -2$ or $\underline{Se^{2-}}$

3.56 Because some of the alpha particles were strongly deflected by the thin foil.

3.57 Alpha, α, He^{2+} particles; beta, β, composed of electrons; gamma, γ rays, high energy light waves.

3.58 Since the helium nucleus, or alpha particle, has twice the charge and 4 times the mass (e /m = 2 /4 or 1 /2), the e /m ratio is half that of the proton and would be deflected less in the mass spectrometer.

3.59 (a) $+3.20 \times 10^{-19}$ C (b) $+1.60 \times 10^{-19}$ C (c) -1.60×10^{-19} C
(d) -1.60×10^{-19} C (e) no charge (f) no charge

3.60 Density = m /v mass = 1.67×10^{-24} g

$v = (4/3)\,\pi\, r^3 = (4/3) \times 3.142 \times (0.500 \times 10^{-13}\ cm)^3$

$= (4/3) \times 3.142 \times 1.25 \times 10^{-40}\ cm^3 = 5.24 \times 10^{-40}\ cm^3$

Density $= 1.67 \times 10^{-24}\ g / 5.24 \times 10^{-40}\ cm^3 = \underline{3.19 \times 10^{15}\ g/cm^3}$

3.61 $v = (4/3)\,\pi\, r^3$ vol. of nucleus $= (4/3)\,\pi\,(1 \times 10^{-13}/2)^3 cm^3$

$= 5 \times 10^{-40}\ cm^3$

vol. of atom $= (4/3)\,\pi\,(2 \times 10^{-8}/2)^3\ cm^3 = 4 \times 10^{-24}\ cm^3$

% occupied by nucleus $= \frac{5 \times 10^{-40}}{4 \times 10^{-24}} \times 100 = \underline{1 \times 10^{-14}\,\%}$

3.62 Mass of the earth in grams is:

$$6.59 \times 10^{21} \text{ tons} \times \frac{2000 \text{ lb}}{\text{ton}} \times \frac{454 \text{ g}}{\text{lb}} = 5.98 \times 10^{27} \text{ g}$$

Use Density $= 3.19 \times 10^{15}$ g /cm^3 from problem 3.60

$$\frac{5.98 \times 10^{27} \text{ g}}{3.19 \times 10^{15} \text{ g/cm}^3} = 1.87 \times 10^{12} \text{ cm}^3$$

Use $v = (4/3)\,\pi\, r^3$ to obtain the radius. $1.87 \times 10^{12} = (4/3)\,\pi\, r^3$

$$r = \sqrt[3]{\frac{1.87 \times 10^{12} \times 3}{4\pi}} = 7.64 \times 10^{3} \text{ cm}$$

Diameter would be: 2 x 7.64×10^3 cm or 1.53×10^4 cm or **153 meters** or **502 ft** or **0.0950 mile**

3.63 Rutherford proposed the existence of neutrons to enable him to account for much of the nuclear mass in excess of that from the number of protons that he observed in his experiments.

3.64 **(a)** A proton has a mass of 1.007276 amu and a charge of 1+.

(b) A neutron has a mass of 1.008665 amu and a charge of 0.

(c) An electron has a mass of 0.0005486 amu and a charge of 1-.

(d) An α-particle has a mass of 4.0 amu and a charge of 2+.

3.65 Because the observed atomic weights are obtained as an average of the masses contributed by each isotope of an atom.

3.66 The mass number is simply the total count of protons plus neutrons and is not quite equal to the atomic mass of an atom.

3.67 ^{132}<u>**Cs**</u> has 55 protons, 77 neutrons and 55 electrons.

^{115}<u>**Cd^{2+}**</u> has 48 protons, 67 neutrons, and 46 electrons.

^{194}<u>**Tl**</u> has 81 protons, 113 neutrons, and 81 electrons.

^{105}<u>**Ag^{+}**</u> has 47 protons, 58 neutrons, and 46 electrons.

^{78}<u>**Se^{2-}**</u> has 34 protons, 44 neutrons, and 36 electrons.

3.68 ^{131}<u>**Ba**</u> has 56 protons, 75 neutrons, and 56 electrons.

^{109}<u>**Cd^{2+}**</u> has 48 protons, 61 neutrons, and 46 electrons.

^{36}<u>**Cl^{-}**</u> has 17 protons, 19 neutrons, and 18 electrons.

^{63}<u>**Ni**</u> has 28 protons, 35 neutrons, and 28 electrons.

^{170}<u>**Tm**</u> has 69 protons, 101 neutrons, and 69 electrons.

3.69 **(a)** ^{55}<u>**Fe**</u> **(b)** ^{86}<u>**Rb**</u> **(c)** ^{204}<u>**Tl**</u> **(d)** ^{170}<u>**Lu**</u> **(e)** ^{169}<u>**Yb**</u>

3.70 **(a)** <u>**29**</u> **(b)** <u>**49**</u> **(c)** <u>**123**</u> **(d)** <u>**99**</u> **(e)** <u>**99**</u>

3.71 <u>**Carbon-12**</u>

3.72 The mass of 47.82% of a mole of ^{151}Eu is:

(150.9 g /mol) x 0.4782 mol = 72.16

The mass of 52.18% of a mole of ^{153}Eu is:

(152.9 g /mol) x 0.5281 mol = 80.75

Total weight of 1 mole of naturally-occuring Eu is: 72.16 + 80.75 = <u>**152.91**</u>

3.73 ^{10}B 10.01294 g /mol x 0.196 mol = 1.96 g

^{11}B 11.00931 g /mol x 0.804 mol = 8.85 g

Average mass of one mole = <u>**10.81 g**</u>

3.74 ^{204}Pb 203.973 g /mol x 0.0148 mol = 3.02

^{206}Pb 205.9745 g /mol x 0.236 mol = 48.6

^{207}Pb 206.9759 g /mol x 0.226 mol = 46.8

^{208}Pb 207.9766 g /mol x 0.523 mol = 109.

Average mass of one mole = **207 g**

3.75 (34.96885 x % ^{35}Cl) + [36.96590 x (100 - % ^{35} Cl)] = 35.453 x 100%

(34.96885% ^{35}Cl) + (3696.590 - 36.96590% ^{35}Cl) = 3545.3

(36.96590 - 34.96885)% ^{35}Cl = 3696.590 - 3545.3

1.99705% ^{35}Cl = 151.3

% ^{35}Cl = **75.76%**

% ^{37}Cl = 100.00 - 75.79

= **24.24%**

3.76 (106.9041 x ?% ^{107}Ag) + 108.9047 (100 - ?% ^{107}Ag) = 107.868 x 100 %

106.9041 x ?% ^{107}Ag + 10890.47 - 108.9047 x ?% ^{107} = 10786.8

2.001 x ?% ^{107}Ag = 103.7

? % ^{107}Ag = **51.82%**

% ^{109}Ag = 100.00 - 51.82 = **48.18%**

4 ELECTRONIC STRUCTURE AND THE PERIODIC TABLE

4.1 See Figure 4.1. Wavelength, λ, is the distance between consecutive peaks in a wave. Frequency, v, is the number of peaks passing a given point per second. They are related to each other by the equation $\lambda \bullet v = c$ where c is the speed of light.

4.2 c = speed of light = **3.00×10^8 m s^{-1}**

4.3 SI unit of frequency is the hertz, 1 Hz = 1 s^{-1}. Units for wavelengths are chosen so that the numbers are simple to comprehend. Thus 320 nm is easier to comprehend than 3.20×10^{-7} m. The visible region of the spectrum runs from about 400 nm to 800 nm.

4.4 **Infrared light has a longer wavelength,** has a lower frequency, and is less energetic than is visible light.

Ultraviolet light has a shorter wavelength, has a higher frequency and is more energetic than visible light.

4.5 (Shortest wavelength) **gamma rays, x rays, ultraviolet light, visible light, infrared light, microwaves, TV waves** (longest wavelength)

4.6 **AM radio** broadcasts have frequencies between **~500 and ~1700 kHz,** while **FM** uses frequencies between **~85 and ~110 MHz.** M= 10^6; k = 10^3

4.7 Wavelength x frequency = speed of light

(a) wavelength x $(8.0 \times 10^{15}\ s^{-1}) = (3.0 \times 10^{8}\ m\ s^{-1})$

wavelength = 3.75×10^{-8} m

two significant figures: **3.8×10^{-8} m** or **38 nm**

(b) 200.0 nm $\left(\frac{10^{-9}\ m}{nm}\right)$ x frequency = speed of light in $m\ s^{-1}$

$(200.0 \times 10^{-9}\ m) \times v = (3.00 \times 10^{8}\ m\ s^{-1})$

$$v = \frac{3.00 \times 10^{8}\ m\ s^{-1}}{200.0 \times 10^{-9}\ m} = 1.50 \times 10^{15}\ s^{-1} \text{ or } \mathbf{1.50 \times 10^{15}\ Hz}$$

(Only 3 significant figures because the speed of light is not an exact number.)

4.8 (a) $\lambda \cdot v = c$ $\lambda \times (9.40 \times 10^{9}\ s^{-1}) = (3.00 \times 10^{8}\ m\ s^{-1})$

$$\lambda = \frac{3.00 \times 10^{8}\ m\ s^{-1}}{9.40 \times 10^{9}\ s^{-1}} = \mathbf{0.0319\ m}$$

(b) λ = **3.19 cm**

4.9 (a) 101.1 MHz = 101.1×10^{6} Hz = $101.1 \times 10^{6}\ s^{-1}$

$\lambda \times v = c$ $\lambda \times (101.1 \times 10^{6}\ s^{-1}) = (3.00 \times 10^{8}\ m\ s^{-1})$

$$\lambda = \frac{3.00 \times 10^{8}\ m\ s^{-1}}{101.1 \times 10^{6}\ s^{-1}} = \mathbf{2.97\ m} \text{ (3 significant figures)}$$

(b) 880 kHz = 880×10^{3} Hz = $880 \times 10^{3}\ s^{-1}$

$\lambda \times (880 \times 10^{3}\ s^{-1}) = (3.00 \times 10^{8}\ m\ s^{-1})$

$$\lambda = \frac{3.00 \times 10^{8}\ m\ s^{-1}}{880 \times 10^{3}\ s^{-1}} \qquad \lambda = \mathbf{341\ m}$$

4.10 $341\ m \times \left(\frac{100\ cm}{m}\right) \times \left(\frac{1\ in.}{2.54\ cm}\right) \times \left(\frac{1\ ft}{12\ in.}\right) = \underline{1120\ ft}$ (>3 football fields)

4.11 A line spectrum results when the light emitted does not contain radiation of all wavelengths as is needed for a continuous spectrum. A continuous spectrum can be obtained by passing sunlight through a prism. If light emitted by a gas discharge tube is passed through a prism, a line spectrum is obtained.

4.12 From the point of view of atomic structure, the lines in the line spectrum are light whose energies are equal to that given off by excited electrons in the atom going to less energetic states. Since only certain excited and ground states are found, this led Bohr to propose the existence of energy levels within an atom.

4.13 The line spectra is also known as the atomic emission spectra, emission spectra and atomic spectra.

4.14 $546\ nm = 546 \times 10^{-9}\ m;\quad \lambda \cdot v = c$

$(546 \times 10^{-9}\ m) \times v = (3.00 \times 10^{8}\ m\ s^{-1})$

$v = \frac{3.00 \times 10^{8}\ m\ s^{-1}}{546 \times 10^{-9}\ m} = \underline{5.49 \times 10^{14}\ s^{-1}}$ or $\underline{5.49 \times 10^{14}\ Hz}$

4.15 The visible lines of the atomic spectrum of hydrogen are at 410.3 nm, 432.4 nm, 486.3 nm, and 656.5 nm. The frequency of each of these is:

(a) (for 410.3 nm) $\lambda \times v = c: (410.3 \times 10^{-9}\ m) \times v = 3.00 \times 10^{8}\ m\ s^{-1}$

$v = \underline{7.31 \times 10^{14}\ s^{-1}}$

(b) (for 432.4 nm) $v = \underline{6.94 \times 10^{14}\ s^{-1}}$

(c) (for 486.3 nm) $v = \underline{6.17 \times 10^{14}\ s^{-1}}$

(d) (for 656.5nm) $v = \underline{4.57 \times 10^{14}\ s^{-1}}$

4.16 Sodium vapor lamps emit intense light at a wavelength of 589 nm. The frequency of the light is:

$$\lambda \times v = c$$

$$(589 \times 10^{-9}\ \text{m}) \times v = (3.00 \times 10^{8}\ \text{m s}^{-1})$$

$$v = \frac{3.00 \times 10^{8}\ \text{m s}^{-1}}{589 \times 10^{-9}\ \text{m}}$$

$$v = \underline{\mathbf{5.09 \times 10^{14}\ s^{-1}}}$$

4.17 Each element has its own characteristic set of emission spectrum lines which can be used to identify the presence of an element in the presence of other elements.

4.18 The Rydberg equation is $1/\lambda = 109{,}678\ \text{cm}^{-1}\left[\frac{1}{n_1^2} - \frac{1}{n_2^2}\right]$

For the Pfund series, $n_a = 5$. For the first two lines of this series n_b would equal 6 and 7. The calculated wavelength of these two lines is:

(When $n_b = 6$) $1/\lambda = 109{,}678\ \text{cm}^{-1}\left[\frac{1}{5^2} - \frac{1}{6^2}\right]$

$$\lambda = 7.45985 \times 10^{-4}\ \text{cm}$$

$$\lambda = \underline{\mathbf{7459.85\ nm}}$$

(When $n_b = 7$) $1/\lambda = 109{,}678\ \text{cm}^{-1}\left[\frac{1}{5^2} - \frac{1}{7^2}\right]$

$$\lambda = 4.65377 \times 10^{-4}\ \text{cm}$$

$$\lambda = \underline{\mathbf{4653.77\ nm}}$$

4.19 $1/\lambda = 109{,}678\ \text{cm}^{-1}\left[\frac{1}{1^2} - \frac{1}{\infty^2}\right]$

$\lambda = 9.11760 \times 10^{-6}\ \text{cm}$ or $9.11760 \times 10^{-8}\ \text{m}$

$\Delta E = h\nu$

$= \frac{hc}{\lambda}$ $\quad h$ = Planck's constant $= 6.63 \times 10^{-34}$ joules x seconds

$$\Delta E = \frac{(6.63 \times 10^{-34}\ \text{J s})(3.00 \times 10^{8}\ \text{m s}^{-1})}{(9.11760 \times 10^{-8}\ \text{m})}$$

$= \underline{\mathbf{2.18 \times 10^{-18}\ joules}}$

To three significant figures, this agrees with the answer obtained in example 4.5.

4.20 Planck's constant is a proportionality constant equal to energy divided by frequency (E /v) which has the units of energy x time.

4.21 A photon is a tiny packet, or quanta, of light energy.

4.22 **(a)** $E = h\nu = (6.63 \times 10^{-34}\ \text{J s})(3 \times 10^{15}\ \text{s}^{-1})$

$= \underline{\mathbf{2 \times 10^{-18}\ J}}$

(b) $E = \frac{hc}{\lambda} = 2 \times 10^{-20}\ \text{J}$

$$\frac{(6.63 \times 10^{-34}\ \text{J s})(3.00 \times 10^{8}\ \text{m s}^{-1})}{\lambda} = 2 \times 10^{-20}\ \text{J}$$

Solving for λ gives: $\lambda = \frac{6.63 \times 10^{-34} \times 3.00 \times 10^{8}\ \text{J m}}{2 \times 10^{-20}\ \text{J}}$

$\lambda = 9.9 \times 10^{-6}\ \text{m} = \underline{\mathbf{10\ \mu m}}$

4.23 (a) 589 nm $= 589 \times 10^{-9}$ m

$$E = \frac{hc}{\lambda} = \frac{(6.63 \times 10^{-34}\ \text{J s})(3.00 \times 10^{8}\ \text{m s}^{-1})}{(589 \times 10^{-9}\ \text{m})} = \mathbf{3.38 \times 10^{-19}\ J}$$

(b) $\frac{3.38 \times 10^{-19}\ \text{J}}{\text{photon}} \times \frac{6.02 \times 10^{23}\ \text{photons}}{\text{mole}} = 2.04 \times 10^{5}$ J /mole =

204 kJ /mol

(c) The specific heat of water is 1.00 cal /g °C (See example 1.13)

$$\frac{1\ \text{cal}}{\text{g °C}} \times ?\text{g} \times ?\text{°C} = ?\ \text{cal}$$

$$\frac{1\ \text{cal}}{\text{g °C}} \times 10.0\ \text{kg} \times \frac{1000\ \text{g}}{\text{kg}} \times ?\ \text{°C} = 2.04 \times 10^{5} \frac{\text{J}}{\text{mole}} \times 1\ \text{mole} \times \frac{1\ \text{cal}}{4.184\ \text{J}}$$

$$?\ \text{°C} = \frac{2.04 \times 10^{5}}{10.0 \times 1000 \times 4.184} = \mathbf{4.88°C}$$

4.24 Planck's relationship (Equation 4.4) and the existence of energy levels in atoms can be used to derive an equation for the atomic emission spectra of hydrogen. Light is emitted by an atom only at certain frequencies and Planck's relationship shows, therefore, that an electron can have only certain discrete amounts of energy with none between. This suggests that the electron is restricted to specific energy levels in the atom.

4.25 The Bohr model imagined that the electrons travel around the nucleus in orbits of fixed size and energy. For this model Bohr mathematically derived an equation for the wavelengths of the light emitted by hydrogen when it produced its atomic spectrum. The model (theory) failed to calculate correctly energies for any atoms more complex than hydrogen.

4.26 In Bohr's theory, when energy is absorbed by an atom, the electron is raised in energy from one level to another and when the electron returns to a lower energy level, light is emitted whose energy is equal to the energy difference between the two levels.

4.27 **(a)** $$\frac{1}{\lambda} = 109{,}678\ \text{cm}^{-1}\left[\frac{1}{2^2} - \frac{1}{4^2}\right]$$

$$\lambda = \underline{\mathbf{4.86273 \times 10^{-5}\ cm}} = \underline{\mathbf{486.273\ nm}}$$

(b) $$\frac{1}{\lambda} = 109{,}678\ \text{cm}^{-1}\left[\frac{1}{3^2} - \frac{1}{6^2}\right]$$

$$\lambda = \underline{\mathbf{1.09411 \times 10^{-4}\ cm}} = \underline{\mathbf{1094.11\ nm}}$$

4.28 $$\Delta E = A\left[\frac{1}{n_a^2} - \frac{1}{n_b^2}\right] = A\left[\frac{1}{1^2} - \frac{1}{3^2}\right] = 0.888889\ A$$

$$\frac{A}{hc} = (109{,}730\ \text{cm}^{-1})$$

$$A = (109{,}730\ \text{cm}^{-1})\ (6.626 \times 10^{-34}\ \text{J s})\ (3.00 \times 10^{8}\ \text{m s}^{-1})\ \left(\frac{10^2\ \text{cm}}{\text{m}}\right)$$

$$= 2.18 \times 10^{-18}\ \text{J}$$

$$\Delta E = 0.888889\ A = (0.888889)\ (2.18 \times 10^{-18}\ \text{J}) = \underline{\mathbf{1.94 \times 10^{-18}\ J}}$$

4.29 The de Broglie relationship treats light as both particles and waves. Using Einstein's equation and Planck's equation, de Broglie derived for particles the equation $\lambda = h/mv$ which contains both wavelength and mass.

4.30 $\lambda = \frac{h}{mv}$; $v = c = 3.00 \times 10^8\ m\ s^{-1}$; $\lambda = 589\ nm = 589 \times 10^{-9}\ m$

$h = 6.626 \times 10^{-34}\ J\ s = 6.626 \times 10^{-34}\ kg\ m^2/s$

$$m = \frac{6.626 \times 10^{-34}\ kg\ m^2/s}{(589 \times 10^{-9}\ m)(3.00 \times 10^8\ m\ s^{-1})} = 3.75 \times 10^{-36}\ kg\ \text{(per photon)}$$

$$m = \left(\frac{3.75 \times 10^{-36}\ kg}{photon}\right) \times \left(\frac{6.02 \times 10^{23}\ photon}{mole}\right) \times \left(\frac{1000\ g}{kg}\right) = \underline{2.26 \times 10^{-9}\ g}$$

4.31 $E = mc^2 = (1.0\ g) \times (3.00 \times 10^8\ m\ s^{-1})^2 = 9.0 \times 10^{16}\ g\ m^2\ s^{-2}$

Recall that: $1\ J = 1\ kg\ m^2\ s^{-2}$

$$E = (9.0 \times 10^{16}\ g\ m^2\ s^{-2}) \times \left(\frac{1\ kg}{10^3\ g}\right)\left(\frac{1\ J}{kg\ m^2\ s^{-2}}\right) = 9.0 \times 10^{13}\ J \times$$

$$\frac{1.0\ g\ H_2O \times 1°C}{4.184\ J \times 100°C} \times \frac{1\ kg}{10^3\ g} \times \frac{2.20\ lb}{kg} \times \frac{1\ ton}{2000\ lb} = \underline{\mathbf{2.4 \times 10^5\ tons}}$$

4.32 K. E. $= \frac{1}{2}mv^2$, $\lambda = \frac{h}{mv}$ or $v = \frac{h}{m\lambda}$

Therefore, K.E. $= \frac{1}{2} m \left(\frac{h^2}{m^2 \lambda^2}\right) = \frac{h^2}{2m\lambda^2}$

$$= \frac{(6.626 \times 10^{-34}\ J\ s)^2}{(2)(9.1091 \times 10^{-31}\ kg)(0.10\ nm)^2} \times \frac{10^9\ nm}{1\ m}^2 \times \frac{1\ kg\ m^2 s^{-2}}{1\ J}$$

$= \underline{\mathbf{2.4 \times 10^{-17}\ J}}$

4.33 $(?\ s)\left(\frac{h}{m\lambda}\right) = \text{distance(d)}$ Time $= \frac{(d)(m\lambda)}{h} = \frac{(10\ cm)(2.0\ g)(0.10\ nm)}{6.626 \times 10^{-34}\ J \cdot s} \times$

$$\left(\frac{1\ J}{1\ kg\ m^2 s^{-2}}\right) \times \left(\frac{1\ kg}{10^3\ g}\right) \times \left(\frac{1\ m}{10^2\ cm}\right) \times \left(\frac{1\ m}{10^9\ nm}\right) = \underline{\mathbf{3.0 \times 10^{19}\ s}}$$

4.34 A diffraction pattern is the pattern of light and dark areas produced on a screen when two beams of diffracted light interact with each other by constructive and destructive interference.

4.35 Because the wavelengths are too small to be detected.

4.36 Electrons and other subatomic particles can be used to produce diffraction patterns.

4.37 A wave whose nodes are stationary. A node is a position where the amplitude of a wave is zero. For an orbital, the node is a place where the probability of finding the electron is zero.

4.38 **n = 1, 2, 3, 4, etc.** The larger the value of n, the greater the average energy of the levels belonging to its associated shell.

4.39 **ℓ = 0, 1, 2, etc., to a maximum value of n-1** The azimuthal quantum number determines the shape of an orbital and, to a certain degree, its energy.

4.40 **m_ℓ = -ℓ to +ℓ including zero** The magnetic quantum number serves to determine an orbital's orientation in space relative to the other orbitals.

4.41 An orbital in an atom has a characteristic energy and can be viewed as a region around the nucleus where the electron can be expected to be found. The region can be described by a wave function.

4.42 **4**

4.43 **s, p, d, f, and g**

4.44 **f**

4.45 **25 orbitals:** 1 s, 3 p's, 5 d's, 7 f's, and 9 g's.

4.46 The ground state is the state of lowest energy.

4.47 (a) Max. electron population: **s 2, p 6, d 10, f 14, g 18, and h 22**

(b) First shell with h subshell has **n = 6**

(c) **-5, -4, -3, -2,-1, 0, 1, 2, 3, 4 and 5**

4.48 In order of increasing energy they are: s < p < d < f

4.49 Bohr's theory could work for hydrogen since hydrogen's electrons can populate only a few, low energy orbitals. His theory failed with an element more complex than hydrogen because it did not account for the many possibilities that exist other than changes in n value for the excited states.

4.50 The circular motion of the charged electron is associated with its "spin" and causes the electron to act as a tiny electromagnet.

4.51 $+\frac{1}{2}$ **and** $-\frac{1}{2}$

4.52 The Pauli exclusion principle states that no two electrons in any one atom may have all four quantum numbers the same. This limits the number of electrons in in any given orbital to two.

4.53

electron no.	n	ℓ	m_ℓ	m_s
1.	2	0	0	+1/2
2.	2	0	0	-1/2
3.	2	1	-1	+1/2
4.	2	1	-1	-1/2
5.	2	1	0	+1/2
6.	2	1	0	-1/2
7.	2	1	+1	+1/2
8.	2	1	+1	-1/2

4.54 **18**

4.55 They are in the same orbital and their spins are in opposite directions.

4.56 Unpaired electrons give atoms, molecules or ions that are paramagnetic, weakly attracted to a magnetic field. Atoms, molecules or ions that have no unpaired electrons are not attracted by a magnetic field and are said to be diamagnetic.

4.57 Hund's rule states that: electrons entering a subshell containing more than one orbital will be spread out over the available orbitals with their spins in the same direction.

4.58 Predicted electron configurations based on position in periodic table.

P; $1s^22s^22p^63s^23p^3$

Ni; $1s^2\ 2s^2\ 2p^6\ 3s^2\ 3p^6\ 4s^2\ 3d^8$

As; $1s^2\ 2s^2\ 2p^6\ 3s^2\ 3p^6\ 4s^2\ 3d^{10}\ 4p^3$

Ba; $1s^2\ 2s^2\ 2p^6\ 3s^2\ 3p^6\ 4s^2\ 3d^{10}\ 4p^6\ 5s^2\ 4d^{10}\ 5p^6\ 6s^2$

Rh; $1s^2\ 2s^2\ 2p^6\ 3s^2\ 3p^6\ 4s^2\ 3d^{10}\ 4p^6\ 5s^2\ 4d^7$

Ho; $1s^2\ 2s^2\ 2p^6\ 3s^2\ 3p^6\ 4s^2\ 3d^{10}\ 4p^6\ 5s^2\ 4d^{10}\ 5p^6\ 6s^2\ 5d^1\ 4f^{10}$

Sn; $1s^2\ 2s^2\ 2p^6\ 3s^2\ 3p^6\ 4s^2\ 3d^{10}\ 4p^6\ 5s^2\ 4d^{10}\ 5p^2$

4.59 Rb; $1s^2\ 2s^2\ 2p^6\ 3s^2\ 3p^6\ 4s^2\ 3d^{10}\ 4p^6\ 5s^1$

Sn; $1s^2\ 2s^2\ 2p^6\ 3s^2\ 3p^6\ 4s^2\ 3d^{10}\ 4p^6\ 5s^2\ 4d^{10}\ 5p^2$

Br; $1s^2\ 2s^2\ 2p^6\ 3s^2\ 3p^6\ 4s^2\ 3d^{10}\ 4p^5$

Cr; $1s^2\ 2s^2\ 2p^6\ 3s^2\ 3p^6\ 4s^1\ 3d^5$

Cu; $1s^2\ 2s^2\ 2p^6\ 3s^2\ 3p^6\ 4s^1\ 3d^{10}$

4.60 K $4s^1$; Al $3s^23p^1$; F $2s^22p^5$; S $3s^23p^4$; Tl $6s^26p^1$; Bi $6s^26p^3$

4.61 Si $3s^23p^2$; Se $4s^24p^4$; Sr $5s^2$; Cl $3s^23p^5$; O $2s^22p^4$; S $3s^23p^4$; As $4s^24p^3$; Ga $4s^24p^1$.

4.62 Because there are no d or f orbitals in periods 1 and 2. Based on the energy-level sequence in Figure 4.12, the 3d subshell does not begin to fill until the 3p and 4s subshells have been filled.

4.63 (a) 15 ($2p^6$ $3p^6$ $4p^3$) (b) 8 ($2p^6$ $3p^2$) (c) 18 ($2p^6$ $3p^6$ $4p^6$)

4.64

(a) P

1s	2s	2p	2p	2p	3s	3p	3p	3p
↑↓	↑↓	↑↓	↑↓	↑↓	↑↓	↑	↑	↑

(b) Ca

1s	2s	2p	2p	2p	3s	3p	3p	3p	4s
↑↓	↑↓	↑↓	↑↓	↑↓	↑↓	↑↓	↑↓	↑↓	↑↓

4.65

		3d	3d	3d	3d	3d	4s	
Sc	[Ar]	↑					↑↓	(P)
Ti	[Ar]	↑	↑				↑↓	(P)
V	[Ar]	↑	↑	↑			↑↓	(P)
Cr	[Ar]	↑	↑	↑	↑	↑	↑	(P)
Mn	[Ar]	↑	↑	↑	↑	↑	↑↓	(P)
Fe	[Ar]	↑↓	↑	↑	↑	↑	↑↓	(P)
Co	[Ar]	↑↓	↑↓	↑	↑	↑	↑↓	(P)
Ni	[Ar]	↑↓	↑↓	↑↓	↑	↑	↑↓	(P)
Cu	[Ar]	↑↓	↑↓	↑↓	↑↓	↑↓	↑	(P)
Zn	[Ar]	↑↓	↑↓	↑↓	↑↓	↑↓	↑↓	(D)

4.66 (a) Sn [Kr] $\frac{\uparrow\downarrow}{5s}$ $\frac{\uparrow}{}$ $\frac{\uparrow}{}$ $\frac{}{}$ ← 5p →

(b) Br [Ar] $\frac{\uparrow\downarrow}{4s}$ $\frac{\uparrow\downarrow}{}$ $\frac{\uparrow\downarrow}{}$ $\frac{\uparrow}{}$ ← 4p →

(c) Ba [Xe] $\frac{\uparrow\downarrow}{6s}$

4.67 Cd, Sr and Kr

4.68 4 orbitals [1s and 3 p's]

4.69 In a Bohr orbit, the electron is confined to a fixed path about the nucleus. In an orbital, the electron is free to move anywhere in the atom. The concept of the probability of locating the electron within a minute volume element at various places applies to orbitals and is a consequence of the uncertainty principle.

4.70 See Figure 4.20.

4.71 The size increases from 1s to 2s, etc., and nodes occur. Their overall shape, however, is spherical.

4.72 The s orbital is spherical while the p orbital is dumbbell-shaped. (See Figures 4.17 and 4.20)

4.73 See Figure 4.21

4.74 Three electrons, which have the same charge, will tend to stay away from each other as far as possible. This they can do by occupying separate p orbitals.

4.75 An atom or ion has no fixed outer limits. Atomic and ionic sizes are usually given in angstroms, nanometers, or picometers.

4.76 (a) 1 Å = 10^{-10} m; therefore, 4.06 Å x $\left(\frac{10^{-10}\text{ m}}{1\text{ Å}}\right)$ = $\underline{4.06 \times 10^{-10}\text{ m}}$

(4.76 continued)

(b) 4.06 Å = 4.06×10^{-10} m = 4.06×10^{-10} m x $\left(\frac{10^9 \text{ nm}}{\text{m}}\right)$ = **$\underline{0.406 \text{ nm}}$**

(c) 4.06 Å = 4.06×10^{-10} m = 4.06×10^{-10} m x $\left(\frac{10^{12} \text{ pm}}{\text{m}}\right)$

= **4.06×10^2 pm** = **$\underline{406 \text{ pm}}$**

4.77 Size trends within the periodic table would predict that Sn is larger.

4.78 (a) Se (b) C (c) Fe^{2+} (d) O^- (e) S^{2-}

4.79 $r_{N^{3-}}$ = 1.71 Å, $r_{O^{2-}}$ = 1.40 Å, r_{F^-} = 1.36 Å. These ions are isoelectonic (i.e., they have identical electron configurations). The effective nuclear charge is increasing N < O < F. This leads to greater attraction for the outer-shell electrons which are pulled closer to the nucleus decreasing the size of the atom. The electron-electron repulsions are the same.

4.80 The lanthanide contraction is the gradual decrease in the sizes of the lanthanide elements that occurs upon the filling of the inner 4f subshell in the lanthanides. As a result, Hf is nearly the same size as Zr, but with a much larger nuclear charge pulling on the outermost electrons. Outer electrons are held more tightly.

4.81 When there are fewer electrons, the interelectron repulsions are less and the outer shell can contract in size under the influence of the nuclear charge.

4.82 <u>Ionization energy</u> is the amount of energy needed to remove an electron from an atom or ion.

<u>Electron affinity</u> is the amount of energy released or absorbed when an electron is added to an atom or an ion.

4.83 As we move from left to right across a period, the increased effective nuclear charge causes the shell to shrink in size and also makes it more difficult to remove an electron.

4.84 (a) Be (b) Be (c) N (d) N (e) Ne (f) S^+ (g) Na^+

4.85 This graph is supposed to illustrate the stability of the noble gas electron configuration.

4.86 (a) Cl (b) S (c) P (predicted from general trends; actually, this is an exception and EA for As is more exothermic.) (d) S

4.87 The second electron that is added must be forced into an already negative ion. This requires work and, therefore, is an endothermic process.

4.88 The Group VIIA elements can attain a stable configuration by acquiring one electron. The octet is a much more stable configuration than just seven electrons and, when the Group VIIA elements do achieve their octet, a relatively large amount of energy is released.

4.89 Ionization energy of H = 1,312 kJ /mol

heat cap. x mass x change in temp. = energy

$$\frac{4.184\text{ J}}{1\text{g}(H_2O) \times 1°\text{C}} \times (\text{mass}) \times (25°\text{C}) = \left(\frac{1{,}312\text{ kJ}}{\text{mol}}\right) \times (1\text{ mol}) \times \left(\frac{10^3\text{ J}}{1\text{kJ}}\right)$$

mass(H_2O) = **$\underline{1.3 \times 10^4\text{ g } H_2O}$**

5 CHEMICAL BONDING: GENERAL CONCEPTS

5.1 Chemical bonds are relatively strong forces of attraction that hold atoms together.

5.2 Ionic compounds tend to be hard and to have high melting points while, on the other hand, molecular compounds tend to be soft and to have low melting points.

5.3 Ionic compounds are able to conduct electricity in the liquid state but not in the solid state. Molecular compounds do not conduct electricity either when melted or in the solid state.

5.4 The presence of mobile ions in an ionic liquid is responsible for its electrical conductivity.

5.5 Lewis symbols help us to keep tabs on the outer shell electrons which are most important in bond formation.

5.6 (a) :Ṡ̤e· (b) :Ḃ̤r: (c) ·Ȧl· (d) ·Ba· (e) ·Ġ̣e· (f) ·P̣̈·

5.7 Elements in a given group all have the same number of valence electrons. Therefore, elements in a given group should all have Lewis symbols that are the same. The atomic symbol changes, but the number of dots or valence electrons does not.

5.8 (a) Two (b) Four (c) Lewis symbols are written in a way that reflects the number of unpaired electrons that are typically involved in bonding and not necessarily the number of unpaired electrons on the atom in its ground state.

5.9 The valence shell of an atom is the outermost shell of an atom that contains electrons when the atom is in its ground state electronic configuration.

5.10

	Elements	Number of valence electrons
(a)	As	5
(b)	I	7
(c)	Ca	2
(d)	Sn	4
(e)	S	6

5.11 An ionic bond results from the attraction between oppositely charged ions.

5.12 Cation is a positively charged ion; anion is a negatively charged ion.

5.13 (a) Ba^{2+} $[Kr]4d^{10}\,5s^2\,5p^6$ or [Xe] (b) Se^{2-} $[Ar]3d^{10}\,4s^2\,4p^6$ or [Kr]

(c) Al^{3+} $[He]2s^2\,2p^6$ or [Ne] (d) Na^+ $[He]\,2s^2\,2p^6$ or [Ne]

(e) Br^- $[Ar]\,3d^{10}\,4s^2\,4p^6$ or [Kr]

5.14 (a) Xe (b) Kr (c) Ne (d) Ne (e) Kr

5.15 The tendency for atoms to achieve an outer-shell configuration with a total of eight electrons (the stable electronic structure of noble gases) forms the basis of the octet rule. The octet rule states that an atom tends to gain or lose electrons until there are eight electrons in its outer shell.

5.16 (a) $Ba^{2+}\,[:\ddot{\underset{..}{O}}:]^{2-}$ (b) $2Na^+\,[:\ddot{\underset{..}{O}}:]^{2-}$ (c) $K^+\,[:\ddot{\underset{..}{F}}:]^-$

(d) $Ca^{2+}\,[:\ddot{\underset{..}{S}}:]^{2-}$ (e) $2Mg^{2+}\,[:\ddot{\underset{..}{C}}:]^{4-}$

5.17 (a) Sr^{2+} (b) $[:\ddot{\underset{..}{N}}:]^{3-}$ (c) $[:\ddot{\underset{..}{O}}:]^{2-}$ (d) $[:\ddot{\underset{..}{Cl}}:]^-$ (e) K^+ (f) Mg^{2+}

5.18 An element in periods 4, 5, or 6 that is also in Groups IIIA to VIIA is a post-transition element.

5.19 (a) $Zn^{2+}[Ar]3d^{10}$ (b) $Sn^{2+}[Kr]4d^{10}\,5s^2$ (c) $Bi^{3+}[Xe]4f^{14}\,5d^{10}\,6s^2$

(d) $Cr^{2+}[Ar]3d^4$ (e) $Fe^{3+}[Ar]3d^5$ (f) $Ag^{+}[Kr]4d^{10}$

5.20 $ns^2\,np^6\,nd^{10}$, Zn^{2+}, Cd^{2+}, Hg^{2+}

5.21 (a) both are [Ar] (d) both are [Kr] (e) both are [Ne]

5.22 Looking at outer-shell configurations

K $4s^1 \longrightarrow 4s^0$	O $2s^22p^4 \longrightarrow 2s^22p^6$
Mg $3s^2 \longrightarrow 3s^0$	N $2s^22p^3 \longrightarrow 2s^22p^6$
Na $3s^1 \longrightarrow 3s^0$	S $3s^23p^4 \longrightarrow 3s^23p^6$
Ba $6s^2 \longrightarrow 6s^0$	Br $4s^24p^5 \longrightarrow 4s^24p^6$

5.23 (a) $CaBr_2$ (b) K_2S (c) Al_2O_3 (d) Ba_3P_2 (e) Mg_3N_2

5.24 (a) should be $\mathbf{Rb_2O}$ (b) should be $\mathbf{K_2S}$ (c) should be **CaO**

(d) should be **KBr**

5.25 $Mg\cdot + \cdot\dot{\underset{\cdot}{C}}\cdot$ (+ $Mg\cdot$) $\longrightarrow 2Mg^{2+}\ [:\ddot{\underset{\cdot\cdot}{C}}:]^{4-}$

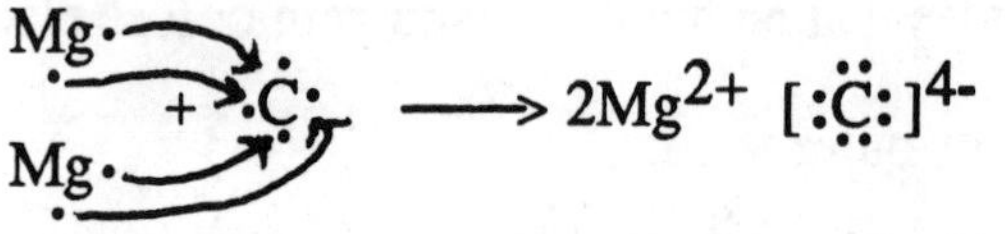

5.26 See Table 5.3 (a) $CrCl_2$, $CrCl_3$, CrS and Cr_2S_3

(b) $MnCl_2$, $MnCl_3$, MnS and Mn_2S_3 (c) $FeCl_2$, $FeCl_3$, FeS and Fe_2S_3

(d) $CoCl_2$, $CoCl_3$, CoS and Co_2S_3 (e) $NiCl_2$ and NiS

(f) CuCl, $CuCl_2$, Cu_2S and CuS (g) AgCl and Ag_2S

5.27 See Table 5.3 (a) AuBr, $AuBr_3$, Au_2O and Au_2O_3 (b) $ZnBr_2$ and ZnO (c) $CdBr_2$ and CdO (d) AgBr and Ag_2O (e) $SnBr_2$, $SnBr_4$, SnO and SnO_2 (f) $PbBr_2$, $PbBr_4$, PbO and PbO_2 (g) $BiBr_3$ and Bi_2O_3

5.28 (a) Ammonium ion (b) Carbonate ion (c) Chromate ion (d) Sulfite ion (e) Acetate ion

5.29 (a) CN^- (b) ClO_4^- (c) MnO_4^- (d) NO_3^- (e) PO_4^{3-} (f) OH^- (g) $C_2O_4^{2-}$ (h) $Cr_2O_7^{2-}$ (i) SO_4^{2-} (j) HCO_3^- (k) SO_3^{2-} (l) NO_2^-

5.30 (a) Na_2CO_3 (b) $Ca(ClO_3)_2$ (c) SrS (d) $CrCl_3$ (e) $Ti(ClO_4)_4$

5.31 (a) $CrCO_3$, $Cr_2(CO_3)_3$, $CrCrO_4$, $Cr_2(CrO_4)_3$, $CrSO_3$, $Cr_2(SO_3)_3$, $Cr(C_2H_3O_2)_2$, $Cr(C_2H_3O_2)_3$

(b) $MnCO_3$, $Mn_2(CO_3)_3$, $MnCrO_4$, $Mn_2(CrO_4)_3$, $MnSO_3$, $Mn_2(SO_3)_3$, $Mn(C_2H_3O_2)_2$, $Mn(C_2H_3O_2)_3$,

(c) $FeCO_3$, $Fe_2(CO_3)_2$, $FeCrO_4$, $Fe_2(CrO_4)_3$, $FeSO_3$, $Fe_2(SO_3)_3$, $Fe(C_2H_3O_2)_2$ and $Fe(C_2H_3O_2)_3$

(d) through (n) Repeat using the other 11 metals.

5.32 (a) $Fe_2(HPO_4)_3$ (b) K_3N (c) $Ni(NO_3)_2$ (d) $Cu(C_2H_3O_2)_2$ (e) $BaSO_3$

5.33 For many of them, their outer shells have two electrons.

5.34 The second shell can contain a maximum of 8 electrons.

5.35 Lattice energy. Exothermic.

5.36

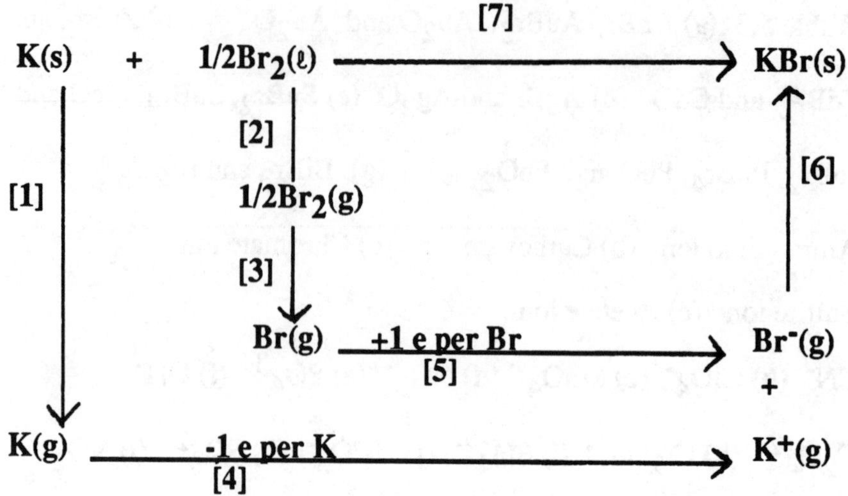

Steps [1], [2], [3,], and [4] are endothermic. Steps [5], [6], and [7] are exothermic. The sum of steps (1) through (6) = step (7) = overall reaction

5.37 The conversion of K(s) and $F_2(g)$ to KF(s) is exothermic primarily because of the lowering effect of the lattice energy.

5.38

$K(s) + 1/2\ Cl_2(g) \xrightarrow{[6]} KCl_2(s)$

[1] K(s) → K(g)

[2] $1/2\ Cl_2(g)$ → Cl(g)

[3] K(g) → K^+ (- 1 e per K)

[4] Cl(g) → Cl^- (+ 1 e per Cl)

[5] Cl^- + K^+ → $KCl_2(s)$

[1] + [2] + [3] + [4] + [5] = [6]

[1] = 90.0 kJ
[2] = 119 kJ
[3] = 419 kJ
[4] = -348 kJ
[5] = -704.2 kJ
[6] = **-424. kJ** (exothermic)

5.39 $Ca(s) + Cl_2(g) \xrightarrow{[7]} CaCl_2(s)$

[1] $Ca(s) \rightarrow Ca(g)$

[4] $Cl_2(g) \rightarrow 2Cl(g)$

$2Cl(g) \xrightarrow[\text{[5]}]{\text{+ 1 e per Cl}} 2Cl^-(g)$

[6] $2Cl^-(g) + Ca^{2+}(g) \rightarrow CaCl_2(s)$

$Ca(g) \xrightarrow[\text{[2]}]{\text{-1 e per Ca}} Ca^+(g) \xrightarrow[\text{[3]}]{\text{- 1 e per } Ca^+} Ca^{2+}(g)$

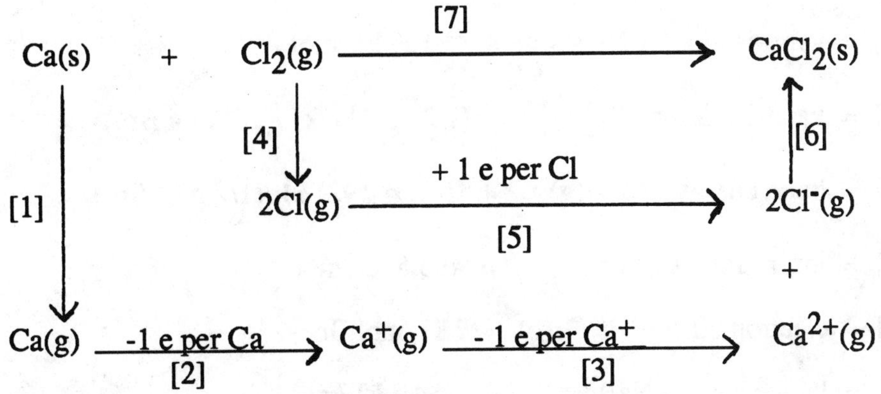

[1] = vaporization energy of Ca(s) = 192 kJ /mol

[2] = 1st ionization energy of Ca(g) = 589.5 kJ /mol

[3] = 2nd ionization energy of Ca(g) = 1146. kJ /mol

[4] = bond energy of Cl_2 = 238 kJ /(mol Cl_2)

[5] = electron affinity of Cl = 2 x (-348) kJ /(2 mol Cl)

[6] = lattice energy of $CaCl_2$ = ? kJ /mol $CaCl_2$

[7] = overall reaction = -795 kJ /mol $CaCl_2$

192 kJ + 589.5 kJ + 1146 kJ + 238 kJ + 2(-348 kJ) + ? kJ = -795 kJ

? = **-2,264 kJ**

5.40

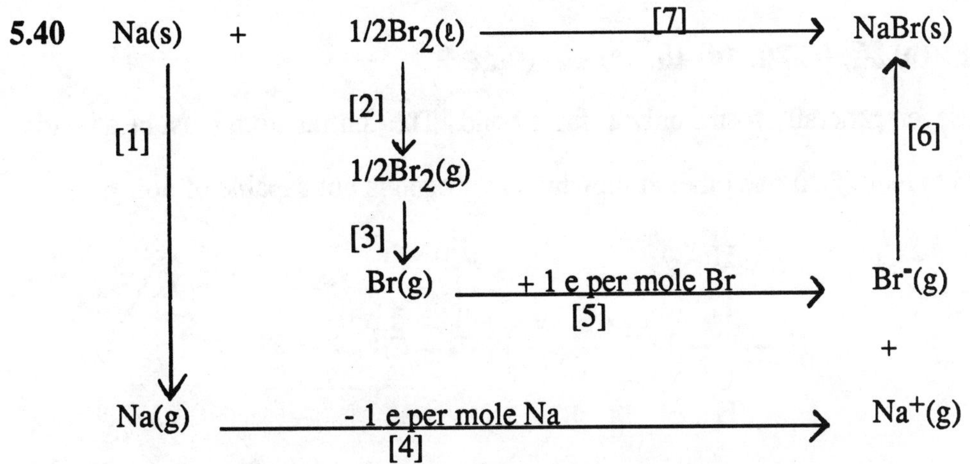

(5.40 continued)

[1] = vaporization of Na(s) = 109 kJ /mol

[2] = vaporization of $Br_2(\ell)$ = (1/2 x 31) kJ /(1/2 mol Br_2)

[3] = bond energy of $Br_2(g)$ = (1/2 x 192) kJ /(1/2 mol Br_2)

[4] = ionization of Na(g) = 495.8 kJ /mol

[5] = electron affinity of Br(g) = ? kJ /mol Br

[6] = lattice energy NaBr = -734.3 kJ /mol

[7] = overall reaction = - 360 kJ /mol

[1] + [2] + [3] + [4] + [5] + [6] = [7]

109 + (1/2 x 31) + (1/2 x 192) + 495.8 + (?) + (-734.3) = -360

? = electron affinity of Br(g) = <u>-342 kJ /mol</u>

5.41 (a) H—N̈—H with H below N (b) Cl—P̈—Cl with Cl below P (c) Cl—S̈: with Cl on S

(d) $[O{=}N\cdot$—O$]^-$ (e) F—B̈r—F with F above and F, F below (f) $[Cl—P—Cl$ with Cl above and Cl below$]^+$

5.42 (a) <u>8</u> (b) <u>26</u> (c) <u>20</u> (d) <u>18</u> (e) <u>42</u> (f) <u>32</u>

5.43 Hydrogen generally forms only a single bond. The central atom must be able to bond to more than one other atom which hydrogen is not capable of doing.

5.44 :C̤̈l—P̈—C̤̈l: with :C̤̈l: below P   H—Si—H with H above and H below Si   :C̤̈l—B—C̤̈l: with :C̈l: above B

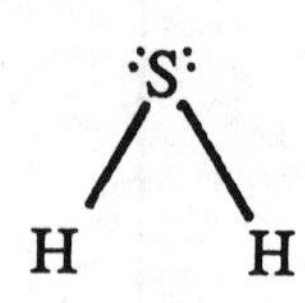

(5.44 continued)

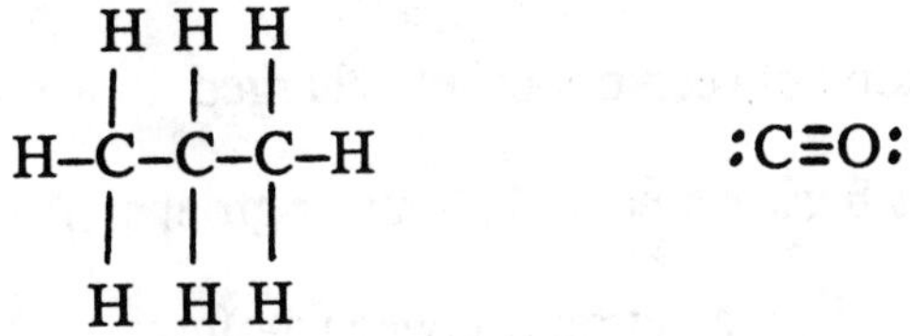

$CH_3CH_2CH_3$ (H–C–C–C–H with H above and below each C) $:C\equiv O:$

5.45 $:\ddot{Cl}-\ddot{Cl}:$, SO_2, OF_2, SnH_4, $H_2C=CH_2$, SCl_2

5.46 $:\ddot{Cl}:^-$, $:\ddot{S}:^{2-}$, $:\ddot{Cl}-\ddot{O}:^-$,

$[ClO_4]^-$ $[SO_3]^{2-}$ $[PO_4]^{3-}$

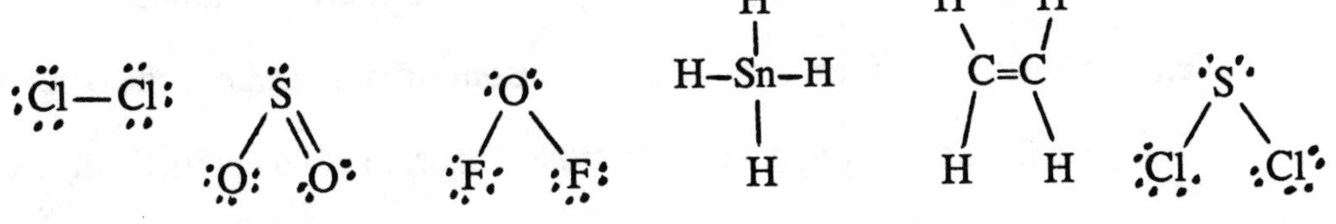

5.47 $[NO_3]^-$ [:N≡O:]$^+$ $[NO_2]^-$ $[CO_3]^{2-}$

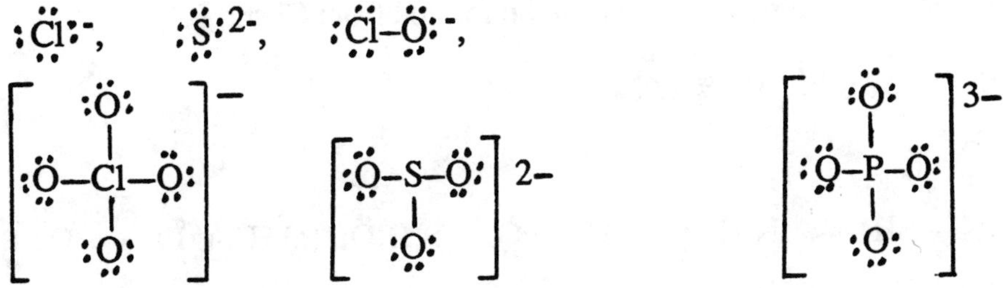

5.48 SeF_6 SeF_4 ICl_3 $AsCl_5$

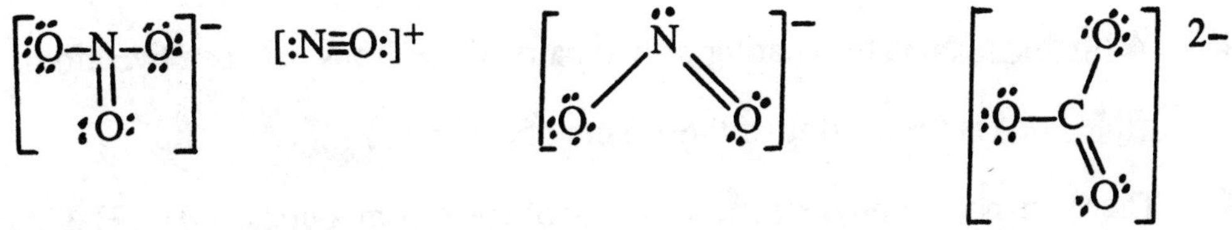

[:Cl–I–Cl:]$^-$ $[ICl_4]^-$ XeF_4

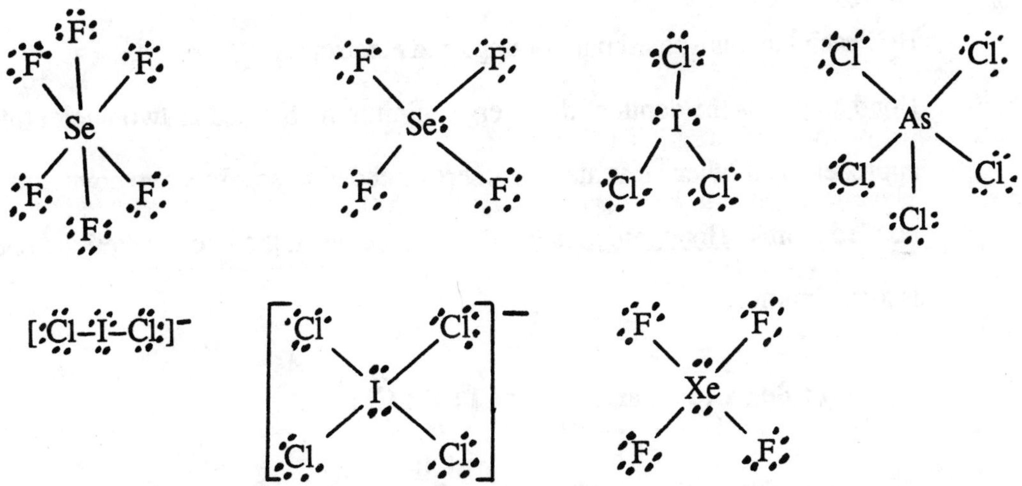

5.49 ClF_3, SF_4, IF_7, NO_2, BCl_3

5.50 The ionic bond results from attraction between oppositely charged ions that can be traced to the transfer of electrons between neutral atoms or groups. A covalent bond results from the sharing of a pair of electrons between atoms.

5.51 Neither Cl nor F can form a stable cation. Both strive to achieve the octet by gaining an electron, not by losing electrons. Therefore, no energetically favored combination of cation and anion can be formed from Cl and F.

5.52 (a) 4 (b) 2 (c) 1 (d) 4 (e) 3

5.53 (a) :Ṅ̤· + 3H· —> H:N̤̈:H (with a third H below N) (b) 2 H· + ·Ọ̇: —> H:Ö̤: (with H above O) (c) H· + ·F̤̈: —> H:F̤̈:

5.54 A double bond is the sharing of two pairs of electrons between two atoms. A triple bond is the sharing of three pairs of electrons.

5.55 There are no unpaired electrons in any of these compounds. NH_3, H_2O, and HCl each have unshared but not unpaired electrons.

5.56 Bond energy is the depth of the energy minimum obtained as two nuclei (atoms) approach each other. It is also the energy needed to separate two covalently bonded atoms. Bond length is the distance between the nuclei when the energy is a minimum.

5.57 (a) :C̤̈l : Be : C̤̈l: and :C̤̈l : B : C̤̈l: (with :C̤l: bonded below B)

(b) 4 in $BeCl_2$ and 6 in BCl_3

5.58 **(a)** <u>4</u> **(b)** <u>4</u> **(c)** <u>2</u> **(d)** <u>2</u>

5.59 **(a)** <u>4</u> **(b)** <u>Yes</u> **(c)** Because in some compounds the d orbitals of phosphorus are utilized. Nitrogen does not possess d orbitals in its valence shell.

5.60 <u>Bond order</u> is the number of covalent bonds that exist between a pair of atoms.

5.61 **(a)** Each C-Cl bond has a bond order of <u>**1**</u>.

(b) In HCN the H-C bond order is <u>**1**</u> and the C≡N bond order is <u>**3**</u>.

(c) In CO_2 each C=O has a bond order of <u>**2**</u>.

(d) In NO^+ the bond order is <u>**3**</u>.

(e) In CH_3NCO the bond order between each hydrogen and the carbon is <u>**1**</u>, between one of the carbons and nitrogen it is <u>**1**</u>, between nitrogen and the other carbon it is <u>**2**</u> and between carbon and the oxygen it is <u>**2**</u>.

5.62 Bond energy <u>increases as bond order increases</u> because the additional electron density between the nuclei increases the attraction of the nuclei for that electron density.

5.63 Bond length <u>decreases as bond order increases</u> because the additional electron density between the nuclei causes the nuclei to be pulled together.

5.64 Bending motions are those that change the bond angles while vibration motions change bond lengths (see Figure 5.7). Strength of bonds will influence the frequency with which a molecule will vibrate.

5.65 The greater the bond order the shorter and stronger the bond and the greater the vibrational frequency. Strong bonds will vibrate faster with shorter amplitude just as will a strong spring compared to a weak spring. Infrared absorption

(5.65 continued)

spectra are used to measure bond vibrational frequencies. When infrared radiation shines on a substance, the infrared frequencies that are the same as the vibrational frequencies of the bonds in the substance are absorbed.

5.66 154pm, 146pm, 140pm and 137pm. Bond energy also increases in this direction.

5.67 A resonance hybrid is the true structure of a compound and is a composite of the contributing structures. We use resonance because it is impossible to draw a single electron-dot formula that obeys the octet rule and is consistent with experimental facts at the same time.

5.68

(5.68 continued)

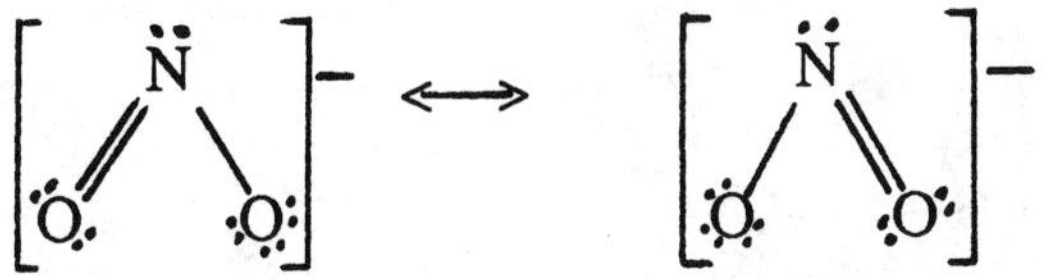

[N / O O]⁻ ⟷ [N / O O]⁻

5.69

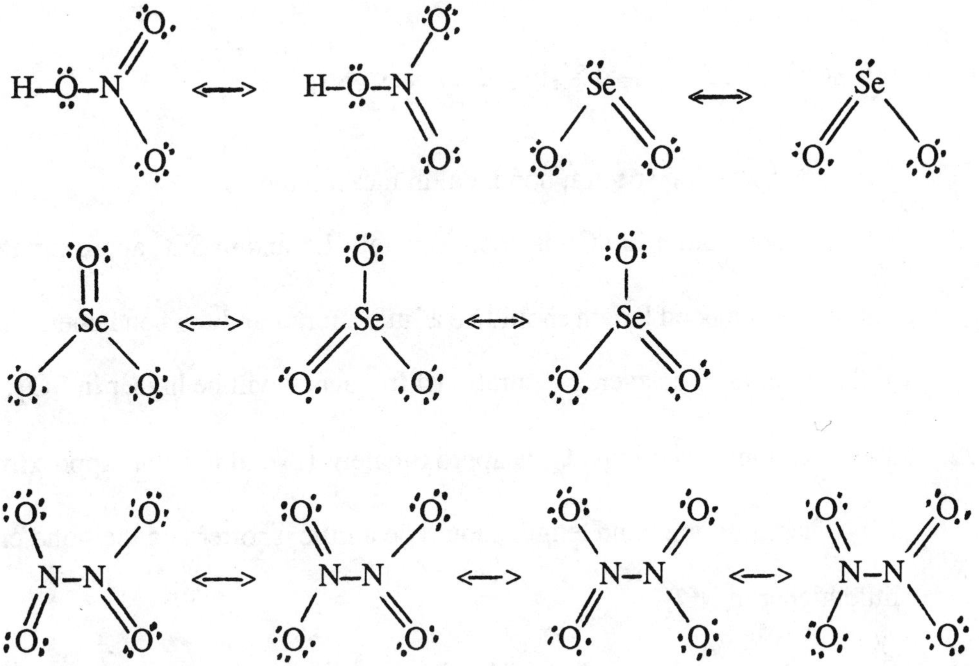

H–O–N(=O)–O ⟷ H–O–N(–O)=O   Se(–O)=O ⟷ Se(=O)–O

O=Se(–O)–O ⟷ O–Se(=O)–O ⟷ O–Se(–O)=O

N–N ⟷ N–N ⟷ N–N ⟷ N–N

5.70

[C–C] 2- ⟷ [C–C] 2- ⟷ [C–C] 2- ⟷

[C–C] 2-

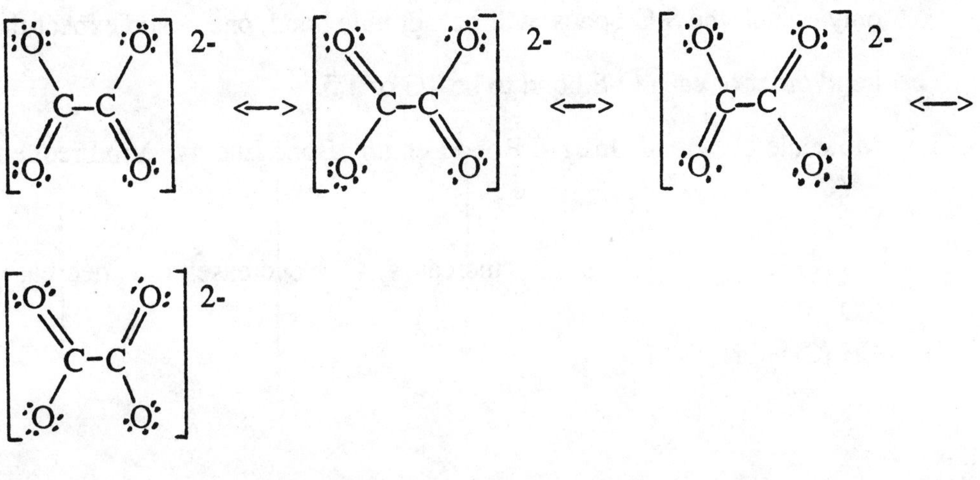

(5.70 continued)

```
[      H          ]-            [      H          ]-
       |                               |
  H—C—C—Ö:            <—>         H—C—C=Ö
       |  ||                              |
       H  :O:                         H   :O:
```

[N=N=N]$^-$ <—> [:N≡N-N:]$^-$ <—> [:N-N≡N:]$^-$

5.71 Infrared absorption spectra, bond length measurements

5.72 The S-O bond order in SO_2 is approximately 1.5 and in SO_3 approximately 1.3. Therefore, the bond length should be a little shorter and the bond energy a little higher in SO_2. The average vibrational frequency will be higher in SO_2.

5.73 The N-O bond order in NO_2^- is approximately 1.5 and in NO_3^- approximately 1.3. Therefore, the bond length should be a little shorter and the bond energy a little higher in NO_2^-.

5.74 Because SO_3 can be represented by three resonance structures in each of which only one of the S-O bonds will be a double bond, one would expect the bond order of each O-S bond to be 4/3 or <u>1.3</u>.

5.75

Molecule	Bond Order	Bond Length	Bond Energy	Vib.Frequency
CO	3			
CO_2	2			
CH_3COO^-	1.5	increases ↓	decreases ↓	decreases ↓
CO_3^{2-}	1.3			
CH_3CH_2OH	1			

5.76 A coordinate covalent bond is one where a pair of electrons from one atom is shared by the two atoms in a bond. It differs from normal covalent bonds in that electrons being shared between two atoms are both coming from one atom instead of one electron from each. It is really only a bookkeeping device; once formed, the coordinate covalent bond is the same as any other covalent bond.

5.77

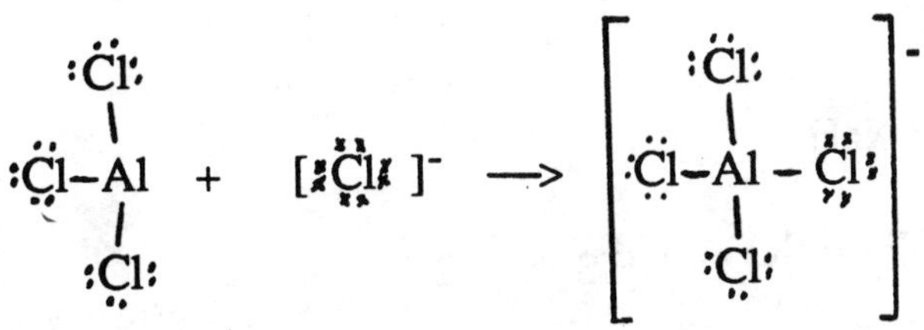

$$AlCl_3 + [:\ddot{Cl}:]^- \longrightarrow [AlCl_4]^-$$

5.78 Since it has neither an unbonded pair of electrons to donate nor any way to accept a pair of electrons, the molecule CH_4 would not be expected to participate in the formation of a coordinate covalent bond.

5.79

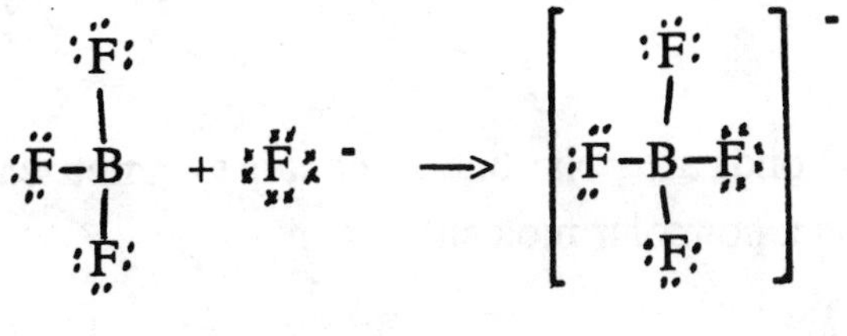

$$BF_3 + [:\ddot{F}:]^- \longrightarrow [BF_4]^-$$

5.80 Electronegativity is the attraction an atom has for electrons in a chemical bond. Electron affinity, which is an energy term referring to an isolated atom, is the energy released or absorbed when an electron is added to a neutral gaseous atom.

5.81 A polar molecule is one that has its positive and negative charges separated by a distance. The resulting molecule is said to be a dipole. The dipole moment is the product of the charge on either end of the dipole times the distance between the charges.

5.82 Fluorine, upper right -hand corner, is the element highest in electronegativity. The values generally decrease down a group and right to left across a period. Elements with low ionization energies generally have low electronegativities and those with high ionization energies also have high electronegativities.

5.83 (a) P–F (b) Al–Cl (c) Se–Cl

5.84 MgO, Al_2O_3 and CsF

5.85 NH_3, BCl_3, BeI_2 and NaH

5.86 $F_2 < H_2Se < H_2S < OF_2 < SO_2 = ClF_3 < SF_2$

5.87 Rb

5.88 Being a nonsymmetrical molecule (bent) with polar bonds, it will be a polar molecule. Since the oxygen is the more electronegative element, the oxygen atoms will have a negative charge and the sulfur end or side will carry the positive charge.

5.89 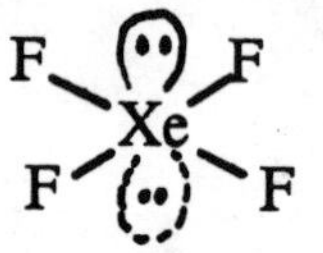 F, F, Xe, F, F — The bonds are polar but, since it is symmetrical, it is a nonpolar molecule.

5.90 The difference between an experimental bond energy and a calculated bond energy is proportional to the electronegativity difference between the bonded atoms.

Compounds	HF	HCl	HBr	HI
Difference between calc. and exp. bond energies (kJ /mol)	270	94	50	10

(continued)

(5.90 continued)

Since the electronegativity of hydrogen is constant in each compound, the differences must be due to the present of the other elements. The change in bond energy indicates a decrease in electronegativity from F to I.

5.91 (See answer to Question 5.90)

Compounds	LiH	NaH	KH	RbH
Difference between calc. and exp. bond energies (kcal /mol)	8.2	13	14	19

Since the bond energy difference is increasing, the electronegativity difference must be increasing. Since the electronegativity of hydrogen is constant, and larger than the electronegativity of any alkali metal, the electronegativities of the alkali metals must decrease from lithium to rubidium.

5.92 $NaBr$ sodium bromide CaO calcium oxide

$FeCl_3$ ferric chloride; iron(III) chloride $AsCl_5$ arsenic pentachloride

$CuCO_3$ cupric carbonate; copper(II) carbonate

CBr_4 carbon tetrabromide P_4O_6 tetraphosphorus hexoxide

$Mn(HCO_3)_2$ manganous hydrogen carbonate; manganous bicarbonate; manganese(II) hydrogen carbonate; manganese(II) bicarbonate

$NaMnO_4$ sodium permanganate O_2F_2 dioxygen difluoride

5.93 $Al(NO_3)_3$, $FeSO_4$, $NH_4H_2PO_4$, IF_5, PCl_3, N_2O_4, $KMnO_4$, $Mg(OH)_2$, H_2Se, NaH

5.94 Chromium(III) oxide or chromic nitrate | Aluminum phosphate

Magnesium dihydrogen phosphate | Magnesium nitride

Copper(II) nitrate or cupric nitrate | Lead(II) oxalate

Calcium sulfate | Ammonium carbonate

Barium hydroxide | Potassium dichromate

5.95 TiO_2 $Ni(HCO_3)_2$

$SiCl_4$ $NaHSO_4$

$CaSe$ $(NH_4)_2Cr_2O_7$

KNO_3 $Ca(C_2H_3O_2)_2$

$Al_2(SO_4)_3$ $Sr(OH)_2$

5.96 (a) $Fe_2(SO_4)_3$ (b) $FeCl_2$ (c) $Hg_2(NO_3)_2$ (d) $CuCl$ (e) $SnCl_4$
(f) $Co(OH)_2$ (g) $AuCl_3$ (from Table 5.3) (h) $Cr(C_2H_3O_2)_3$

5.97 (a) chromium(II) carbonate, chromium(III) carbonate, chromium(II) chromate, chromium(III) chromate, chromium(II) sulfite, chromium(III) sulfite, chromium(II) acetate, and chromium(III) acetate [Parts (b) through (n) are not answered in this solutions manual.]

6 COVALENT BONDING AND MOLECULAR STRUCTURE

6.1 See the figures with Section 6.1.

6.2 180°

6.3 planar triangular, 120°; tetrahedral, 109.5°; octahedral, 90°.

6.4 Within triangular plane, 120°; between triangular plane and apex, 90°.

6.5 (a) 4 (b) 6 (c) 5

6.6 Covalent bonds between any bonded species consist of a sharing of electron pairs. The geometric arrangements of atoms, or groups of atoms, about some central atom is determined solely by the mutual repulsion between the electron pairs (both bonding and lone pairs) present in the valence shell of the central atom.

6.7 (a) AX_3E; pyramidal (b) AX_4; tetrahedral (c) AX_3; planar triangular (d) AX_2E; V-shaped (e) AX_4E; distorted tetrahedral (f) AX_2E_3; linear (g) AX_5E; square pyramidal (h) AX_4; tetrahedral (i) AX_6; octahedral (j) AX_5; trigonal bipyramidal (k) AX_2E; V-shaped

6.8

	(1)	(2)
(a)	planar triangular	planar triangular (distorted)
(b)	tetrahedral	pyramidal
(c)	octahedral	octahedral
(d)	tetrahedral	pyramidal
(e)	tetrahedral	pyramidal
(f)	tetrahedral	tetrahedral
(g)	planar triangular	planar triangular
(h)	tetrahedral	tetrahedral
(i)	tetrahedral	nonlinear (bent)
(j)	octahedral	square planar

6.9

	(1)	(2)
(a)	tetrahedral	bent
(b)	tetrahedral	bent
(c)	octahedral	octahedral
(d)	tetrahedral	tetrahedral
(e)	octahedral	square planar
(f)	tetrahedral	tetrahedral
(g)	planar triangular	planar triangular
(h)	trigonal bipyramidal	T-shaped
(i)	planar triangular	planar triangular
(j)	tetrahedral	pyramidal
(k)	tetrahedral	tetrahedral

6.10 **(a)** planar triangular to tetrahedral

(b) trigonal bipyramidal to octahedral

(c) T-shaped to square planar

(d) nonlinear (V-shaped) to distorted tetrahedral

(6.10 continued)

(e) linear to planar "double" bent

$$\begin{matrix} H & & H \\ & C{=}C & \\ H & & H \end{matrix}$$

(f) planar triangular to linear

6.11 Figure 6.2(b), the X–A–X angle will be less than 120° (e.g., SO_2).

Figure 6.3 (b) and (c). X–A–X angles will be compressed to less than the 109.5° found in perfect tetrahedron (e.g., H_2O and NH_3).

Figure 6.4 (b) distorted tetrahedral (arrows indicate direction of distortion).

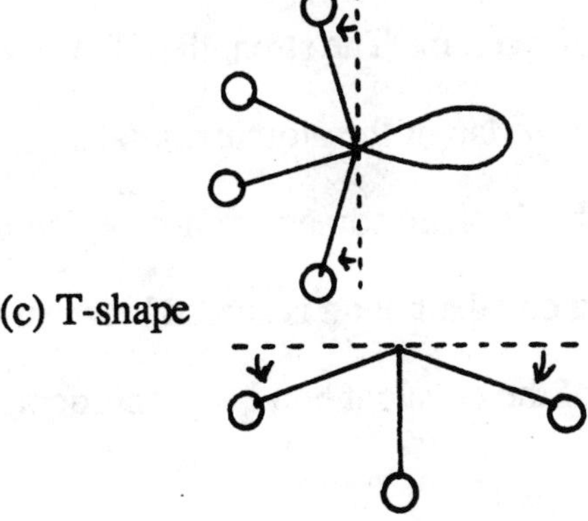

(c) T-shape

Figure 6.5 (b) square pyramid

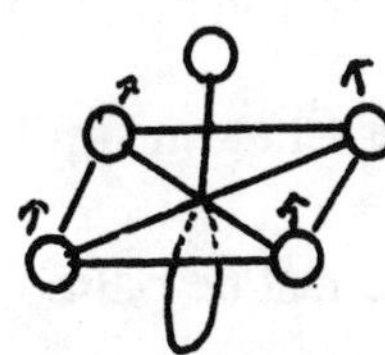

6.12 When two atoms joined by a covalent bond differ in electronegativity, the bond will be polar due to the resulting uneven distribution of electrons. A dipole exists when opposite ends of the molecule carry opposite electrical charges.

6.13 Molecules with polar bonds may be nonpolar molecules if there is complete cancellation of the effects of the bond dipoles due to a symmetrical arrangement of the bonds.

6.14 Because SO_2 is V-shaped(bent), its bond dipoles do not cancel each other. The result is a polar molecule. The dipoles in the planar triangular arrangement in SO_3 do cancel and the molecule is nonpolar.

6.15 (a), (c), (d), (g), (h) and (j)

6.16 Planar triangular

6.17 When two atoms come together to form a covalent bond, an atomic orbital of one atom overlaps with an atomic orbital of the other, and a pair of electrons is shared between the two atoms in the region of overlap. The strength of the covalent bond is proportional to the amount of overlap of the atomic orbitals.

6.18 Orbital overlap means that the two orbitals share some common region in space. The pair of electrons associated with a covalent bond is shared between the two atoms in this region and the strength of the covalent bond is proportional to the amount of overlap.

6.19 The p orbital with one electron on one Cl atom overlaps with the p orbital with one electron on the other Cl atom similar to the overlap of p_z orbitals shown in Figure 6.31. The spins must be paired if bonding is to occur.

6.20 The s orbital on hydrogen with one electron overlaps with the p orbital with one electron on the Cl atom. See Figure 6.10, 6.11 or 6.12.

6.21 See Figure 5.6.

6.22 Hybrid orbitals are produced when two or more atomic orbitals are mixed, producing a new set of orbitals. In hybrid orbitals one lobe is much larger than (continued)

(6.22 continued)

the other. Some atoms prefer to use hybrid orbitals because hybrid orbitals tend to form stronger covalent bonds than those from ordinary atomic orbitals.

6.23 (a) linear (b) planar triangular (c) tetrahedral (d) trigonal bipyramidal (e) octahedral

6.24 (a) 109.5° (b) 120° (c) 180° (d) 90°

6.25 We must employ hybrid orbitals in order to account for the H-C-H bond angle of 109° in CH_4 and the equivalence of the four C-H bonds.

6.26 Experimental evidence indicates that the lone pair(s) of electrons project out from the central atoms rather than being spread symmetrically as is the s orbital. .

6.27 The overlap of the unpaired electrons in the p orbitals of As with the unpaired electron in the s orbital of the hydrogens will yield bonding with a bond angle of close to 90°.

6.28 p orbitals

6.29 The bond angle of 104° is much closer to that of sp^3 orbital bonding than it is to that of p orbital bond.

P ↑↓ (3s) ↑ ↑ ↑ (3p) F ↑↓ (2s) ↑↓ ↑↓ ↑ (2p) F ↑↓ (2s) ↑↓ ↑↓ ↑ (2p) F ↑↓ (2s) ↑↓ ↑↓ ↑ (2p)

hybridized to

P ↑↓ ↑ ↑ ↑ (sp^3) F ↑↓ (2s) ↑↓ ↑↓ ↑ (2p) F ↑↓ (2s) ↑↓ ↑↓ ↑ (2p) F ↑↓ (2s) ↑↓ ↑↓ ↑ (2p)

The hybridized sp^3 orbitals of P have 3 unpaired electrons. Each sp^3 orbital of P containing an unpaired electron will overlap with a 2p electron of F containing an unpaired electron.

6.30 No. Our explanation is no better than the quality of the experimental evidence on this compound and very similar compounds. There is considerable evidence that indicates that fluorine uses hybrid orbitals.

6.31 Sn has the valence shell configuration, $5s^2\ 5p^2$. If the Cl atoms' orbitals overlap with the p orbitals of Sn, a nonlinear (bent) molecule should result with a bond angle of about 90° (actual Cl-Sn-Cl angle in $SnCl_2$ is 95°).

6.32
(a) planar triangular, sp^2 bonding
(b) tetrahedral, sp^3 bonding
(c) trigonal bipyramidal, sp^3d bonding
(d) octahedral, sp^3d^2 bonding
(e) linear, sp bonding
(f) octahedral, sp^3d^2 bonding
(g) pyramidal, sp^3 bonding
(h) distorted tetrahedral, sp^3d bonding
(i) tetrahedral, sp^3 bonding

6.33 (a) sp^3 (b) sp^3 (c) sp^2 (d) sp^2 (e) sp^3d (f) sp^3d (g) sp^3d^2 (h) sp^3 (i) sp^3d^2 (j) sp^3d (k) sp^2

6.34 (a) sp^2 (b) sp^3 (c) sp^3d^2 (d) sp^3 (e) sp^3 (f) sp^3 (g) sp^2 (h) sp^3 (i) sp^3 (j) sp^3d^2

6.35 Sb ↑↓ (5s) ↑ ↑ ↑ (5p) _ _ _ _ _ (5d)

x = Cl electrons

$SbCl_5$ ↑x ↑x ↑x ↑x ↑x (sp^3d) _ _ _ _ (unhybridized 5d orbitals)

6.36 Si has a relatively low-energy d subshell in its valence shell, whereas C does not.

6.37 Boron in BCl_3 is sp^2 hybridized. Nitrogen in NH_3 is sp^3 hybridized. In order for boron to accept two electrons from the nitrogen to form Cl_3BNH_3, it must first become sp^3 hybridized. The geometry of B changes from planar triangular to tetrahedral. The N does not change geometry nor hybridization.

6.38 A coordinate covalent bond "exists" in NH_4^+, $AlCl_6^{3-}$, $SbCl_6^-$ and ClO_4^-. After formation, the coordinate covalent bond is (of course) identical to the "normal" covalent bond.

6.39 Sn is sp^3 hybridized. The Sn-Cl bond would be formed by sp^3-p overlap.

6.40 In NH_3, the N-H bonds are polar with the negative ends of the bond dipoles at the nitrogen. The lone pair, if it were in a nonbonded sp^3 orbital, would also produce a contribution to the dipole moment of the molecule, with its negative end pointing <u>away</u> from the nitrogen.

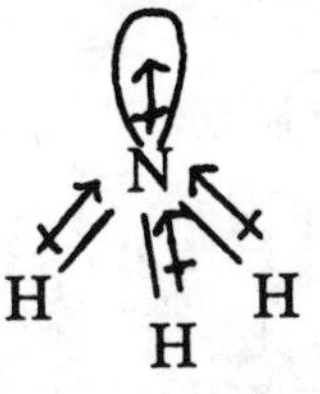

(effects of the bond dipoles and lone pair dipole are additive)

All dipoles are additive and produce a large net molecular dipole. In NF_3, the fluorines are more electronegative than nitrogen, producing bond dipoles with their positive ends at nitrogen. These, therefore, tend to offset the contribution of the lone pair in the sp^3 orbital on nitrogen, thereby giving a very small net dipole moment for the NF_3 molecule.

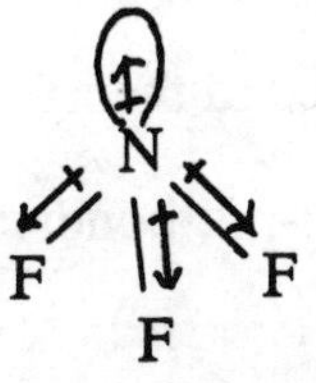

(The bond dipoles cancel the effects of the lone pair dipole.)

6.41 The σ-bond results from a head-on overlap of atomic orbitals that concentrates electron density along the imaginary line joining the bound nuclei. A π-bond is produced by the sideways overlap of atomic p orbitals providing electron density above and below the line connecting the bound nuclei. A double bond consists of one σ-bond and one π-bond. A triple bond is usually made by overlap of orbitals to give one σ and two π-bonds.

6.42

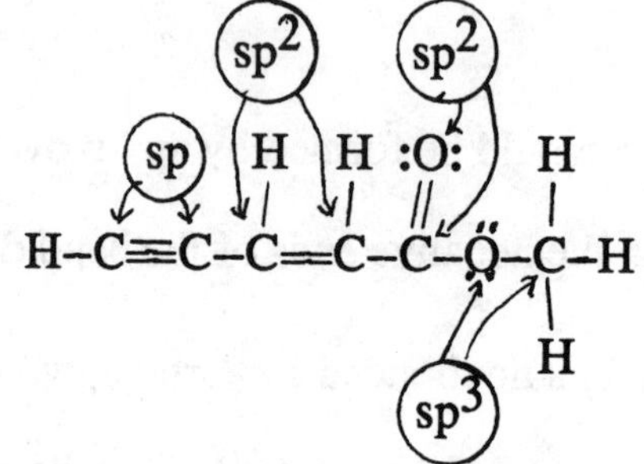

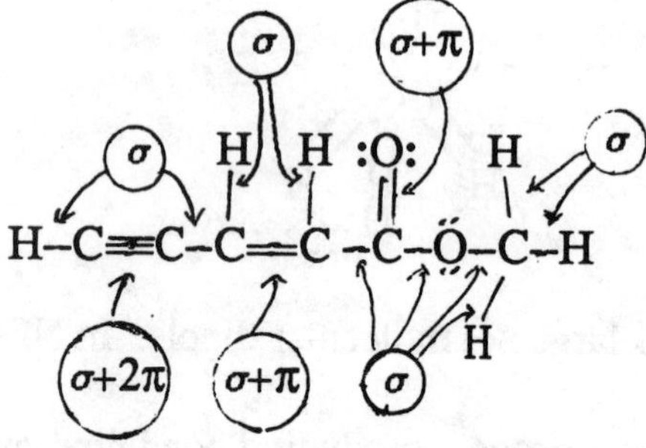

6.43 Valence bond theory would show that the N_2 triple bond consists of one p-p σ and two p-p π-bonds.

6.44 Valence bond theory shows that the CN^- triple bond consists of one sp-sp σ and two p-p π-bonds.

6.45 H, C=O: (σ+π) bonds; H, σ bonds; H, C=O: s-sp^2, p-p, sp^2-sp^2

6.46 $[\ddot{N}, O, O]^-$ <—> $[\ddot{N}, O, O]^-$ sp^2 hybrid orbitals are used; p orbitals used

6.47 Period-2 nonmetals are smaller than period-3 nonmetals and are able to approach each other more closely. As a result, more effective sideways overlap of the p orbitals can occur. Therefore, period-2 nonmetals form much stronger pi bonds. Since period-3 nonmetals do not form very strong pi bonds, they tend to form sigma bonds with several atoms rather than multiple bonds to a single atom.

6.48 Because they can exist without involving a pi bond as they form a σ bond.

6.49 Allotropes are different forms of the same element as the result of differences in molecular structure as with O_2 and O_3 or as the result of differences in packing of molecules in the solid state.

6.50 Diatomic oxygen (O_2) and ozone (O_3).

6.51 The most stable form of elemental sulfur contains 8 sulfur atoms, each sigma bonded to two neighbors, to form an 8-member, puckered crown-like ring. (see Figure 6.28)

6.52 White phosphorus consists of P_4 molecules in which each phosphorus atom lies at a corner of a tetrahedron. (See Figure 6.29)

6.53 White phosphorus is very reactive because the very small P-P-P bond angle (~60°) does not allow effective overlap of orbitals and results in a bond that is easily broken or, stated another way, is very reactive.

6.54 In diamond each carbon atom is sigma bonded to 4 other carbon atoms. This produces a gigantic three-dimensional network made up of sp^3-sp^3 σ bonds. In graphite each carbon atom is sigma bonded to 3 other carbon atoms. The atoms are arranged in the form of hexagonal rings connected together in large planar sheets. The carbons are sp^2 hybridized in graphite with one p-electron on each carbon being involved in π bonding. (See Figs. 6.24, 6.25, 6.26, & 6.27)

6.55 Because Si has no apparent tendency to form multiple bonds.

6.56 From the point of view of molecular orbital theory the electronic structure of a molecule is similar to the electronic structure of an atom in that (1) no more than two electrons can populate a single orbital, (2) each electron will occupy the lowest energy orbital available, and (3) electrons are spread out as much as possible, with unpaired spins, over orbitals of the same energy. The electronic structures of atoms and molecules differ in that (1) atomic orbitals and molecular orbitals are very different and (2) in molecular orbital theory, distinctly different bonding and antibonding orbitals exist unlike anything that exists in the electonic structure of an atom.

6.57 See Figure 6.30. The σ_{1s} molecular orbital will stabilize a molecule while the $\sigma_{1s}{}^*$ will destabilize the molecule. The effect of the two will cancel each other. The $\sigma_{1s}{}^*$ is said to be an antibonding orbital because it destabilizes a molecule when it is filled.

6.58 See Figure 6.31.

6.59 See Figure 6.33. The net result is one bonding sigma bond and two bonding pi bonds.

6.60 The molecular orbital diagram of N_2 can be seen in Figure 6.33. The species N_2^+ would have one less π_{2p} electron and N_2^- would have an additional electron located in the π_{2p}^* molecular orbital. The net bond order of N_2 is 3 and N_2^+ and N_2^- is each 2.5. Both N_2^+ and N_2^- are less stable than N_2 and both would have a longer bond length than N_2.

6.61 The molecular orbital diagram of O_2 can be seen in Figure 6.33. The species O_2^+ would have one less π_{2p}^* electron and the species O_2^- would have one additional π_{2p}^* electron. Net bond orders: $O_2 = 2$, $O_2^+ = 2.5$, and $O_2^- = 1.5$. The stability, therefore, would be $O_2^+ > O_2 > O_2^-$. The bond lengths would be, $O_2^+ < O_2 < O_2^-$. Vibrational frequencies would be, $O_2^- < O_2 < O_2^+$.

6.62 See Figure 6.33. The O_2 molecule has the net bonding of a double bond while the O_2^{2-} ion has the net bonding of a single sigma bond. Therefore, the bond order of O_2 is 2 and that of O_2^{2-} is 1. The bond energy of O_2 would be greater, its bond length would be less, and its vibrational frequency would be greater than that of O_2^{2-}.

6.63

	Li_2	Be_2	B_2	C_2
$\sigma_{2p_z}^*$	—	—	—	—
$\pi_{2p_x}^*$ $\pi_{2p_y}^*$	— —	— —	— —	— —
π_{2p_x} π_{2p_y}	— —	— —	— —	↑ ↑
σ_{2p_z}	—	—	↑↓	↑↓
σ_{2s}^*	—	↑↓	↑↓	↑↓
σ_{2s}	↑↓	↑↓	↑↓	↑↓

Be_2 should not exist and C_2 is paramagnetic.

6.64 **(a)** Because a bonding electron is removed in each case, Li_2^+, B_2^+, and C_2^+ would be less stable than the neutral X_2 species. Be_2^+ would be more stable than Be_2 because an antibonding electron is removed.

(b) Li_2^- would be less stable, Be_2^-, B_2^-, and C_2^- would be more stable than the neutral X_2 species. The extra electron is antibonding in Li_2^- but is bonding in Be_2^-, B_2^-, and C_2^-.

6.65 It allows for the formation of molecular orbitals that extend over more than two nuclei. This delocalization is the equivalent of valence bond resonance.

6.66 H_2^+ Bond order = 1/2; $(\sigma_{1s})^1$

He_2^+ Bond order = 1/2; $(\sigma_{1s})^2\,(\sigma_{1s}{}^*)^1$

6.67 Valence Bond Description: In all three species the central atom is sp^2 hybridized. In SO_2 the two resonance structures arise from alternating the double bond between the unhybridized p orbital on S and p orbitals on the oxygens. In NO_3^- three resonance structures arise because there are three O atoms which can π-bond to the unhybridized p orbital on N. In HCO_2^- the C-H bond is a single bond, and two resonance structures result by forming two possible double bonds as in the case of SO_2.

Molecular Orbital Description: Again, the central atom is sp^2 hybridized in all three cases. Delocalized π clouds are formed over three atoms in both SO_2 and HCO_2^-(i.e., over O-S-O and over O-C-O). In NO_3^- a delocalized π cloud extends over all 4 atoms as in the case of SO_3.

7 CHEMICAL REACTIONS AND THE PERIODIC TABLE

7.1 Water is one of the most abundant chemicals in nature and serves as a good solvent for many substances, both ionic and molecular. Because of the homogeneous nature of solutions, dissolved substances are intimately mixed and chemical reactions occur rapidly.

7.2 Solvent: substance present in the greatest proportion in a solution

Solutes: all other substances present

Concentrated: relatively large amounts of solute present in the solvent

Dilute: only a small amount of solute in the solvent

Saturated: at a given temperature, the maximum amount of solute that the solvent can hold in contact with undissolved solute

Supersaturated: at a given temperature, the solvent contains more solute than it can usually hold in the presence of excess solute

Unsaturated: the solvent contains less than the maximum amount of solute at a given temperature

7.3 Solubility: the amount of solute required to produce a saturated solution at a particular temperature

7.4 Usually, the solubility of a solute in a particular solvent changes with temperature

7.5 Yes, for a solute which has a limited solubility in a particular solvent, a saturated solution will have a relatively small proportion of solute to solvent.

7.6 If a crystal of solute is added to a supersaturated solution, additional solute crystallizes on this "seed" crystal until the concentration drops to saturation.

7.7 To prepare a supersaturated solution of sugar in water, heat the water and add enough sugar to form a saturated solution at the elevated temperature. When the solution is allowed to cool, a supersaturated solution is the result.

7.8 If the solution is at 25°C, it would be described as supersaturated. At some higher temperature it would be saturated and above that temperature unsaturated. Because of the low solubility of $PbSO_4$ in water, all of these soltuions would be considered to be dilute solutions.

7.9 An electrolyte is a substance which when dissolved in a solvent produces ions which make the solution able to conduct electricity. A nonelectrolyte is a substance which, when dissolved in a solvent, does not produce ions; therefore, it does not make a solution able to conduct electricity.

7.10 We can distinguish between strong and weak electrolytes with the aid of the apparatus shown in Figure 7.2. A strong electrolyte will cause the bulb to glow brightly and a weak electrolyte will cause the bulb to glow dimly. Ions are present in solutions of electrolytes but not in solutions of nonelectrolytes.

7.11 $KCl(s) \rightarrow K^+(aq) + Cl^-(aq)$

$(NH_4)_2SO_4(s) \rightarrow 2NH_4^+(aq) + SO_4^{2-}(aq)$

(7.11 continued)

$Na_3PO_4(s) \rightarrow 3Na^+(aq) + PO_4^{3-}(aq)$

$NaOH(s) \rightarrow Na^+(aq) + OH^-(aq)$ $\quad$ $HCl(g) \rightarrow H^+(aq) + Cl^-(aq)$

7.12 H^+ is the short form of H_3O^+. We often leave out the H_2O which is merely a carrier for the H^+ ion.

7.13 A dynamic equilibrium is one in which opposing processes occur at equal rates, so there is no net change in the system, e.g. ions react to form molecules while molecules react to form ions.

7.14 $CdSO_4(aq) \rightleftharpoons Cd^{2+}(aq) + SO_4^{2-}(aq)$

7.15 $H_2O \rightleftharpoons H^+ + OH^-$ (or, $2H_2O \rightleftharpoons H_3O^+ + OH^-$)

7.16 By position of equilibrium, we mean the relative proportions of reactants and products in a chemical system when the system is at equilibrium.

7.17 It lies mainly to the left, in favor of undissociated H_2O. For HCl the position of equilibrium lies virtually 100% in favor of the ionic products.

7.18 $H{:}\ddot{\underset{\cdot\cdot}{Br}}{:} + H{:}\ddot{\underset{\cdot\cdot}{O}}{:} \rightarrow \left[H{:}\ddot{\underset{\cdot\cdot}{O}}{:}H\right]^+ + \left[{:}\ddot{\underset{\cdot\cdot}{Br}}{:}\right]^-$ (with H below O in $H{:}\ddot{O}{:}$ and H below O in $[H{:}\ddot{O}{:}H]^+$)

7.19 The rate of the reverse reaction would decrease because the concentrations of $C_2H_3O_2^-$ and H_3O^+ would be less and there would be fewer collisions between them. The rate of the forward reaction would also decrease, but by a lesser amount, because the concentration of $HC_2H_3O_2$ would be less and the concentration of H_2O would be more (only slightly more for dilute solutions).

The percentage ionization increases as the solution is made more dilute.

7.20 Precipitate

7.21 Metathesis is the kind of reaction in which the cations and anions have changed partners. This is also known as double replacement.

7.22 A <u>spectator ion</u> is an ion that does not change during a reaction.

7.23 By filtering the mixture as shown in Figure 7.4

7.24 In a molecular equation all reactants and products are written as if they were molecules. An ionic equation more accurately represents a reaction as it actually occurs in solution by showing all soluble ionic substances as being dissociated. A net ionic equation represents the net chemical change that occurs by eliminating the spectator ions.

7.25 The net ionic equation focuses attention on the species that participate in the changes occurring in the solution and emphasizes that any substances that produce the same species in solution will react in the same way.

7.26 $Ca^{2+}(aq) + 2Cl^-(aq) + 2K^+(aq) + CO_3^{2-}(aq) \longrightarrow CaCO_3(s) + 2K^+(aq) + 2Cl^-(aq)$

Net ionic $Ca^{2+}(aq) + CO_3^{2-}(aq) \longrightarrow CaCO_3(s)$

7.27 (a) $Cu^{2+} + 2Cl^- + Pb^{2+} + 2NO_3^- \longrightarrow Cu^{2+} + 2NO_3^- + PbCl_2(s)$

Net ionic $Pb^{2+}(aq) + 2Cl^-(aq) \longrightarrow PbCl_2(s)$

(b) $Fe^{2+} + SO_4^{2-} + 2Na^+ + 2OH^- \longrightarrow Fe(OH)_2(s) + 2Na^+ + SO_4^{2-}$

Net ionic $Fe^{2+}(aq) + 2OH^-(aq) \longrightarrow Fe(OH)_2(s)$

(c) $Zn^{2+} + SO_4^{2-} + Ba^{2+} + 2Cl^- \longrightarrow Zn^{2+} + 2Cl^- + BaSO_4(s)$

Net ionic $Ba^{2+}(aq) + SO_4^{2-}(aq) \longrightarrow BaSO_4(s)$

(7.27 continued)

(d) $2Ag^+ + 2NO_3^- + 2K^+ + SO_4^{2-} \longrightarrow Ag_2SO_4(s) + 2K^+ + 2NO_3^-$

Net ionic $2Ag^+(aq) + SO_4^{2-}(aq) \longrightarrow Ag_2SO_4(s)$

(e) $2NH_4^+ + CO_3^{2-} + Ca^{2+} + 2Cl^- \longrightarrow 2NH_4^+ + 2Cl^- + CaCO_3(s)$

Net ionic $Ca^{2+}(aq) + CO_3^{2-}(aq) \longrightarrow CaCO_3(s)$

7.28 (a) $Cu^{2+} + 2NO_3^- + 2Na^+ + 2OH^- \longrightarrow Cu(OH)_2(s) + 2Na^+ + 2NO_3^-$

$Cu^{2+}(aq) + 2OH^-(aq) \longrightarrow Cu(OH)_2(s)$ (Net ionic)

(b) $3Ba^{2+} + 6Cl^- + 2Al^{3+} + 3SO_4^{2-} \longrightarrow 3BaSO_4(s) + 2Al^{3+} + 6Cl^-$

$Ba^{2+}(aq) + SO_4^{2-}(aq) \longrightarrow BaSO_4(s)$ (Net ionic)

(c) $Hg_2^{2+} + 2NO_3^- + 2H^+ + 2Cl^- \longrightarrow Hg_2Cl_2(s) + 2H^+ + 2NO_3^-$

$Hg_2^{2+}(aq) + 2Cl^-(aq) \longrightarrow Hg_2Cl_2(s)$ (Net ionic)

(d) $2Bi^{3+} + 6NO_3^- + 6Na^+ + 3S^{2-} \longrightarrow Bi_2S_3(s) + 6Na^+ + 6NO_3^-$

$2Bi^{3+}(aq) + 3S^{2-}(aq) \longrightarrow Bi_2S_3(s)$ (Net ionic)

(e) $Ca^{2+} + 2Cl^- + 2Na^+ + SO_4^{2-} \longrightarrow CaSO_4(s) + 2Na^+ + 2Cl^-$

$Ca^{2+}(aq) + SO_4^{2-}(aq) \longrightarrow CaSO_4(s)$ (Net ionic)

7.29 Solutions of acids have a sour taste and solutions of bases have a bitter taste. Another property is their effect on indicators, e.g., a basic solution turns the dye litmus blue and an acidic solution turns it pink. An acid reacts with a base to produce a salt and water; a base reacts with an acid to produce a salt and water (neutralization).

7.30 An <u>acid</u> is any substance that increases the concentration of hydronium ions in a solution. A <u>base</u> is any substance that increases the concentration of hydroxide ions in a solution.

7.31 Use an indicator, e.g., dip a strip of pink litmus paper into the solution; if the litmus paper turns blue, the solution is basic.

7.32 A strong acid is essentially 100% ionized in solution while only a small fraction of a weak acid ionizes in solution.

7.33

Hydrochloric acid	HCl	$HCl + H_2O \longrightarrow H_3O^+ + Cl^-$
Hydrobromic acid	HBr	$HBr + H_2O \longrightarrow H_3O^+ + Br^-$
Hydroiodic acid	HI	$HI + H_2O \longrightarrow H_3O^+ + I^-$
Chloric acid	$HClO_3$	$HClO_3 + H_2O \longrightarrow H_3O^+ + ClO_3^-$
Perchloric acid	$HClO_4$	$HClO_4 + H_2O \longrightarrow H_3O^+ + ClO_4^-$
Periodic acid	HIO_4	$HIO_4 + H_2O \longrightarrow H_3O^+ + IO_4^-$
Nitric acid	HNO_3	$HNO_3 + H_2O \longrightarrow H_3O^+ + NO_3^-$
Sulfuric acid	H_2SO_4	$H_2SO_4 + H_2O \longrightarrow H_3O^+ + HSO_4^-$

(note: only the first dissociation of H_2SO_4 is strong)

7.34 (a) $H_2SO_3 \rightleftharpoons H^+ + HSO_3^-$

$HSO_3^- \rightleftharpoons H^+ + SO_3^{2-}$

(b) $H_3AsO_4 \rightleftharpoons H^+ + H_2AsO_4^-$

$H_2AsO_4^- \rightleftharpoons H^+ + HAsO_4^{2-}$

$HAsO_4^{2-} \rightleftharpoons H^+ + AsO_4^{3-}$

7.35 (a) A <u>monoprotic acid</u> is able to furnish only one hydrogen ion per molecule.

(b) A <u>diprotic acid</u> is able to furnish two hydrogen ions per molecule of acid.

(c) A <u>triprotic acid</u> is able to furnish three hydrogen ions per molecule of acid.

(d) A <u>polyprotic acid</u> is an acid which is able to furnish more than one hydrogen ion per molecule of acid; includes diprotic and triprotic acids.

7.36 Acid anhydride - nonmetal oxides that react with H_2O to yield acidic solutions.

e.g. $CO_2 + H_2O \rightleftharpoons H_2CO_3$

$H_2CO_3 + H_2O \rightleftharpoons H_3O^+ + HCO_3^-$

Basic anhydride - metal oxides that react with H_2O to give corresponding hydroxides. e.g. $BaO + H_2O \longrightarrow Ba(OH)_2$

7.37 (a) acidic (b) basic (c) acidic (d) acidic (e) basic

7.38 $H_2O + N_2O_5 \longrightarrow 2HNO_3$

7.39 Phosphoric acid, H_3PO_4 : $P_4O_{10} + 6H_2O \longrightarrow 4H_3PO_4$

7.40 A base turns litmus blue. Therefore, the element would be classified as a metal because metal oxides yield bases on reaction with water.

7.41 The two kinds of bases are ionic hydroxides and molecular substances that react with water to produce OH^-.

7.42 $O^{2-} + H_2O \longrightarrow 2OH^-$

7.43 potassium hydroxide, KOH

7.44 $NH_3(aq) + H_2O \rightleftharpoons NH_4^+(aq) + OH^-(aq)$ Ammonia is a weak base.

7.45 $N_2H_4(aq) + H_2O \rightleftharpoons N_2H_5^+(aq) + OH^-(aq)$

7.46

```
                             [    H   ]+
 H-N̈-N̈-H  +  H:Ö:   ⇌    [ H-N̈-N̈-H ]   +  [:Ö:H]-
   | |           ..        [   | |    ]        ..
   H H           H         [   H H    ]
```

7.47 $H_3O^+ + OH^- \longrightarrow 2H_2O$ or $H^+ + OH^- \longrightarrow H_2O$

7.48 (a) $KOH + HCl \longrightarrow KCl + H_2O$

(b) $NaOH + HC_2H_3O_2 \longrightarrow NaC_2H_3O_2 + H_2O$

(c) $NH_3(aq) + HCl \longrightarrow NH_4Cl(aq)$

(d) $CuO + 2HBr \longrightarrow CuBr_2 + H_2O$

(e) $Fe_2O_3 + 3H_2SO_4 \longrightarrow Fe_2(SO_4)_3 + 3H_2O$

7.49 Acid salts are the products of partial neutralization of a polyprotic acid. Examples include $NaHCO_3$, $NaHSO_4$, and Na_2HPO_4.

KH_2PO_4 potassium dihydrogen phosphate

K_2HPO_4 dipotassium hydrogen phosphate

K_3PO_4 tripotassium phosphate (or potassium phosphate)

7.50 <u>Brønsted-Lowry definition of acids and bases</u>

Acid: substance that is able to donate a proton to some other substance.

Base: substance that is able to accept a proton from an acid.

7.51 (a) NH_2^- (b) NH_3 (c) $C_2H_3O_2^-$ (d) $H_2PO_4^-$ (e) NO_3^-

7.52 (a) H_2SO_4 (b) HSO_4^- (c) H_3O^+ (d) HCl (e) $HCHO_2$

7.53 The Brønsted-Lowry definition is less restrictive than the Arrhenius concept because it recognizes acid-base phenomena in other than just aqueous solutions.

7.54 Acid-base conjugate pairs (acid written first in each pair)

(a) $HC_2H_3O_2$, $C_2H_3O_2^-$ and H_2O, OH^- (b) HF, F^- and NH_4^+, NH_3

(c) $Zn(OH)_2$, ZnO_2^{2-} and H_2O, OH^-

(7.54 continued)

(d) $Al(H_2O)_6^{3+}$, $Al(H_2O)_5OH^{2+}$ and H_2O, OH^-

(e) $N_2H_5^+$, N_2H_4 and H_2O, OH^- (f) NH_3OH^+, NH_2OH and HCl, Cl^-

(g) OH^-, O^{2-} and H_2O, OH^- (h) H_2, H^- and H_2O, OH^-

(i) NH_3, NH_2^- and N_2H_4, $N_2H_3^-$ (j) HNO_3, NO_3^- and $H_3SO_4^+$, H_2SO_4

7.55 Acid-base conjugate pairs (acids written first in each pair)

(a) $HClO_4$, ClO_4^- and $N_2H_5^+$, N_2H_4

(b) H_3PO_3, $H_2PO_3^-$ and H_2SO_3, HSO_3^-

(c) $C_5H_5NH^+$, C_5H_5N and $(CH_3)_3NH^+$, $(CH_3)_3N$

(d) H_2O, OH^- and HCO_3^-, CO_3^{2-}

(e) $HCHO_2$, CHO_2^- and $HC_7H_5O_2$, $C_7H_5O_2^-$

(f) $H_2C_2O_4$, $HC_2O_4^-$ and $CH_3NH_3^+$, CH_3NH_2

(g) H_2CO_3, HCO_3^- and H_3O^+, H_2O (h) C_2H_5OH, $C_2H_5O^-$ and NH_3, NH_2^-

(i) $N_2H_5^+$, N_2H_4 and HNO_2, NO_2^- (j) H_2CN^+, HCN and H_2SO_4, HSO_4^-

7.56 (a) $2H_2O \rightleftharpoons H_3O^+ + OH^-$ (b) $2NH_3 \rightleftharpoons NH_4^+ + NH_2^-$

(c) $2HCN \rightleftharpoons H_2CN^+ + CN^-$

7.57 acid, $(CH_3)_2NH_2^+$; base, $(CH_3)_2N^-$

7.58 $HCO_3^- + H_2O \rightleftharpoons CO_3^{2-} + H_3O^+$ (as an acid)

$HCO_3^- + H_2O \rightleftharpoons H_2CO_3 + OH^-$ (as a base)

7.59 The highly charged Cr^{3+} ion polarizes the O-H bonds of the water molecules attached to it, thereby making it easier for the H^+ to be transferred to neighboring H_2O molecules.

7.60 (a) $HClO_3$ (b) HNO_3 (c) H_3PO_4 (d) $CHCl_2COOH$

(e) CH_2FCOOH (f) H_2SO_4 (g) $HClO_3$ (h) $HBrO_3$

7.61 (a) H_2Se (b) HBr (c) PH_3

7.62 CH_3SH

7.63 The additional oxygen in HNO_3 draws more electron density from the nitrogen which gives it a greater partial positive charge. The nitrogen in turn draws electron density from the N-OH bond. This in turn draws the electron density from the O-H bond making HNO_3 a stronger acid than HNO_2.

7.64 Cl^- is a larger ion than F^- so the HCl bond is much weaker than the HF bond, thus making it more acidic.

7.65 HCl is much more polar than H_2S.

7.66 Lewis base: a substance that can donate a pair of electrons to the formation of a covalent bond

Lewis acid: a substance that can accept a pair of electrons to form a covalent bond.

7.67 Ammonia acts as a Lewis base by donating a pair of electrons to form a covalent bond with H^+ which acts as a Lewis acid.

7.68

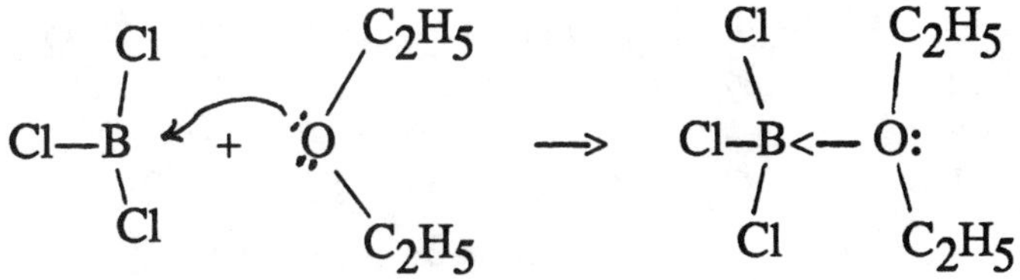

```
        Cl           C2H5              Cl     C2H5
        |           /                    \     |
     Cl—B  <-- +  :O:        —>       Cl–B<—— O:
        \           \                    /     \
        Cl           C2H5              Cl      C2H5
```

7.69

```
H       ..                   ..          H     ..
 \      O:            H -> :O:            \   O:
  \  ..  ||                  |                /
   :O: -> C   —>     H–O–C     —>    H–O–C
   /  ..  ||             ..  ||           ..  ||
  /       ||                 ||               ||
H       :O:                :O:              :O:
```

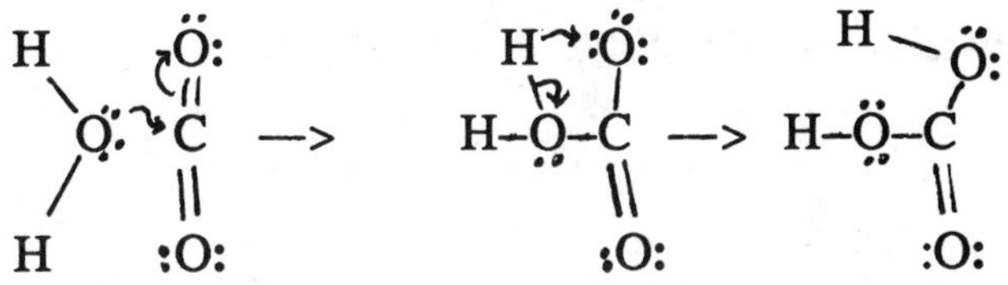

Water acts as a Lewis base by donating a pair of electrons to form a covalent bond with CO_2.

7.70 $H_3N: \rightarrow Ag^+ \leftarrow :NH_3 \longrightarrow [H_3N\text{-}Ag\text{-}NH_3]^+$ NH_3 is a Lewis base which forms coordinate covalent bonds to the Lewis acid, Ag^+.

7.71 Oxidation is the process of losing electrons. Reduction is the process of gaining electrons. Oxidation state is the charge an atom would have if both electrons in the bond were assigned to the more electronegative element. An oxidizing agent is that material being reduced (causing oxidation). A reducing agent is that material being oxidized (causing reduction).

7.72 **(a) K = +1, Cl = +3, O = -2** **(b) Ba = +2, Mn = +6, O = -2**

(c) Fe = +8/3, O = -2 **(d) O = +1, F = -1**

(e) I = +5, F = -1 **(f) H = +1, O = -2, Cl = +1**

(g) Ca = +2, S = +6, O = -2 **(h) Cr = +3, S = +6, O = -2**

(i) O = 0 **(j) Hg = +1, Cl = -1**

7.73

H_2	S	O_4,	C	Br_4,	O	F_2,	H_2	O_2,	Cr	Cl_3,	Mn_2	O_7
+1	+6	-2	+4	-1	+2	-1	+1	-1	+3	-1	+7	-2

K	Mn	O_4,	H_2	C_2	O_4,	K	Cl	O_3,	Li	N	O_3
+1	+7	-2	+1	+3	-2	+1	+5	-2	+1	+5	-2

7.74 (a) **oxidation** (b) **reduction** (c) **oxidation** (d) **oxidation**

(e) **reduction**

7.75 C_2H_5OH, C = -2; C_2H_4O, C = -1; CH_3CO_2H, C = 0; CO_2, C = +4

7.76 (a) $10HNO_3 + 4Zn \longrightarrow 4Zn(NO_3)_2 + 3H_2O + NH_4NO_3$

(b) $10K + 2KNO_3 \longrightarrow N_2 + 6K_2O$

(c) $3C_3H_7OH + 2Na_2Cr_2O_7 + 8H_2SO_4 \longrightarrow$

$2Cr_2(SO_4)_3 + 2Na_2SO_4 + 11H_2O + 3HC_3H_5O_2$

(d) $3H_2S + 2HNO_3 \longrightarrow 3S + 2NO + 4H_2O$

(e) $4Fe(OH)_2 + O_2 + 2H_2O \longrightarrow 4Fe(OH)_3$

7.77

	Ox. Agent	Red. Agent
(a)	HNO_3	Zn
(b)	KNO_3	K
(c)	$Na_2Cr_2O_7$	C_3H_7OH
(d)	HNO_3	H_2S
(e)	O_2	$Fe(OH)_2$

7.78 **(a)** $3Cu + 8HNO_3 \longrightarrow 3Cu(NO_3)_2 + 2NO + 4H_2O$

(b) $MnO_2 + 4HBr \longrightarrow Br_2 + MnBr_2 + 2H_2O$

(c) $3(CH_3)_2CHOH + 2CrO_3 + 3H_2SO_4 \longrightarrow$

$3(CH_3)_2CO + Cr_2(SO_4)_3 + 6H_2O$

(d) $3PbO_2 + 2Sb + 2NaOH \longrightarrow 3PbO + 2NaSbO_2 + H_2O$

(e) $3NO_2 + H_2O \longrightarrow 2HNO_3 + NO$

7.79

	Substance oxidized	Substance reduced
(a)	Cu	HNO_3
(b)	HBr	MnO_2
(c)	$(CH_3)_2CHOH$	CrO_3
(d)	Sb	PbO_2
(e)	NO_2	NO_2

7.80 **(a)** $8H^+ + 2NO_3^- + 3Cu \longrightarrow 2NO + 3Cu^{2+} + 4H_2O$

(b) $10H^+ + NO_3^- + 4Zn \longrightarrow NH_4^+ + 4Zn^{2+} + 3H_2O$

(c) $2Cr + 6H^+ \longrightarrow 2Cr^{3+} + 3H_2$

(d) $8H^+ + Cr_2O_7^{2-} + 3H_3AsO_3 \longrightarrow 2Cr^{3+} + 4H_2O + 3H_3AsO_4$

(e) $10H^+ + SO_4^{2-} + 8I^- \longrightarrow 4I_2 + H_2S + 4H_2O$

(f) $4H_2O + 8Ag^+ + AsH_3 \longrightarrow H_3AsO_4 + 8Ag + 8H^+$

(g) $H_2O + S_2O_8^{2-} + HNO_2 \longrightarrow NO_3^- + 2SO_4^{2-} + 3H^+$

(7.80 continued)

(h) $4H^+ + MnO_2 + 2Br^- \longrightarrow Mn^{2+} + Br_2 + 2H_2O$

(i) $2S_2O_3^{2-} + I_2 \longrightarrow 2I^- + S_4O_6^{2-}$

(j) $IO_3^- + 3HSO_3^- \longrightarrow I^- + 3SO_4^{2-} + 3H^+$

7.81 (a) $8H^+ + Cr_2O_7^{2-} + 3CH_3CH_2OH \longrightarrow 2Cr^{3+} + 3CH_3CHO + 7H_2O$

(b) $4H^+ + PbO_2 + 2Cl^- \longrightarrow Pb^{2+} + Cl_2 + 2H_2O$

(c) $14H^+ + 2Mn^{2+} + 5BiO_3^- \longrightarrow 2MnO_4^- + 5Bi^{3+} + 7H_2O$

(d) $3H_2O + ClO_3^- + 3HAsO_2 \longrightarrow 3H_3AsO_4 + Cl^-$

(e) $2H_2O + PH_3 + 2I_2 \longrightarrow H_3PO_2 + 4I^- + 4H^+$

(f) $16H^+ + 2MnO_4^- + 10S_2O_3^{2-} \longrightarrow 5S_4O_6^{2-} + 2Mn^{2+} + 8H_2O$

(g) $4H^+ + 2Mn^{2+} + 5PbO_2 \longrightarrow 2MnO_4^- + 5Pb^{2+} + 2H_2O$

(h) $2H^+ + As_2O_3 + 2NO_3^- + 2H_2O \longrightarrow 2H_3AsO_4 + N_2O_3$

(i) $8H_2O + 2P + 5Cu^{2+} \longrightarrow 5Cu + 2H_2PO_4^- + 12H^+$

(j) $6H^+ + 2MnO_4^- + 5H_2S \longrightarrow 2Mn^{2+} + 5S + 8H_2O$

7.82 (a) $H_2O + CN^- + AsO_4^{3-} \longrightarrow AsO_2^- + CNO^- + 2OH^-$

(b) $2CrO_2^- + 3HO_2^- \longrightarrow 2CrO_4^{2-} + H_2O + OH^-$

(c) $7OH^- + 4Zn + NO_3^- + 6H_2O \longrightarrow 4Zn(OH)_4^{2-} + NH_3$

(d) $4OH^- + Cu(NH_3)_4^{2+} + S_2O_4^{2-} \longrightarrow 2SO_3^{2-} + Cu + 4NH_3 + 2H_2O$

(e) $N_2H_4 + 2Mn(OH)_3 \longrightarrow 2Mn(OH)_2 + 2NH_2OH$

(7.82 continued)

(f) $4OH^- + 2MnO_4^- + 3C_2O_4^{2-} \longrightarrow 2MnO_2 + 6CO_3^{2-} + 2H_2O$

(g) $6OH^- + 7ClO_3^- + 3N_2H_4 \longrightarrow 6NO_3^- + 7Cl^- + 9H_2O$

7.83 (a) $3H_2O + P_4 + 3OH^- \longrightarrow PH_3 + 3H_2PO_2^-$

(b) $12H^+ + 12Cu + 12Cl^- + As_4O_6 \longrightarrow 12CuCl + 4As + 6H_2O$

(c) $9H_2O + 5IPO_4 \longrightarrow I_2 + 3IO_3^- + 5H_2PO_4^- + 8H^+$

(d) $3NO_2 + H_2O \longrightarrow 2NO_3^- + NO + 2H^+$

(e) $12OH^- + 6Br_2 \longrightarrow 10Br^- + 2BrO_3^- + 6H_2O$

(f) $4HSO_2NH_2 + 6NO_3^- \longrightarrow 4SO_4^{2-} + 2H^+ + 5N_2O + 5H_2O$

(g) $4H^+ + 2ClO_3^- + 2Cl^- \longrightarrow 2ClO_2 + Cl_2 + 2H_2O$

(h) $2OH^- + 2ClO_2 \longrightarrow ClO_2^- + ClO_3^- + H_2O$

(i) $6OH^- + 3Se \longrightarrow 2Se^{2-} + SeO_3^{2-} + 3H_2O$

(j) $3H_2O + 5ICl \longrightarrow 2I_2 + IO_3^- + 5Cl^- + 6H^+$

(k) $4OH^- + 2FNO_3 \longrightarrow O_2 + 2F^- + 2NO_3^- + 2H_2O$

(l) $2H_2O + 4Fe(OH)_2 + O_2 \longrightarrow 4Fe(OH)_3$

7.84 (a) $Zn + 2H_2O + 2OH^- \longrightarrow Zn(OH)_4^{2-} + H_2$

(b) $2CrO_2^- + 3HO_2^- \longrightarrow 2CrO_4^{2-} + H_2O + OH^-$

7.85 Metals usually have positive oxidation states in all of their compounds.

7.86 Metals are elements that have low ionization energies and small electron affinities. They therefore tend to react by the loss of electrons to form positive ions, i.e., they become oxidized and serve as reducing agents.

7.87 The only effective oxidizing agent in aqueous solutions of HCl is H^+.

7.88 $Mn(s) + 2HCl(aq) \longrightarrow H_2(g) + MnCl_2(aq)$

7.89 (a) $2Na + 2H_2O \longrightarrow 2NaOH + H_2(g)$

(b) $2Rb + 2H_2O \longrightarrow 2RbOH + H_2(g)$

(c) $Sr + 2H_2O \longrightarrow Sr(OH)_2 + H_2(g)$

7.90 $2Al(s) + 6HBr(aq) \longrightarrow 2AlBr_3(aq) + 3H_2(g)$

7.91 A solution of HNO_3 contains not only H^+ but also the nitrate ion, which is a stronger oxidizing agent than H^+.

7.92 (a) $Ag(s) + NO_3^-(aq) + 2H^+(aq) \longrightarrow Ag^+(aq) + NO_2(g) + H_2O$

(b) $3Ag(s) + NO_3^-(aq) + 4H^+(aq) \longrightarrow 3Ag^+(aq) + NO(g) + 2H_2O$

7.93 If silver metal is placed in a solution of hydrochloric acid, nothing happens. A stronger oxidizing agent than H^+, such as NO_3^-, is needed to oxidize silver.

7.94 $4Zn(s) + NO_3^-(aq) + 10H^+(aq) \longrightarrow 4Zn^{2+}(aq) + NH_4^+(aq) + 3H_2O$

7.95 $4Zn(s) + HSO_4^-(aq) + 9H^+(aq) \xrightarrow{\text{hot}} 4Zn^{2+}(aq) + H_2S(g) + 4H_2O$

7.96 The easily oxidized metals are located on the left side of the periodic table including IA metals and IIA metals except beryllium. The least easily oxidized metals are located in the lower center portion of the block of transition metals.

7.97 (a) Rb (b) Rb (c) Na (d) Ca

7.98 They all react with water to liberate hydrogen.

7.99 Because they are indifferent toward oxidizing agents that attack other metals.

7.100 (a) $Mg + 2HCl \longrightarrow MgCl_2 + H_2$ (b) $2Al + 6HCl \longrightarrow 2AlCl_3 + 3H_2$

7.101 (a) $2Cr + 6HCl \longrightarrow 2CrCl_3 + 3H_2$ (b) $Ni + H_2SO_4 \longrightarrow NiSO_4 + H_2$

7.102 For 7.100: (a) $Mg + 2H^+ \longrightarrow Mg^{2+} + H_2$

(b) $2Al + 6H^+ \longrightarrow 2Al^{3+} + 3H_2$

For 7.101 (a) $2Cr + 6H^+ \longrightarrow 2Cr^{3+} + 3H_2$ (The oxidizing agent is H^+ in each of these reactions.)

(b) $Ni + 2H^+ \longrightarrow Ni^{2+} + H_2$

7.103 Ca should react more rapidly because it has a lower ionization energy than Mg and, therefore, should be more reactive.

7.104 1 part concentrated HNO_3 and 3 parts concentrated HCl, by volume.

7.105 A single displacement reaction is a reaction in which one element replaces another element from a compound.

7.106 (a) $2Al(s) + 3Zn^{2+}(aq) \longrightarrow 2Al^{3+}(aq) + 3Zn(s)$

(b) $Sn(s) + Cu^{2+}(aq) \longrightarrow Sn^{2+}(aq) + Cu(s)$

(c) $Ag(s) + Co^{2+}(aq) \longrightarrow$ No reaction

(d) $Mn(s) + Pb^{2+}(aq) \longrightarrow Mn^{2+}(aq) + Pb(s)$

(e) $Cu(s) + Mg^{2+}(aq) \longrightarrow$ No reaction

(f) $Hg(\ell) + H^+(aq) \longrightarrow$ No reaction

(7.106 continued)

(g) $Ni(s) + 2H^+(aq) \longrightarrow Ni^{2+}(aq) + H_2(g)$

(h) $Cd(s) + H_2O \longrightarrow$ No reaction

(i) $Ba(s) + 2H_2O \longrightarrow Ba(OH)_2(aq) + H_2(g)$

(j) $H_2(g) + Pt^{2+} \longrightarrow Pt(s) + 2H^+(aq)$

7.107 (a) $C < N < O < F$ (b) $I < Br < Cl < F$

7.108 (a) $F_2 + 2Cl^- \longrightarrow 2F^- + Cl_2$

(b) $Br_2 + Cl^- \longrightarrow$ No reaction

(c) $I_2 + Cl^- \longrightarrow$ No reaction

(d) $Br_2 + 2I^- \longrightarrow 2Br^- + I_2$

7.109 (a) The oxidizing ability of nonmetals increases to the right across a period.

(b) The oxidizing ability of nonmetals decreases down a group.

7.110 Combustion is a rapid oxidation of a substance with oxygen that evolves a large amount of heat and light.

7.111 Rust is the product of a direct reaction of iron with oxygen in the presence of moisture to form an iron oxide whose crystals contain water molecules in variable amounts.

$$2Fe(s) + 3/2\ O_2(g) + X\ H_2O(\ell) \longrightarrow Fe_2O_3 \cdot X\ H_2O(s)$$

7.112 The product of the corrosion of aluminum is aluminum oxide, Al_2O_3. This thin oxide layer covers and adheres tightly to the aluminum surface and effectively protects it from further oxidation.

7.113 $2Mg(s) + O_2(g) \longrightarrow 2MgO(s)$

7.114 (a) $2Fe(s) + 3O_2(g) \longrightarrow 2Fe_2O_3(s)$

(b) $4Li(s) + O_2(g) \longrightarrow 2Li_2O(s)$

(c) $2Ca(s) + O_2(g) \longrightarrow 2CaO(s)$

(d) $2Mg(s) + O_2(g) \longrightarrow 2MgO(s)$

(e) $4Al(s) + 3O_2(g) \longrightarrow 2Al_2O_3(s)$

7.115 (a) $C(s) + O_2(g) \longrightarrow CO_2(g)$

(b) $S(s) + O_2(g) \longrightarrow SO_2(g)$

(c) $P_4(s) + 5O_2(g) \longrightarrow P_4O_{10}(s)$

7.116 $2C(s) + O_2(g) \longrightarrow 2CO(g)$

7.117 (a) $C_9H_{20} + 14O_2 \longrightarrow 9CO_2 + 10H_2O$

(b) $2C_2H_4(OH)_2 + 5O_2 \longrightarrow 4CO_2 + 6H_2O$

(c) $2(CH_3)_2S + 9O_2 \longrightarrow 4CO_2 + 6H_2O + 2SO_2$

7.118 $2CH_4 + 3O_2 \longrightarrow 2CO + 4H_2O$ (somewhat limited supply of O_2)

$CH_4 + O_2 \longrightarrow C + 2H_2O$ (extremely limited supply of O_2)

7.119 $2C_{20}H_{42} + 21O_2 \longrightarrow 40C + 42H_2O$

$2C_{20}H_{42} + 41O_2 \longrightarrow 40CO + 42H_2O$

(CO_2 will also be formed)

8 IONIC REACTIONS IN SOLUTION - A CLOSER LOOK

8.1 The three "driving forces" for metathesis reactions are: **(a)** formation of a precipitate, **(b)** formation of a weak electrolyte and **(c)** formation of a gas.

8.2

Soluble	Insoluble
KCl	$PbSO_4$
$(NH_4)_2SO_4$	$Mn(OH)_2$
$AgNO_3$	$FePO_4$
$Zn(ClO_4)_2$	$CaCO_3$
$Ba(C_2H_3O_2)_2$	NiO

8.3

Soluble	Insoluble
KNO_3	$NiCO_3$
$FeCl_2$	Hg_2Cl_2
$(NH_4)_2HPO_4$	$Al(OH)_3$
CuI_2	PbI_2
$SrBr_2$	CoS

8.4 (a) $Al(OH)_3(s) + 3H^+(aq) + 3Cl^-(aq) \longrightarrow Al^{3+}(aq) + 3Cl^-(aq) + 3H_2O$

Net ionic $Al(OH)_3(s) + 3H^+(aq) \longrightarrow Al^{3+}(aq) + 3H_2O$

(b) $CuCO_3(s) + 2H^+(aq) + SO_4^{2-} \longrightarrow Cu^{2+}(aq) + SO_4^{2-} + H_2O + CO_2(g)$

Net ionic $CuCO_3(s) + 2H^+(aq) \longrightarrow Cu^{2+}(aq) + H_2O + CO_2(g)$

(c) $Cr_2(CO_3)_3(s) + 6H^+ + 6NO_3^- \longrightarrow 2Cr^{3+} + 6NO_3^- + 3H_2O + 3CO_2(g)$

Net ionic $Cr_2(CO_3)_3(s) + 6H^+(aq) \longrightarrow 2Cr^{3+}(aq) + 3H_2O + 3CO_2(g)$

8.5 (a) $Ag^+(aq) + Br^-(aq) \longrightarrow AgBr(s)$

(b) $CoCO_3(s) + 2H^+(aq) \longrightarrow Co^{2+}(aq) + CO_2(g) + H_2O$

(c) $C_2H_3O_2^-(aq) + H^+(aq) \longrightarrow HC_2H_3O_2(aq)$

(d) $Pb^{2+}(aq) + SO_4^{2-}(aq) \longrightarrow PbSO_4(s)$

(e) $H_2S(aq) + Cu^{2+}(aq) \longrightarrow 2H^+(aq) + CuS(s)$

(f) $NH_4^+(aq) + OH^-(aq) \longrightarrow NH_3(g) + H_2O$

8.6 (a) $CoS(s) + 2H^+(aq) \longrightarrow H_2S(g) + Co^{2+}(aq)$

(b) $PbCO_3(s) + 2H^+(aq) \longrightarrow H_2O + CO_2(g) + Pb^{2+}(aq)$

(c) $PbCO_3(s) + 2H^+(aq) + SO_4^{2-}(aq) \longrightarrow PbSO_4(s) + H_2O + CO_2(g)$

(d) $Sn^{2+}(aq) + 2OH^-(aq) \longrightarrow Sn(OH)_2(s)$

(e) $Ag_2O(s) + 2H^+(aq) + 2Cl^-(aq) \longrightarrow 2AgCl(s) + 2H_2O$

(f) (This reaction does not have a true driving force.)

8.7 (a) $Na_2SO_4(aq) + BaCl_2(aq) \longrightarrow BaSO_4(s) + 2NaCl(aq)$

$2Na^+(aq) + SO_4^{2-}(aq) + Ba^{2+}(aq) + 2Cl^- \longrightarrow BaSO_4(s) + 2Na^+ + 2Cl^-$

$Ba^{2+}(aq) + SO_4^{2-}(aq) \longrightarrow BaSO_4(s)$

(b) $Ca(NO_3)_2(aq) + (NH_4)_2CO_3(aq) \longrightarrow CaCO_3(s) + 2NH_4NO_3(aq)$

$Ca^{2+}(aq) + 2NO_3^-(aq) + 2NH_4^+ + CO_3^{2-} \longrightarrow CaCO_3(s) + 2NH_4^+ + 2NO_3^-$

$Ca^{2+}(aq) + CO_3^{2-}(aq) \longrightarrow CaCO_3(s)$

(c) $NaC_2H_3O_2(aq) + HNO_3(aq) \longrightarrow NaNO_3(aq) + HC_2H_3O_2(aq)$

$Na^+ + C_2H_3O_2^- + H^+ + NO_3^- \longrightarrow Na^+ + NO_3^- + HC_2H_3O_2(aq)$

$H^+(aq) + C_2H_3O_2^-(aq) \longrightarrow HC_2H_3O_2(aq)$

(d) $2NaOH(aq) + CuCl_2(aq) \longrightarrow 2NaCl(aq) + Cu(OH)_2(s)$

$2Na^+ + 2OH^-(aq) + Cu^{2+}(aq) + 2Cl^- \longrightarrow 2Na^+(aq) + 2Cl^- + Cu(OH)_2(s)$

$Cu^{2+}(aq) + 2OH^-(aq) \longrightarrow Cu(OH)_2(s)$

(e) $(NH_4)_2CO_3(aq) + 2HNO_3(aq) \longrightarrow 2NH_4NO_3(aq) + H_2O + CO_2(g)$

$2NH_4^+ + CO_3^{2-} + 2H^+ + 2NO_3^- \longrightarrow 2NH_4^+ + 2NO_3^- + H_2O + CO_2(g)$

$2H^+(aq) + CO_3^{2-}(aq) \longrightarrow H_2O + CO_2(g)$

8.8 (a) No reaction

(b) $2NH_4Br(aq) + MnSO_4(aq) \longrightarrow (NH_4)_2SO_4(aq) + MnBr_2(aq)$

$2NH_4^+ + 2Br^- + Mn^{2+} + SO_4^{2-} \longrightarrow 2NH_4^+ + SO_4^{2-} + Mn^{2+} + 2Br^-$

No net ionic reaction.

(8.8 continued)

(c) $K_2S(aq) + Ni(C_2H_3O_2)_2(aq) \longrightarrow 2KC_2H_3O_2(aq) + NiS(s)$

$2K^+(aq) + S^{2-}(aq) + NI^{2+}(aq) + 2C_2H_3O_2^-(aq) \longrightarrow 2K^+(aq) + 2C_2H_3O_2^-(aq) + NiS(s)$

$Ni^{2+}(aq) + S^{2-}(aq) \longrightarrow NiS(s)$

(d) $MgSO_4(aq) + 2LiOH(aq) \longrightarrow Li_2SO_4(aq) + Mg(OH)_2(s)$

$Mg^{2+}(aq) + SO_4^{2-} + 2Li^+ + 2OH^-(aq) \longrightarrow 2Li^+ + SO_4^{2-} + Mg(OH)_2(s)$

$Mg^{2+}(aq) + 2OH^-(aq) \longrightarrow Mg(OH)_2(s)$

(e) $AgC_2H_3O_2(aq) + KCl(aq) \longrightarrow AgCl(s) + KC_2H_3O_2(aq)$

$Ag^+(aq) + C_2H_3O_2^-(aq) + K^+(aq) + Cl^-(aq) \longrightarrow AgCl(s) + K^+ + C_2H_3O_2^-$

$Ag^+(aq) + Cl^-(aq) \longrightarrow AgCl(s)$

8.9 **(a)** $AgBr(s) + KI(aq) \longrightarrow AgI(s) + KBr(aq)$

$AgBr(s) + K^+(aq) + I^-(aq) \longrightarrow AgI(s) + K^+(aq) + Br^-(aq)$

$AgBr(s) + I^-(aq) \longrightarrow AgI(s) + Br^-(aq)$

(b) $SO_2(aq) + H_2O + BaCl_2(aq) \longrightarrow BaSO_3(s) + 2HCl(aq)$

$SO_2(aq) + H_2O + Ba^{2+}(aq) + 2Cl^-(aq) \longrightarrow BaSO_3(s) + 2H^+ + 2Cl^-(aq)$

$SO_2(aq) + H_2O + Ba^{2+}(aq) \longrightarrow BaSO_3(s) + 2H^+(aq)$

(c) $Na_2C_2O_4(aq) + 2HCl(aq) \longrightarrow 2NaCl(aq) + H_2C_2O_4(aq)$

$2Na^+(aq) + C_2O_4^-(aq) + 2H^+(aq) + 2Cl^- \longrightarrow 2Na^+ + 2Cl^- + H_2C_2O_4(aq)$

$2H^+(aq) + C_2O_4^{2-}(aq) \longrightarrow H_2C_2O_4(aq)$

(8.9 continued)

(d) $K_2SO_3(aq) + 2HCl(aq) \longrightarrow 2KCl(aq) + H_2SO_3(aq)$

$H_2SO_3(aq) \longrightarrow H_2O + SO_2(aq)$

$2K^+(aq) + SO_3^{2-}(aq) + 2H^+(aq) + 2Cl^- \longrightarrow 2K^+ + 2Cl^- + 2H^+ + SO_3^{2-}$

$2H^+(aq) + SO_3^{2-}(aq) \longrightarrow H_2O + SO_2(g)$

$SO_3^{2-}(aq) + 2H^+(aq) \longrightarrow H_2O + SO_2(g)$

(e) $BaCO_3(s) + H_2SO_4(aq) \longrightarrow BaSO_4(s) + H_2O + CO_2(g)$

$BaCO_3(s) + 2H^+(aq) + SO_4^{2-}(aq) \longrightarrow BaSO_4(s) + H_2O + CO_2(g)$

The net ionic equation is the same as the ionic equation.

8.10 $H_2O + CO_2 \longrightarrow H_2CO_3$

$H_2CO_3 + 2NaOH(excess) \longrightarrow Na_2CO_3 + 2H_2O$

8.11 One possible set of reactions is:

(a) $Ba(C_2H_3O_2)_2(aq) + (NH_4)_2SO_4(aq) \longrightarrow BaSO_4(s) + 2NH_4C_2H_3O_2(aq)$

(b) $3FeCl_2(aq) + 2H_3PO_4(aq) \longrightarrow Fe_3(PO_4)_2(s) + 6HCl(aq)$

(c) $Cu(NO_3)_2(aq) + Na_2CO_3(aq) \longrightarrow CuCO_3(s) + 2NaNO_3(aq)$

(d) $2NaOH(aq) + MgSO_4(aq) \longrightarrow Na_2SO_4(aq) + Mg(OH)_2(s)$

(e) $(NH_4)_2SO_4(aq) + Pb(NO_3)_2(aq) \longrightarrow 2NH_4NO_3(aq) + PbSO_4(s)$

8.12 One possible set of reactions is:

(a) See (d) above

(b) $MnCl_2(aq) + Ba(OH)_2(aq) \longrightarrow Mn(OH)_2(s) + BaCl_2(aq)$

(c) $FeCl_2(aq) + Pb(C_2H_3O_2)_2(aq) \longrightarrow Fe(C_2H_3O_2)_2(aq) + PbCl_2(s)$

(d) $NiCl_2(aq) + Pb(ClO_4)_2(aq) \longrightarrow PbCl_2(s) + Ni(ClO_4)_2(aq)$

(e) $(NH_4)SO_3(aq) + BaCl_2(aq) \longrightarrow 2NH_4Cl(aq) + BaSO_3(s)$

8.13 One possible set of reactions is:

(a) $CaCO_3(s) + 2HCl(aq) \longrightarrow CaCl_2(aq) + CO_2(g) + H_2O$

(b) $MnCO_3(s) + 2HClO_4(aq) \longrightarrow Mn(ClO_4)_2(aq) + H_2O + CO_2(g)$

(c) $BaSO_3(s) + H_2SO_4(aq) \longrightarrow BaSO_4(s) + H_2O + SO_2(g)$

(d) $NaOH(aq) + NH_4NO_3(aq) \longrightarrow NaNO_3(aq) + H_2O + NH_3(g)$

(e) $(NH_4)_2CO_3(aq) + 2HC_2H_3O_2 \longrightarrow 2NH_4C_2H_3O_2 + H_2O + CO_2(g)$

8.14 (a) $Ca(OH)_2(aq) + 2HNO_3(aq) \longrightarrow Ca(NO_3)_2(aq) + 2H_2O$

(b) $2NaOH(aq) + H_2C_2O_4(aq) \longrightarrow Na_2C_2O_4(aq) + 2H_2O$

(c) $Fe(OH)_2 + 2H_2SO_4(aq) \longrightarrow 2H_2O + Fe(HSO_4)_2(aq)$

(d) $Al_2O_3(s) + 6HClO_4(aq) \longrightarrow 2Al(ClO_4)_3(aq) + 3H_2O$

(e) $NiO(s) + 2HBr(aq) \longrightarrow NiBr_2(aq) + H_2O$

8.15 (a) $Cu(NO_3)_2(aq) + 2NaOH(aq) \longrightarrow Cu(OH)_2(s) + 2NaNO_3(aq)$

$Cu(OH)_2(s) + 2HCl(aq) \longrightarrow CuCl_2(aq) + 2H_2O$

(8.15 continued)

(b) $BaBr_2(aq) + Na_2SO_3(aq) \longrightarrow BaSO_3(s) + 2NaBr(aq)$

$BaSO_3(s) + 2HCl(aq) \longrightarrow BaCl_2(aq) + H_2O + SO_2(g)$

(c) $Na_2SO_4(aq) + Ba(ClO_4)_2(aq) \longrightarrow 2NaClO_4(aq) + BaSO_4(s)$

(d) $MgCl_2(aq) + Pb(C_2H_3O_2)_2(aq) \longrightarrow Mg(C_2H_3O_2)_2(aq) + PbCl_2(s)$

(e) $Na_2SO_3(aq) + Ba(OH)_2(aq) \longrightarrow 2NaOH(aq) + BaSO_3(s)$

$2NaOH(aq) + H_2CO_3(aq)(CO_2 + H_2O) \longrightarrow Na_2CO_3(aq) + 2H_2O$

8.16 number of grams of solute per 100 g of solution

8.17 number of grams of solute per million (10^6) grams of solution

8.18 number of grams of solute per billion (10^9) grams of solution

8.19 (a) $\frac{0.001 \text{ g F}^-}{1{,}000 \text{ g soln.}} \times 100 = \underline{1 \times 10^{-4}\% \text{ F}^- \text{ by weight}}$

(b) $\frac{0.001 \text{ g F}^-}{1{,}000 \text{ g soln.}} \times 1{,}000{,}000 = \underline{1.0 \text{ parts F}^- \text{ per million}}$

(c) $\frac{0.001 \text{ g F}^-}{1{,}000 \text{ g soln.}} \times 1{,}000{,}000{,}000 = \underline{1.0 \times 10^3 \text{ parts F}^- \text{ per billion}}$

8.20 $\frac{2.1 \times 10^{-5} \text{ mol Hg}}{25.0 \text{ g sample}} \times \frac{200.59 \text{ g Hg}}{\text{mol Hg}} \times 1{,}000{,}000 = 1.7 \times 10^2 \text{ ppm}$

1.7×10^2 ppm is greater than the allowed 0.50 ppm. Therefore, the shipment must be <u>confiscated</u>.

8.21 (a) $\frac{1.50 \text{ mol NaCl}}{2.00 \text{ L soln.}} = \underline{0.750 \text{ M}}$ (b) $\underline{0.992 \text{ M}}$ (c) $\underline{0.556 \text{ M}}$

(d) $\frac{85.5 \text{ g HNO}_3}{1.00 \text{ L soln.}} \times \frac{1 \text{ mol HNO}_3}{63.01 \text{ g HNO}_3} = \underline{1.36 \text{ M}}$

(8.21 continued)

(e) $\frac{44.5 \text{ g } NH_4C_2H_3O_2}{600 \text{ mL soln.}} \times \frac{1000 \text{ mL}}{\text{L}} \times \frac{1 \text{ mol } NH_4C_2H_3O_2}{77.1 \text{ g } NH_4C_2H_3O_2} = \underline{\textbf{0.962 M}}$

8.22 (a) $\frac{0.100 \text{ moles solute}}{\text{L soln.}} \times 0.250 \text{ L soln.} = \underline{\textbf{0.0250 mol KCl}}$

(b) **$\underline{2.31 \text{ moles } HClO_4}$** (c) **$\underline{2.50 \times 10^{-4} \text{ mole } HC_2H_3O_2}$**

8.23 $\frac{0.150 \text{ mol } Na_2CO_3}{\text{L soln.}} \times 0.300 \text{ L soln.} \times \frac{106 \text{ g } Na_2CO_3}{\text{mol}} = \underline{\textbf{4.77 g } \mathbf{Na_2CO_3}}$

8.24 $\frac{0.300 \text{ mol } OH^-}{\text{L soln.}} \times \frac{1 \text{ mol } Ba(OH)_2}{2 \text{ mol } OH^-} \times \frac{171 \text{ g } Ba(OH)_2}{\text{mol } Ba(OH)_2} \times 0.250 \text{ L soln.} =$

$\underline{6.41 \text{ g } Ba(OH)_2}$

8.25 In pure nitric acid, nitric acid is both the solute and the solution. Therefore, a density of 1.513 g /mL can be expressed as 1.513 g solute /mL solution.

$\frac{1.513 \text{ g } HNO_3}{\text{mL soln.}} \times \frac{1{,}000 \text{ mL soln.}}{\text{L soln.}} \times \frac{1 \text{ mole } HNO_3}{63.01 \text{ g } HNO_3^-} = \underline{\textbf{24.01 M}}$

8.26 $\frac{273.8 \text{ g salt}}{\text{L soln.}} \times \frac{1 \text{ L}}{1{,}000 \text{ mL}} \times \frac{100 \text{ g soln.}}{22.0 \text{ g salt}} = \frac{1.24 \text{ g soln.}}{\text{mL soln}}$

$\underline{\text{Density} = 1.24 \text{ g /mL}}$

$\frac{273.8 \text{ g } MgSO_4}{1.000 \text{ L soln.}} \times \frac{1 \text{ mol } MgSO_4}{120.4 \text{ g } MgSO_4} = 2.274 \text{ mol } MgSO_4 \text{ /L} = \underline{\textbf{2.274 M}}$

8.27 $\frac{825 \text{ g}}{10^6 \text{ g}} \times 100 = 8.25 \times 10^{-2}\% = \underline{\textbf{0.0825\%}}$

$\frac{825 \text{ g benzene}}{10^6 \text{ g soln.}} \times \frac{1\text{g}}{1 \text{ mL}} \times \frac{1{,}000 \text{ mL}}{\text{L}} \times \frac{1 \text{ mol benzene}}{78.11 \text{ g}} = \underline{\textbf{0.0106 M}}$

8.28 (a) 0.100 M Li^+ and 0.100 M Cl^-

(b) 0.250 M Ca^{2+} and 0.500 M Cl^-

(c) 2.40 M NH_4^+ and 1.20 M SO_4^{2-}

(d) 0.600 M Na^+, ~ 0.600 M HSO_4^-

(e) 0.800 M Fe^{3+} and 1.20 M SO_4^{2-}

8.29 (a) 0.0250 M Ba^{2+} and 0.0500 M OH^-

(b) 0.300 M Cd^{2+} and 0.600 M NO_3^-

(c) 0.800 M Na^+ and 0.400 M HPO_4^{2-}

(d) 0.200 M Cr^{3+} and 0.300 M SO_4^{2-}

(e) 0.0450 M Hg_2^{2+} and 0.0900 M NO_3^-

8.30 0.100 M (See problem 8.31 for an example of the method for obtaining this answer.)

8.31 $$\frac{0.160 \text{ mol Cl}^-}{\text{L}} \times \frac{1 \text{ mol FeCl}_3}{3 \text{ mol Cl}^-} = \frac{0.0533 \text{ mol FeCl}_3}{\text{L}} = 0.0533 \text{ M FeCl}_3$$

8.32 0.0700 M (See problem 8.31 for an example of the method for obtaining this answer.)

8.33 (a) 0.0100 mol Na^+ and 0.0100 mol Cl^-

(b) 0.00480 mol Ca^{2+} and 0.00960 mol Cl^-

(c) 0.0351 mol Na^+ and 0.0176 mol SO_4^{2-}

(d) 0.221 mol NH_4^+ and 0.111 mol SO_4^{2-}

(e) 0.0375 mol Al^{3+} and 0.0562 mol SO_4^{2-}

8.34 M.W. of $CuSO_4 \cdot 5H_2O$ = 249.7 The concentration of the solution is:

$$\frac{10.45 \text{ g salt}}{150.0 \text{ mL soln.}} \times \frac{1{,}000 \text{ mL}}{\text{L}} \times \frac{1 \text{ mol salt}}{249.7 \text{ g}} = 0.2790 \text{ M salt}$$

The salt solution will contain: **<u>0.2790 M Cu^{2+}</u>** and **<u>0.2790 M SO_4^{2-}</u>**

8.35 $2NaOH(aq) + H_2SO_4(aq) \longrightarrow Na_2SO_4(aq) + 2H_2O$

$$5.00 \times 10^{-3} \text{ mol } H_2SO_4 \times \frac{2 \text{ mol NaOH}}{\text{mol } H_2SO_4} \times \frac{1 \text{ L NaOH soln.}}{0.100 \text{ mol NaOH}} =$$

0.100 L NaOH soln. or **<u>100 mL</u>**

8.36 $$3.22 \text{ g Cu} \times \frac{1 \text{ mol Cu}}{63.55 \text{ g Cu}} \times \frac{8 \text{ mol } HNO_3}{3 \text{ mol Cu}} \times \frac{1 \text{ L soln.}}{1.250 \text{ mol } HNO_3} =$$

0.1081 L soln. = **<u>108 mL</u>** (based upon H^+ needed)

8.37 **(a)** Molecular equation: $CuCO_3(s) + 2HClO_4 \longrightarrow H_2O + CO_2(g) + Cu(ClO_4)_2$

Net ionic eq.: $\mathbf{2H^+(aq) + CuCO_3(s) \rightarrow CO_2(g) + H_2O(\ell) + Cu^{2+}(aq)}$

(b) To show the formation of $Cu(ClO_4)_2$ the molecular equation must be used.

Solid $Cu(ClO_4)_2$ can be obtained by evaporation.

$2HClO_4(aq) + CuCO_3(s) \longrightarrow CO_2(g) + H_2O + Cu(ClO_4)_2(aq)$

$$5.25 \text{ g } Cu(ClO_4)_2 \times \frac{1 \text{ mol } Cu(ClO_4)_2}{262.5 \text{ g}} \times \frac{2 \text{ mol } HClO_4}{1 \text{ mol } Cu(ClO_4)_2} \times$$

$$\frac{1 \text{ L soln.}}{1.35 \text{ mol } HClO_4} \times \frac{1{,}000 \text{ mL}}{\text{L}} = \mathbf{\underline{29.6 \text{ mL}}}$$

(8.37 continued)

(c) $5.25\ g\ Cu(ClO_4)_2 \times \frac{1\ mol\ Cu(ClO_4)_2}{262.5\ g} \times \frac{1\ mol\ CuCO_3}{1\ mol\ Cu(ClO_4)_2} \times$

$\frac{123.6\ g\ CuCO_3}{mol\ CuCO_3} = \underline{\mathbf{2.47\ g\ CuCO_3}}$

8.38 (a) $H_3PO_4(aq) + 3NaOH(aq) \longrightarrow Na_3PO_4(aq) + 3H_2O$

$\frac{0.170\ mol\ H_3PO_4}{L\ soln.} \times 0.500\ L\ soln. \times \frac{3\ mol\ NaOH}{mol\ H_3PO_4} \times \frac{1\ L\ NaOH\ soln.}{0.300\ mol\ NaOH} =$

$0.850\ L\ NaOH\ soln. = \underline{\mathbf{850\ mL}}$

(b) $H_3PO_4(aq) + 2NaOH(aq) \longrightarrow Na_2HPO_4(aq) + 2H_2O$

$\frac{0.170\ mol\ H_3PO_4}{L\ soln.} \times 0.500\ L\ soln. \times \frac{2\ mol\ NaOH}{mol\ H_3PO_4} \times \frac{1\ L\ NaOH\ soln.}{0.300\ mol\ NaOH} =$

$0.567\ L\ NaOH\ soln. = \underline{\mathbf{567\ mL}}$

(c) $H_3PO_4(aq) + NaOH(aq) \longrightarrow NaH_2PO_4(aq) + H_2O$

$\frac{0.170}{1} \times \frac{.500}{1} \times \frac{1}{1} \times \frac{1}{0.300} = 0.283\ L$ or $\underline{\mathbf{283\ mL}}$

8.39 $BaCl_2(aq) + H_2SO_4(aq) \longrightarrow 2HCl(aq) + BaSO_4(s)$

$\frac{0.200\ mol\ H_2SO_4}{L} \times 0.0250\ L \times \frac{1\ mol\ BaCl_2}{mol\ H_2SO_4} \times \frac{1\ L\ BaCl_2\ soln.}{0.100\ mol\ BaCl_2}$

$= 0.0500\ L\ BaCl_2\ soln. = \underline{\mathbf{50.0\ mL\ BaCl_2\ soln.}}$

8.40 $3BaCl_2(aq) + Fe_2(SO_4)_3(aq) \longrightarrow 3BaSO_4(s) + 2FeCl_3(aq)$

$$\frac{0.200\ \text{mol}\ Fe_2(SO_4)_3}{L} \times 0.0250\ L \times \frac{3\ \text{mol}\ BaCl_2}{\text{mol}\ Fe_2(SO_4)_3} \times \frac{1\ L\ BaCl_2\ \text{soln.}}{0.100\ \text{mol}\ BaCl_2}$$

$$\times \frac{1{,}000\ \text{mL}}{L} = \underline{\mathbf{150\ mL\ BaCl_2\ soln.}}$$

8.41 $1NaOH + 1$ monoprotic acid $\longrightarrow$ salt $+ 1H_2O$

$$\frac{1\ L\ NaOH\ \text{soln.}}{0.100\ \text{mol NaOH}} \times \frac{1}{0.0200\ L\ NaOH\ \text{soln.}} \times \frac{1\ \text{mol NaOH}}{\text{mol benzoic acid}} \times$$

0.244 g benzoic acid = **<u>122 g benzoic acid /mol benzoic acid</u>**

8.42 **(a)** Molecular equation: $AgNO_3(aq) + NaCl(aq) \longrightarrow NaNO_3(aq) + AgCl(s)$

Net ionic equation: $\underline{Ag^+(aq) + Cl^-(aq) \longrightarrow AgCl(s)}$

(b) 20.0 mL of 0.200 M $AgNO_3$ contains: $0.0200\ L \times \frac{0.200\ \text{mol}}{L}$ or

0.00400 mole of Ag^+

30.0 mL of 0.200 M NaCl contains: $0.0300\ L \times \frac{0.200\ \text{mol}}{L}$ or

0.00600 mole of Cl^-

From this, one can see that the Ag^+ is the limiting reagent and that only

<u>0.00400 mole of AgCl</u> can be precipitated.

(c) $0.00400\ \text{mol AgCl} \times \frac{143.3\ \text{g AgCl}}{\text{mol}} = \underline{\mathbf{0.573\ g\ AgCl}}$

(d) The amount of each ion before reaction is: $Ag^+ = 0.00400$ moles, $NO_3^- =$ 0.00400 moles, $Na^+ = 0.00600$ moles, and $Cl^- = 0.00600$ moles. The precipitation process will remove 0.00400 moles of Ag^+ and 0.00400 moles of

(8.42 continued)

Cl^- leaving in solution 0.0 moles Ag^+, 0.00200 moles Cl^-, 0.00400 moles NO_3^- and 0.00600 moles Na^+. The concentration of each ion will be the number of moles of ion in the final solution divided by the total volume of solution.

$Ag^+ = \underline{\mathbf{0\ M}}$ $\qquad Cl^- = \dfrac{0.00200\text{ mol}}{0.0500\text{ L}} = \underline{\mathbf{0.0400\ M}}$

$NO_3^- = \dfrac{0.00400\text{ mol}}{0.0500\text{ L}} = \underline{\mathbf{0.0800\ M}}$ $\qquad Na^+ = \dfrac{0.00600\text{ mol}}{0.0500\text{ L}} = \underline{\mathbf{0.120\ M}}$

8.43 $AgNO_3(aq) + HCl(aq) \longrightarrow AgCl(s) + HNO_3(aq)$ (The limiting reactant is HCl.)

$$\frac{0.050\text{ mol HCl}}{\text{L}} \times 0.0250\text{ L} \times \frac{1\text{ mol AgCl}}{1\text{ mol HCl}} \times \frac{143\text{ g AgCl}}{\text{mol}} = \underline{\mathbf{0.18\ g\ AgCl}}$$

8.44 $3BaCl_2(aq) + Fe_2(SO_4)_3(aq) \longrightarrow 3BaSO_4(s) + 2FeCl_3(aq)$

$$\frac{0.240\text{ mol }BaCl_2}{\text{L}} \times 0.0500\text{ L} \times \frac{1\text{ mol }Ba^{2+}}{\text{mol }BaCl_2} = 0.0120\text{ mol }Ba^{2+}$$

$$\frac{0.180\text{ mol }Fe_2(SO_4)_3}{\text{L}} \times 0.0450\text{ L} \times \frac{3\text{ mol }SO_4^{2-}}{1\text{ mol }Fe_2(SO_4)_3} = 0.0243\text{ mol }SO_4^{2-}$$

Ba^{2+} and SO_4^{2-} combine in a 1-to-1 mole ratio to form the insoluble $BaSO_4$. Therefore, in this situation the Ba^{2+} is the limiting reagent since there are fewer moles of Ba^{2+} present.

(8.44 continued)

(a) Mass of $BaSO_4$ formed?

$$0.0120 \text{ mol } Ba^{2+} \times \frac{1 \text{ mol } BaSO_4}{\text{mol } Ba^{2+}} \times \frac{233.4 \text{ g } BaSO_4}{\text{mol } BaSO_4} = \underline{\mathbf{2.80 \text{ g } BaSO_4}}$$

(b) Concentrations of remaining ions? $\underline{\mathbf{0\ M\ Ba^{2+}}}$

$$\frac{0.240 \text{ mol } BaCl_2}{L} \times 0.0500 \text{ L} \times \frac{2 \text{ mol } Cl^-}{1 \text{ mol } BaCl_2} \times \frac{1}{0.0950 \text{ L}} = \underline{\mathbf{0.253\ M\ Cl^-}}$$

$$\frac{(0.0243 \text{ mol } SO_4^{2-} - 0.0120 \text{ mol } SO_4^{2-})}{0.0950 \text{ L}} = \underline{\mathbf{0.129\ M\ SO_4^{2-}}}$$

$$\frac{0.180 \text{ mol } Fe_2(SO_4)_3}{L} \times 0.0450 \text{ L} \times \frac{2 \text{ mol } Fe^{3+}}{\text{mol } Fe_2(SO_4)_3} \times \frac{1}{0.0950 \text{ L}} =$$

$\underline{\mathbf{0.171\ M\ Fe^{3+}}}$

8.45 $2Cr^{3+}(aq) + 3SO_4^{2-}(aq) + 6NaOH \longrightarrow 2Cr(OH)_3(s) + 6Na^+ + 3SO_4^{2-}$

$2Cr(OH)_3(s) + 6HNO_3(aq) \longrightarrow 2Cr^{3+}(aq) + 6H_2O + 6NO_3^-(aq)$

From the sequential reactions shown above, one can see that 1 mole of $Cr_2(SO_4)_3(s)$ in the first reaction will eventually react with 6 moles of nitric acid.

$$0.500 \text{ g } Cr_2(SO_4)_3 \times \frac{1 \text{ mol } Cr_2(SO_4)_3}{392.2 \text{ g}} \times \frac{6 \text{ mol } HNO_3}{\text{mol } Cr_2(SO_4)_3} \times$$

$$\frac{1 \text{ L } HNO_3 \text{ soln.}}{0.400 \text{ mol } HNO_3} = 0.0191 \text{ L } HNO_3 \text{ soln. or } \underline{\mathbf{19.1 \text{ mL } HNO_3 \text{ soln.}}}$$

8.46 (a) $\frac{0.0500 \text{ mol NaOH}}{\text{L NaOH soln.}} \times 0.0172 \text{ L NaOH soln.} \times \frac{1 \text{ mol cap. acid}}{1 \text{ mol NaOH}}$

$= 0.000860$ mol cap. acid $\qquad \frac{0.100 \text{ g cap. acid}}{0.000860 \text{ mol}} = \underline{\textbf{116 g/mol = M.W.}}$

(b) C_3H_6O empirical formula weight = 58.1

From its molecular weight and its empirical formula weight, its molecular formula must be twice its empirical formula. $\underline{\mathbf{C_6H_{12}O_2}}$

8.47 $Ba(OH)_2(aq) + 2HCl(aq) \longrightarrow Ba^{2+}(aq) + 2Cl^-(aq) + 2H_2O$

$\frac{0.273 \text{ mol } Ba(OH)_2}{\text{L}} \times 0.380 \text{ L} = 0.104 \text{ mol } Ba(OH)_2$

$\frac{0.520 \text{ mol HCl}}{\text{L}} \times 0.500 \text{ L} = 0.260 \text{ mol HCl}$

(a) HCl is in excess. Therefore, the mixture will be **acidic**.

(b) To calculate the excess of HCl:

$0.104 \text{ mol } Ba(OH)_2 \times \frac{2 \text{ mol HCl}}{1 \text{ mol } Ba(OH)_2} = 0.208 \text{ mol HCl (reacted)}$

$\frac{0.260 \text{ mol HCl total} - 0.208 \text{ mol reacted}}{0.380 \text{ L} + 0.500 \text{ L}} = 0.059 \text{ M HCl} = \underline{\mathbf{0.059 \text{ M } H^+}}$

8.48 (a) $3Ba(OH)_2(aq) + Al_2(SO_4)_3(aq) \longrightarrow 2Al(OH)_3(s) + 3BaSO_4(s)$

(b) $\frac{0.270 \text{ mol } Ba(OH)_2}{\text{L}} \times 0.040 \text{ L} = 0.0108 \text{ mol } Ba(OH)_2$

$\frac{0.330 \text{ mol } Al_2(SO_4)_3}{\text{L}} \times 0.025 \text{ L} = 0.00825 \text{ mol } Al_2(SO_4)_3$

$Ba(OH)_2$ is the limiting reagent.

(8.48 continued)

$$0.0108 \text{ mol Ba(OH)}_2 \times \frac{3 \text{ mol BaSO}_4}{3 \text{ mol Ba(OH)}_2} \times \frac{233.4 \text{ g BaSO}_4}{\text{mol BaSO}_4} =$$

<u>2.52 g of $BaSO_4$ precipitated</u>

$$0.0108 \text{ mol Ba(OH)}_2 \times \frac{2 \text{ mol Al(OH)}_3}{3 \text{ mol Ba(OH)}_2} \times \frac{78.0 \text{ g Al(OH)}_3}{\text{mol Al(OH)}_3} =$$

<u>0.562 g of $Al(OH)_3$ precipitated</u>

Total weight of ppt. is 2.52 + 0.562 = **<u>3.08 g</u>**

(c) **<u>0 M Ba^{2+}</u>, <u>~0 M OH^-</u>**

$$0.00825 \text{ mol Al}_2(\text{SO}_4)_3 \times \frac{3 \text{ mol SO}_4^{2-}}{\text{mol Al}_2(\text{SO}_4)_3} = 0.0248 \text{ mol SO}_4^{2-} \text{ before ppt.}$$

$$\frac{0.0248 \text{ mol SO}_4^{2-} \text{ total} - 0.0108 \text{ mol SO}_4^{2-} \text{ ppt.}}{0.0650 \text{ L}} = \mathbf{0.215 \text{ M SO}_4^{2-}}$$

$$0.00825 \text{ mol Al}_2(\text{SO}_4)_3 \times \frac{2 \text{ mol Al}^{3+}}{\text{mol Al}_2(\text{SO}_4)_3} = 0.0165 \text{ mol Al}^{3+} \text{ before ppt.}$$

$$\frac{0.0165 \text{ mol Al}^{3+} - 0.00721 \text{ mol Al}^{3+} \text{ ppt.}}{0.0650 \text{ L}} = \mathbf{0.143 \text{ M Al}^{3+}}$$

8.49 Chemical analysis is the experimental determination of chemical composition.

8.50 $$0.694 \text{ g AgCl} \times \frac{1 \text{ mol AgCl}}{143.4 \text{ g}} \times \frac{1 \text{ mol Cl}}{\text{mol AgCl}} = 0.00484 \text{ mol Cl}$$

$$0.00484 \text{ mol Cl} \times \frac{35.45 \text{ g Cl}}{\text{mol}} = 0.172 \text{ g Cl}$$

g Ti = 0.249 g of sample - 0.172 g Cl = 0.077 g Ti

(8.50 continued)

$$0.077 \text{ g Ti} \times \frac{1 \text{ mol Ti}}{47.9 \text{ g}} = 0.00161 \text{ mol Ti}$$

Formula is: $Ti_{0.00161}Cl_{0.00484}$ or $Ti_{0.00162/0.00162}Cl_{0.00484/0.00162}$

or $\underline{TiCl_3}$

8.51 $PbCO_3(s) + 2HNO_3(aq) \longrightarrow H_2O + CO_2(g) + Pb^{2+}(aq) + 2NO_3^-(aq)$

$Pb^{2+}(aq) + Na_2SO_4(aq) \longrightarrow PbSO_4(s) + 2Na^+(aq)$

$$1.081 \text{ g } PbSO_4 \times \frac{1 \text{ mol } PbSO_4}{303.3 \text{ g } PbSO_4} \times \frac{1 \text{ mol } PbCO_3}{1 \text{ mol } PbSO_4} \times \frac{267.2 \text{ g } PbCO_3}{\text{mol } PbCO_3} =$$

$0.9523 \text{ g } PbCO_3$ $\qquad \frac{0.9523 \text{ g } PbCO_3}{1.526 \text{ g sample}} \times 100 = \underline{62.40\% \ PbCO_3}$

8.52 $2AgCl(\text{excess}) + CuBr_2 \longrightarrow 2AgBr + CuCl_2$

$$1.800 \text{ g AgCl(init.)} \times \frac{1 \text{ mol AgCl}}{143.32 \text{ g AgCl}} = 0.012559 \text{ mol AgCl(init.)}$$

0.012559 mol AgCl(init.) = mol AgBr + mol AgCl(excess)

mol AgBr = X $\qquad$ mol AgCl(final) = 0.012559 - X

2.052 g sample = (X mol AgBr x 187.77 g /mol) +

[(0.012559 - X) mol AgCl x 143.32 g /mol]

$2.052 = 187.77X + 1.8000 - 143.32X$ $\qquad X = 0.00567$ mol AgBr

$$0.00567 \text{ mol AgBr} \times \frac{1 \text{ mol } CuBr_2}{2 \text{ mol AgBr}} \times \frac{223.35 \text{ g}}{\text{mol } CuBr_2} = 0.633 \text{ g}$$

$$\frac{0.633 \text{ g } CuBr_2}{1.850} \times 100 = \underline{34.2\%}$$

8.53 The difference in mass of 0.4120 g and 0.4881 g is brought about by the following reaction and the change in mass of the silver solids.

$AgCl(s) + Br^-(aq) \longrightarrow AgBr(s) + Cl^-(aq)$

The moles NaCl in original sample = moles AgCl reacting = moles AgBr formed. Therefore;

0.4881 g - 0.4120 g = mass AgBr - mass AgCl

0.0761 = (X mol AgBr formed x 187.78 g AgBr /mol)

- (X mol AgCl reacted x 143.32 g AgCl /mol)

0.0761 = 187.78X - 143.32X = 44.46X   X = 0.00171

1.71×10^{-3} moles AgCl present in sample

$$\frac{1.71 \times 10^{-3} \times 58.44 \text{ g/mol}}{0.200 \text{ g sample}} \times 100 = \underline{50.0\% \text{ NaCl}}$$

$AgBr(s) + I^-(aq) \longrightarrow AgI(s) + Br^-(aq)$

0.5868 g - 0.4881 g = mass AgI - mass AgBr

0.0987 = (X mol AgI x 234.77 g /mol) - (X mol AgBr x 187.77 g /mol)

0.0987 = 234.8X - 187.8X = 47.0X

X = 0.00210 mol AgBr in intermediate sample

0.00210 mol AgBr - 0.00171 mol AgCl converted in previous step = 0.00039 mol AgBr formed from NaBr = 0.00039 mol NaBr in original.

$$\frac{0.00039 \text{ mol NaBr} \times 102.89 \text{ g/mol}}{0.200 \text{ g sample}} \times 100 = \underline{20\% \text{ NaBr}}$$

To calculate amount of NaI in original sample:

(8.53 continued)

$0.2000\text{g} = (0.00171 \text{ mol NaCl} \times 58.44 \text{ g/mol})$

$+ (0.00039 \text{ mol NaBr} \times 102.89 \text{ g/mol}) + \text{mass NaI}$

mass NaI = 0.2000 - 0.100 - 0.040 = 0.060 g

$\frac{0.060 \text{ g NaI}}{0.2000 \text{ g sample}} \times 100 =$ **<u>30% NaI</u>**

8.54 (a) A buret is a long tube fitted at one end with a valve (called a stopcock) and is precisely graduated in milliliters and tenths of milliliters. It is used to deliver known quantities of a liquid or solution.

(b) Titration is an analytical procedure that allows us to measure the amount of one solution needed to react exactly with the contents of another solution.

(c) The titrant is the solution delivered via the buret.

(d) The end point in a titration is the point that delivery of the titrant is stopped and is usually signaled by the color change of an indicator.

8.55 An indicator signals when the reaction is complete.

(a) colorless

(b) pink

8.56 $H_2SO_4(aq) + 2NaOH(aq) \longrightarrow Na_2SO_4(aq) + H_2O$

$$\frac{0.150 \text{ mol NaOH}}{\text{L NaOH soln.}} \times 0.02130 \text{ L NaOH soln} \times \frac{1 \text{ mol } H_2SO_4}{2 \text{ mol NaOH}}$$

$$\times \frac{1}{0.0150 \text{ L } H_2SO_4 \text{ soln.}} = \frac{0.106 \text{ mol } H_2SO_4}{\text{L } H_2SO_4 \text{ soln.}} = \underline{\mathbf{0.106\ M\ H_2SO_4}}$$

8.57 $CaCO_3 \longrightarrow CaO \longrightarrow Ca(OH)_2$

$Ca(OH)_2(aq) + 2HCl(aq) \longrightarrow CaCl_2(aq) + 2H_2O$

$$\frac{0.120\ \text{mol HCl}}{\text{L}} \times 0.03725\ \text{L} \times \frac{1\ \text{mol Ca(OH)}_2}{2\ \text{mol HCl}} = 0.002235\ \text{mol Ca(OH)}_2$$

$0.002235\ \text{mol Ca(OH)}_2 = 0.002235\ \text{mol CaCO}_3$

$$\frac{0.002235\ \text{mol CaCO}_3 \times 100.1\ \text{g mol}^{-1}}{1.030\ \text{g sample}} \times 100 = \underline{\mathbf{21.7\%}}$$

8.58 (See Problem 8.57) $\frac{0.1000\ \text{mol HCl}}{\text{L}} \times 0.0303\ \text{L} \times \frac{1\ \text{mol Ca(OH)}_2}{2\ \text{mol HCl}}$

$= 0.001515\ \text{mol Ca(OH)}_2 = 0.001515\ \text{mol CaO} = 0.001515\ \text{mol CaCO}_3$

$0.001515\ \text{mol CaO} \times 56.08\ \text{g /mol} = 0.08496\ \text{g CaO}$

$0.200\ \text{g sample} - 0.08496\ \text{g CaO} = 0.1150\ \text{g other material}$

$0.001515\ \text{mol CaCO}_3 \times 100.1\ \text{g /mol} = 0.1517\ \text{g CaCO}_3$

$$\frac{0.1517\ \text{g CaCO}_3}{0.1517\ \text{g CaCO}_3 + 0.1150\ \text{g others}} \times 100 = \underline{\mathbf{56.9\%\ CaCO_3}}$$

8.59 $\frac{0.0200\ \text{mol NaOH}}{\text{L}} \times 0.0152\ \text{L} \times \frac{1\ \text{mol acid}}{2\ \text{mol NaOH}} \times \frac{176.1\ \text{g acid}}{\text{mol}} = 0.0268\ \text{g acid}$

$$\frac{0.0268\ \text{g}}{0.1000\ \text{g sample}} \times 100 = \underline{\mathbf{26.8\%}}$$

8.60 $\frac{0.0500\ \text{mol NaOH}}{\text{L}} \times 0.0204\ \text{L} \times \frac{1\ \text{mol acids}}{1\ \text{mol NaOH}} = \underline{0.00102\ \text{mol acids}}$

Let X = moles L.A.; then 0.00102 - X = moles C.A. 0.1000 g =

(X mol L.A. x 90.09 g /mol) + {[(0.00102 - X) mol C.A.] (116.18 g /mol)}

(8.60 continued)

$0.1000 = 90.09X + 0.1185 - 116.18X$

$0.0185 = 26.09X$

$X = 0.000709$

Mass L.A. = 0.000709 mol x 90.09 g /mol = **<u>0.064 g Lactic Acid</u>**

Mass C.A. = (0.00102 - 0.000709 mol) (116.18 g /mol) =

<u>0.036 g Caproic Acid</u>

8.61 $\frac{1.00 \text{ mol NaOH}}{\text{L}} \times 19.6 \times 10^{-3}\text{ L} \times \frac{1 \text{ mol HCl excess}}{1 \text{ mol NaOH}} =$

0.0196 mol HCl excess

$\frac{1.00 \text{ mol HCl}}{\text{L}} \times 0.100 \text{ L HCl} = 0.100 \text{ mol HCl total}$

0.100 mol HCl total - 0.0196 mol HCl excess = 0.0804 mol HCl reacted

$0.0804 \text{ mol HCl react.} \times \frac{1 \text{ mol CaO + MgO}}{2 \text{ mol HCl}} = 0.0402 \text{ mol CaO + MgO}$

Let X = moles CaO and 0.0402 - X = moles of MgO. Then:

$2.00 \text{ g} = (X)(56.08 \text{ g /mol}) + (0.0402 - X)(40.31)$

$2.00 = 56.08X + 1.620 - 40.31X$

$0.38 = 15.77X$

X = 0.024 = moles CaO = moles $CaCO_3$

0.016 = moles MgO = moles $MgCO_3$

% $CaCO_3$ =

(8.61 continued)

$$\frac{0.024 \text{ mol } CaCO_3 \text{ x } 100.1 \text{ g/mol}}{(0.024 \text{ mol } CaCO_3 \text{ x } 100.1 \text{ g/mol}) + (0.016 \text{ mol } MgCO_3 \text{ x } 84.31 \text{ g/mol})}$$

$$\text{x } 100 = \frac{2.40 \text{ x } 100}{2.40 + 1.35} = \underline{64\% \; CaCO_3}$$

$$\% \; MgCO_3 = \frac{1.35}{2.40 \text{ x } 1.35} \text{ x } 100 = \underline{36\% \; MgCO_3}$$

8.62 (a) $\frac{0.05000 \text{ mol HCl}}{\text{L}} \text{ x } 0.0500 \text{ L} = 0.00250 \text{ mol HCl total}$

$$\frac{0.06000 \text{ mol NaOH}}{\text{L}} \text{ x } 0.03057 \text{ L x } \frac{1 \text{ mol HCl neut.}}{1 \text{ mol NaOH}} =$$

0.001834 mol HCl neut. by NaOH

0.00250 mol HCl total = 0.001834 mol HCl neut. by NaOH

+ X mol HCl neut. by NH_3

X = <u>0.00067 mol HCl neutralized by NH_3</u>

(b) $0.00067 \text{ mol HCl x } \frac{1 \text{ mol } NH_3}{\text{mol HCl}} \text{ x } \frac{1 \text{ mol N}}{\text{mol } NH_3} \text{ x } \frac{14.01 \text{ g N}}{\text{mol N}} = \underline{0.0093 \text{ g N}}$

(c) $\frac{0.0093 \text{ g N}}{0.0500 \text{ g sample}} \text{ x } 100 = \underline{19\% \text{ N in sample}}$

$$\frac{14.01 \text{ g N in gly}}{75.08 \text{ g gly}} \text{ x } 100 = \underline{18.66\% \text{ N in gly}}$$

Glycine and the sample have the same percent nitrogen to two significant figures.

8.63 Chlorine is generally not used in the laboratory as an oxidizing agent because it is a poisonous gas and requires special precautions if used.

8.64 (a) CrO_4^{2-} ------- yellow

(b) $Cr_2O_7^{2-}$ --------red-orange

(c) MnO_4^- ------ purple

8.65 (a) $3SO_3^{2-}(aq) + 5H_2O + 2CrO_4^{2-}(aq) \longrightarrow 2Cr(OH)_3(s) + 4OH^- + 3SO_4^{2-}$

(b) $5Sn^{2+}(aq) + 2MnO_4^- + 16H^+(aq) \longrightarrow 5Sn^{4+}(aq) + 2Mn^{2+}(aq) + 8H_2O$

(c) $4Cl_2(aq) + S_2O_3^{2-}(aq) + 5H_2O \longrightarrow 8Cl^-(aq) + 2SO_4^{2-}(aq) + 10H^+(aq)$

8.66 $3HSO_3^-(aq) + Cr_2O_7^{2-}(aq) + 5H^+(aq) \longrightarrow 3SO_4^{2-}(aq) + 2Cr^{3+}(aq) + 4H_2O$

or $3H_2SO_3 + Cr_2O_7^{2-}(aq) + 2H^+(aq) \longrightarrow 3SO_4^{2-}(aq) + 2Cr^{3+}(aq) + 4H_2O$

(if very acidic)

8.67 $3SO_3^{2-}(aq) + 2MnO_4^-(aq) + H_2O \longrightarrow 3SO_4^{2-}(aq) + 2MnO_2(s) + 2OH^-(aq)$

8.68 $I_3^-(aq) + 2S_2O_3^{2-}(aq) \longrightarrow 3I^-(aq) + S_4O_6^{2-}(aq)$

8.69 $3SO_3^{2-}(aq) + 2CrO_4^{2-}(aq) + H_2O \longrightarrow 3SO_4^{2-}(aq) + 2CrO_2^-(aq) + 2OH^-(aq)$

8.70 Because iodine adsorbs on the surface of the starch molecules to form a deep blue-black colored species that can be detected in very low concentrations of iodine.

8.71 $KMnO_4$ is a convenient titrant because it is a powerful oxidizing agent and because of its color. MnO_4^- is purple, whereas Mn^{2+}, its reduced form, is almost colorless.

8.72 (a) $MnO_4^- + 5Fe^{2+} + 8H^+ \longrightarrow Mn^{2+} + 5Fe^{3+} + 4H_2O$

(b) $\frac{0.0281 \text{ mol } KMnO_4}{L} \times 0.03942 \text{ L} \times \frac{1 \text{ mol } MnO_4^-}{\text{mol } KMnO_4} \times \frac{5 \text{ mol } Fe^{2+}}{\text{mol } MnO_4^-} \times$

$\frac{1 \text{ mol } Fe_3O_4}{3 \text{ mol } Fe^{2+}} \times \frac{231.5 \text{ g } Fe_3O_4}{\text{mol } Fe_3O_4} = 0.427 \text{ g } Fe_3O_4$

$\frac{0.427 \text{ g}}{1.362 \text{ g sample}} \times 100 =$ **31.4%**

8.73 (a) $5H_2C_2O_4(aq) + 2MnO_4^-(aq) + 6H^+(aq) \longrightarrow 10CO_2 + 2Mn^{2+}(aq) + 8H_2O$

$\frac{0.2000 \text{ mol } KMnO_4}{L} \times 0.01964 \text{ L} \times \frac{1 \text{ mol } MnO_4^-}{\text{mol } KMnO_4} \times \frac{5 \text{ mol } H_2C_2O_4}{2 \text{ mol } MnO_4^-}$

$\times \frac{1 \text{ mol } CaC_2O_4}{1 \text{ mol } H_2C_2O_4} =$ **0.009820 mol CaC_2O_4 ppt.**

(b) $0.009820 \text{ mol } CaC_2O_4 \times \frac{1 \text{ mol } CaCl_2}{\text{mol } CaC_2O_4} \times \frac{110.98 \text{ g } CaCl_2}{\text{mol}} = 1.090 \text{ g } CaCl_2$

$\frac{1.090 \text{ g } CaCl_2}{2.385 \text{ g sample}} \times 100 =$ **45.70% $CaCl_2$**

8.74 (a) $I_3^-(aq) + 2S_2O_3^{2-}(aq) \longrightarrow 3I^-(aq) + S_4O_6^{2-}(aq)$

$\frac{0.1000 \text{ mol } Na_2S_2O_3}{L} \times 0.02534 \text{ L} \times \frac{1 \text{ mol } S_2O_3^{2-}}{\text{mol } Na_2S_2O_3} \times$

$\frac{1 \text{ mol } I_3^-}{2 \text{ mol } S_2O_3^{2-}} =$ **0.001267 moles I_3^-**

(8.74 continued)

(b) $0.001267 \text{ moles } I_3^- \times \frac{\text{2 mol } Cu^{2+}}{\text{mol } I_3^-} \times \frac{\text{1 mol Cu}}{\text{mol } Cu^{2+}} \times$

$\frac{\text{63.55 g Cu}}{\text{mol}} = 0.1610 \text{ g Cu}$ $\frac{\text{0.1610 g Cu}}{\text{0.244 g sample}} \times 100 = \underline{\text{66.0\% Cu}}$

8.75 For acids and bases, an equivalent is the amount of substance that supplies or reacts with one mole of H^+. For redox, an equivalent is the amount of substance that gains or loses one mole of electrons.

8.76 The equivalence point is the point in a titration when equal numbers of equivalents of reactants have been combined. If the indicator has been properly selected, the end point and the equivalence point will be very nearly the same point in a titration.

8.77 The number of equivalents of A that react is exactly equal to the number of equivalents of B that react.

8.78 $0.200 \text{ mol } Ba(OH)_2 \times \frac{\text{2 eq. } Ba(OH)_2}{\text{mol}} = \underline{\text{0.400 eq. } Ba(OH)_2}$

8.79 $5.00 \text{ eq. } H_3PO_4 \times \frac{\text{1 mol } H_3PO_4}{\text{3 eq.}} = \underline{\text{1.67 mol } H_3PO_4}$

8.80 $0.140 \text{ mol } H_3AsO_4 \times \frac{\text{2 eq. } H_3AsO_4}{\text{mol}} = \underline{\text{0.280 eq. } H_3AsO_4}$

8.81 (a) $1 \text{ mol } HIO_3 \times \frac{\text{1 eq. } HIO_3}{\text{mol}} = \underline{\text{1 eq. } HIO_3}$ (as an acid)

(b) $2HIO_3 + 10H^+ + 10e^- \text{ ---> } I_2 + 6H_2O$

$1 \text{ mol } HIO_3 \times \frac{\text{10 eq. } HIO_3}{\text{2 mol } HIO_3} = \underline{\text{5 eq. } HIO_3}$ (when being reduced to I_2)

8.82 (a) $MnSO_4 \longrightarrow Mn_2O_3$ or $Mn^{2+} \longrightarrow Mn^{3+}$ (1 electron change)

F.W. of $MnSO_4$ = 151.00 $\quad$ eq. wt. = $\frac{151.00\ g}{mol} \times \frac{1\ mol}{eq.}$ = **151.00 g /eq.**

(b) $Mn^{2+} \longrightarrow Mn^{4+}$ $\quad$ eq. wt. = $\frac{151.00\ g}{mol} \times \frac{1\ mol}{2\ eq.}$ = **75.50 g /eq.**

(c) $Mn^{2+} \longrightarrow Mn^{6+}$ $\quad$ eq. wt. = $\frac{151.00\ g}{mol} \times \frac{1\ mol}{4\ eq.}$ = **37.75 g /eq.**

(d) $Mn^{2+} \longrightarrow Mn^{7+}$ $\quad$ eq. wt. = $\frac{151.00\ g}{mol} \times \frac{1\ mol}{5\ eq.}$ = **30.20 g /eq.**

8.83 $Cr^{6+} \longrightarrow Cr^{3+}$

0.400 eq. Na_2CrO_4 $\times \frac{1\ mol}{3\ eq.} \times \frac{161.98\ g}{mol}$ = **21.6 g Na_2CrO_4**

8.84 $Mn^{2+} \longrightarrow Mn^{7+}$

$\frac{0.100\ eq.}{L} \times 0.300\ L \times \frac{1\ mol}{5\ eq.} \times \frac{259.1\ g}{mol}$ = **1.55 g $MnSO_4 \cdot 6H_2O$**

8.85 $Bi^{5+} \longrightarrow Bi^{3+}$ $(-2e^-)$ $\quad$ and $Mn^{2+} \longrightarrow Mn^{7+}$ $(+5e^-)$

eq. wt. of $NaBiO_3$ = $\frac{280.0\ g\ /mole}{2\ eq.\ /mole}$ = 140 g /eq.

eq. wt. of $Mn(NO_3)_2$ = $\frac{178.9\ g\ /mole}{5\ eq.\ /mole}$ = 35.79 g /eq.

$$0.500\ g\ Mn(NO_3)_2 \times \frac{1\ eq.\ Mn(NO_3)_2}{35.79\ g\ Mn(NO_3)_2} \times \frac{1\ eq.\ NaBiO_3}{1\ eq.\ Mn(NO_3)_2} \times \frac{140.0\ g\ NaBiO_3}{1\ eq.\ NaBiO_3}$$

= **1.96 g $NaBiO_3$**

8.86 (a) $\frac{98.01\text{ g } H_3PO_4}{\text{mol}} \times \frac{1\text{ mol}}{2\text{ eq.}} = \mathbf{49.00\ g\ H_3PO_4\ /eq.}$

(b) $\frac{100.5\text{ g } HClO_4}{\text{mol}} \times \frac{1\text{ mol}}{\text{eq.}} = \mathbf{100.5\ g\ HClO_4\ /eq.}$

(c) $I^{5+} \longrightarrow I^-$ $(-6e^-)$ $\frac{197.89\text{ g } NaIO_3}{\text{mol}} \times \frac{1\text{ mol}}{6\text{ eq.}} = \mathbf{32.98\ g\ NaIO_3\ /eq.}$

(d) $I^{5+} \longrightarrow I^0$ $(-5e^-)$ $\frac{197.89\text{ g } NaIO_3}{\text{mol}} \times \frac{1\text{ mol}}{5\text{ eq.}} = \mathbf{39.58\ g\ NaIO_3\ /eq.}$

(e) $\frac{78.01\text{ g } Al(OH)_3}{\text{mol}} \times \frac{1\text{ mol}}{3\text{ eq.}} = \mathbf{26.00\ g\ Al(OH)_3\ /eq.}$

8.87 (a) $\frac{22.0\text{ g } Sr(OH)_2}{0.800\text{ L soln.}} \times \frac{1\text{ mol } Sr(OH)_2}{121.64\text{ g}} \times \frac{2\text{ eq. } Sr(OH)_2}{\text{mol}} = 0.452\text{ eq. /L}$

N = 0.452

(b) $\frac{0.25\text{ mol}}{\text{L}} \times \frac{2\text{ eq.}}{\text{mol}} = 0.50\text{ eq. /L}$ **N = 0.50**

(c) $\frac{0.150\text{ mol}}{\text{L}} \times \frac{2\text{ eq.}}{\text{mol}} = 0.300\text{ eq. /L}$ **N = 0.300**

(d) $Cr_2O_7^{2-} \longrightarrow 2Cr^{3+} + 6e^-$

$\frac{41.7\text{ g } K_2Cr_2O_7}{0.600\text{ L soln.}} \times \frac{1\text{ mol } K_2Cr_2O_7}{294.2\text{ g}} \times \frac{6\text{ eq.}}{\text{mol}} = 1.42\text{ eq. /L}$ **N = 1.42**

(e) $Na_2O \longrightarrow 2NaOH$ 2 eq. /mol Na_2O

$\frac{25.0\text{ g } Na_2O}{1.50\text{ L soln.}} \times \frac{1\text{ mol } Na_2O}{61.9\text{ g}} \times \frac{2\text{ eq.}}{\text{mol}} = 0.538\text{ eq. /L}$ **N = 0.538**

(f) $\frac{0.135\text{ eq.}}{0.400\text{ L soln.}} = 0.338\text{ eq. /mol}$ **N = 0.338**

8.88 $\frac{0.850 \text{ eq. Ba(OH)}_2}{\text{L}} \times 0.129 \text{ L} \times \frac{1 \text{ eq. acid}}{1 \text{ eq. Ba(OH)}_2} = 0.1096$ equivalents acid

$\frac{4.93 \text{ g acid}}{0.1096 \text{ eq. acid}} =$ **45.0 g /eq.**

8.89 Use $V_1N_1 = V_2N_2$; 50.0 mL $H_2C_2O_4$ x 0.250 N = 45.0 mL $KMnO_4$ x ?N

?N = 0.278 N $KMnO_4$ for MnO_4^- —> Mn^{2+}

(0.278 eq. /L) x (1 mol /5 eq.) = 0.0556 mol $KMnO_4$ /L

For $K_2C_2O_4$, in which $KMnO_4$ —> MnO_2 - $3e^-$

(0.250 eq. $K_2C_2O_4$ /L) x 0.025 L x (1 eq. $KMnO_4$ /eq. $K_2C_2O_4$) x

(1 mol $KMnO_4$ /3 eq.) x [1 L $KMnO_4$ /0.0556 mol (from above)] =

0.0375 L or **37.5 mL**

8.90 Use $V_aN_a = V_bN_b$ and $V_{dil}N_{dil} = V_{conc}N_{conc}$

For neutralization: 41.0 mL(B) x 0.255 N(B) = 5.0 mL(A) x ?N(A)

N(A) = 2.1 N HCl (the dil. HCl)

From dilution: 50.0 mL x 2.1 N = 10.0 mL x ?N

N = 10.5 **10 N HCl or 10 M HCl**

8.91 $5Fe^{2+} + MnO_4^- + 8H^+ \longrightarrow 5Fe^{3+} + Mn^{2+} + 4H_2O$

(Assuming this titration was performed in acidic solution.)

$\frac{0.00400 \text{ mol } MnO_4^-}{\text{L}} \times 0.0158 \text{ L} \times \frac{5 \text{ mol } Fe^{2+}}{\text{mol } MnO_4^-}$

$\times \frac{1 \text{ mol } FeSO_4}{\text{mol } Fe^{2+}} \times \frac{151.9 \text{ g } FeSO_4}{\text{mol } FeSO_4} = 0.0480 \text{ g } FeSO_4$

(8.91 continued)

$$\frac{\underline{0.0480 \text{ g } FeSO_4}}{0.1000 \text{ g sample}} \times 100 = \underline{\mathbf{48.0\% \ FeSO_4}}$$

8.92 Use $V_{ox}N_{ox} = V_{red}N_{red}$

$V(K_2Cr_2O_7) \times 0.500 \text{ N} = 120 \text{ mL} \times 0.850 \text{ N}$

Vol. of $K_2Cr_2O_7$ soln. = 204 mL

8.93 Use $V_{conc}N_{conc} = V_{dil}N_{dil}$ $\quad$ $85.0 \text{ mL} \times 1.00 = V_{dil} \times 0.650 \text{ N}$

$V_{dil} = 131 \text{ mL}$

H_2O added = 131mL - 85.0 mL = **46 mL**

8.94 First find the conc. of the dil. H_2SO_4 soln.

Use $V_aN_a = V_bN_b$

$25.0 \text{ mL} \times N(H_2SO_4) = 15.0 \text{ mL} \times 0.750 \text{ N}$

$0.450 \text{ N } H_2SO_4$

Then calc. how this soln. could be prepared from 1.40 M H_2SO_4.

$$\frac{1.40 \text{ mol } H_2SO_4}{\text{L}} \times \frac{2 \text{ eq. } H_2SO_4}{\text{mol}} = 2.80 \text{ N } H_2SO_4$$

$V_{conc}N_{conc} = V_{dil}N_{dil}$

$250 \text{ mL} \times 2.80\text{N} = V_{dil} \times 0.450\text{N}$

$V_{dil} = 1{,}560 \text{ mL}$ or **1.56 L**

9 PROPERTIES OF GASES

9.1 Pressure is force per unit area. As long as there is a space above the mercury column the pressures acting along the reference level will be the same regardless of the size and length of the tube. If the diameter of the tube is doubled, there will be twice the weight of Hg acting over twice the area. The ratio of F/A remains unchanged.

9.2 The SI unit of pressure is the pascal; 1 atm = 101,325 Pa

9.3 **(a)** $1.50 \text{ atm} \times \frac{760 \text{ torr}}{\text{atm}} = \underline{\mathbf{1{,}140 \text{ torr}}}$

(b) $785 \text{ torr} \times \frac{1 \text{ atm}}{760 \text{ torr}} = \underline{\mathbf{1.03 \text{ atm}}}$

(c) $3.45 \text{ atm} \times \frac{101{,}325 \text{ Pa}}{\text{atm}} = 350{,}000 \text{ Pa} = \underline{\mathbf{3.50 \times 10^5 \text{ Pa}}}$

(d) $3.45 \text{ atm} \times \frac{101.325 \text{ kPa}}{\text{atm}} = \underline{\mathbf{350 \text{ kPa}}}$

(e) $165 \text{ torr} \times \frac{1 \text{ atm}}{760 \text{ torr}} \times \frac{101{,}325 \text{ Pa}}{\text{atm}} = \underline{\mathbf{2.20 \times 10^4 \text{ Pa}}}$

(f) $342 \text{ kPa} \times \frac{1 \text{ atm}}{101.3 \text{ kPa}} = \underline{\mathbf{3.38 \text{ atm}}}$

(g) $11.5 \text{ kPa} \times \frac{1 \text{ atm}}{101.3 \text{ kPa}} \times \frac{760 \text{ torr}}{\text{atm}} = \underline{\mathbf{86.3 \text{ torr}}}$

9.4 $\frac{76.0 \text{ cm Hg}}{\text{atm}} \times 1 \text{ atm} \times \frac{13.6 \text{ g}}{\text{mL}} \times \frac{1 \text{ mL}}{\text{cm}^3} \times (2.54 \text{ cm /in.})^2 \times \frac{1 \text{ lb}}{454 \text{ g}}$

$= \underline{14.7 \text{ lb /in.}^2}$

9.5 Sketch would be similar to that shown in Figure 9.3(c). The difference in the height of mercury in the two arms would be 25 mm.

9.6 It is not necessary to measure the atmospheric pressure in order to use it.

9.7 It is dense, it is a liquid over a large temperature range and it has a very low vapor pressure.

9.8 $15.8 \text{ cm} \times \frac{1 \text{ torr}}{\text{mm}} \times \frac{10 \text{ mm}}{\text{cm}} = \underline{158 \text{ torr}}$

9.9 (65 mm x 1 torr /mm) + 733 torr = **798 torr**

9.10 (774 torr - 535 torr) x 1 mm /torr = **239 mm**

9.11 (755 mm Hg + 17 mm Hg) x 1 torr /mm Hg = **772 torr**

9.12 836 torr + (74.0 cm x 0.847 g oil /mL x 1 mL /13.6 g Hg x 10 torr /cm)

= **882 torr**

9.13 $1 \text{ atm} \times \frac{76.0 \text{ cm Hg}}{\text{atm}} \times \frac{13.6 \text{ g Hg}}{\text{mL Hg}} \times \frac{1 \text{ mL } H_2O}{1 \text{ g } H_2O} \times \frac{1 \text{ in.}}{2.54 \text{ cm}} \times \frac{1 \text{ ft}}{12 \text{ in.}}$

= 33.9 ft (maximum height of a column of water in a sealed column at 1 atm of external pressure)

No, the person will not be able to draw water a height of 35 ft.

9.14 Boyle's law states that at a constant temperature, the volume occupied by a fixed quantity of gas is inversely proportional to the applied pressure. All gases do not always obey Boyle's law. A gas that does would be called an ideal gas.

9.15 $P_iV_i = P_fV_f$ (740 torr) x (350 mL) = (900 torr) x (? mL)

? mL = **288 mL**

9.16 $P_iV_i = P_fV_f$ (2.75 atm) x (1.45 L) = [(800/760)atm] x (? L)

? L = **3.79 L**

9.17 $P_iV_i = P_fV_f$ (475 torr) x (540 mL) = (? torr) x (320 mL)

? torr = **802 torr**

9.18 $P_iV_i = P_fV_f$ (20.0 lb in.$^{-2}$) x (35 ft^3) = (? lb in.$^{-2}$) x (40.0 ft^3)

(? lb in.$^{-2}$) = **17.5 lb/in.^{2}**

9.19 $P_iV_i = P_fV_f$ (1 atm) x (75.0 cm x area) = (5.50 atm) x (? length x area)

? length = 13.6 cm

length of downstroke = 75.0 cm - 13.6 cm = **61.4 cm**

9.20 Charles' law states that at a constant pressure, the volume of a given quantity of a gas is directly proportional to its absolute temperature. A temperature of -273.15°C represents that temperature below which gases would have a negative volume. That is impossible.

9.21 During the trip the tires become warm and the air pressure in them rises (Gay-Lussac's law).

9.22 Cooling the gas causes it to contract in volume. This means that a given volume will contain more oxygen at the lower pressure.

9.23 The hot air in the balloon has a lower density than the air surrounding the balloon.

9.24 $\frac{V_i}{T_i} = \frac{V_f}{T_f}$ $\quad \frac{1.50\ L}{(273 + 25)\ K} = \frac{?\ L}{(273 + 100)\ K}$ $\quad ?\ L = $ **1.88 L**

9.25 $\frac{V_i}{T_i} = \frac{V_f}{T_f}$ $\quad \frac{2.0\ L}{(273 + 25)\ K} = \frac{?\ L}{(273 - 28.9)\ K}$ $\quad ?\ L = $ **1.6 L**

9.26 $\frac{V_i}{T_i} = \frac{V_f}{T_f}$ $\quad \frac{2.00\ L}{(273 + 26)\ K} = \frac{?\ L}{(273 + 100)\ K}$ $\quad ?\ L = $ **2.49 L**

9.27 $\frac{V_i}{T_i} = \frac{V_f}{T_f}$ $\quad \frac{285\ mL}{(273 + 25)\ K} = \frac{350\ mL}{(273 + ?°C)\ K}$ $\quad ?\ °C = $ **93°C**

9.28 $\frac{V_i}{T_i} = \frac{V_f}{T_f}$ $\quad \frac{400\ mL}{(273 + 32)\ K} = \frac{850\ mL}{(273 + ?°C)\ K}$ $\quad ?\ °C = $ **375°C**

9.29 Heating the can causes the pressure of the gas inside to rise. This causes the can to explode.

9.30 $\frac{P_i}{T_i} = \frac{P_f}{T_f}$ $\quad \frac{350\ torr}{(273 + 20)\ K} = \frac{?\ torr}{(273 + 40)\ K}$ $\quad ?\ torr = $ **374 torr**

9.31 $\frac{P_i}{T_i} = \frac{P_f}{T_f}$ $\quad \frac{655\ torr}{(273 + 25)\ K} = \frac{825\ torr}{(273 + ?°C)\ K}$ $\quad ?\ °C = $ **102°C**

9.32 29 lb /in.^{2} is a total pressure of 14.7 + 29 lb /in.^{2}

65°F = ? °C $\quad$? °C = (5/9) (65 - 32) = 18.3°C

130°F = ? °C $\quad$? °C = (5/9) (130 - 32) = 54.4°C

$\frac{P_i}{T_i} = \frac{P_f}{T_f}$ $\quad \frac{14.7 + 29}{18.3 + 273°C} = \frac{14.7 + ?\ P}{54.4 + 273°C}$ $\quad ?\ P = $ **34 lb /in.^{2}**

9.33 STP stands for standard temperature and pressure, 0°C (273 K) and one standard atmosphere (760 torr). It is a reference set of conditions.

9.34 (a) $P_iV_i = P_fV_f$ (645 torr)(50.0 mL) = (? torr)(65.0 mL) ? torr = **496 torr**

(b) $\frac{P_iV_i}{T_i} = \frac{P_fV_f}{T_f}$ $\frac{(645 \text{ torr})(50.0 \text{ mL})}{(273 + 25) \text{ K}} = \frac{(? \text{ torr})(65.0 \text{ mL})}{(273 + 35) \text{ K}}$? torr = **513 torr**

9.35 $\frac{(450 \text{ torr})(300 \text{ mL})}{(273 + 27) \text{ K}} = \frac{(? \text{ torr})(200 \text{ mL})}{(273 + 20) \text{ K}}$? torr = **659 torr**

9.36 $\frac{(700 \text{ torr})(2.00 \text{ L})}{(273 + 25) \text{ K}} = \frac{(585 \text{ torr})(5.00 \text{ L})}{(273 + ?°\text{C}) \text{ K}}$? °C = **350°C**

9.37 $\frac{(1 \text{ atm})(1\text{L})}{(273 + 0) \text{ K}} = \frac{(650 / 760 \text{ atm})(? \text{ L})}{(273 + 25) \text{ K}}$? L = 1.276 L

D = 1.96 g / 1.276 L = **1.54 g / L**

9.38 $\frac{(450 \text{ torr})(50.0 \text{ mL})}{(273 + 35) \text{ K}} = \frac{(760 \text{ torr})(? \text{ mL})}{(273 + 0) \text{ K}}$? mL = **26.2 mL**

9.39 Dalton's law states that the total pressure exerted by a mixture of gases is equal to the sum of the partial pressures of each gas in the mixture. Partial pressures cannot be measured after the gases are mixed. However, given sufficient data, partial pressures can be deduced.

9.40 200 torr + 500 torr + 150 torr = **850 torr**

9.41 $P_{N_2} = 300 \text{ torr} \times \frac{2.00 \text{ L}}{1.00 \text{ L}} = 600 \text{ torr}$

$P_{H_2} = 80 \text{ torr} \times \frac{2.00 \text{ L}}{1.00 \text{ L}} = 160 \text{ torr}$

$P_T = P_{N_2} + P_{H_2} = 600 + 160 = 760$ torr or **1.00 atm**

9.42 $P_{N_2} = 740 \text{ torr} \times \frac{20.0 \text{ mL}}{50.0 \text{ mL}} = 296 \text{ torr}$

$P_{O_2} = 640 \text{ torr} \times \frac{30.0 \text{ mL}}{50.0 \text{ mL}} = 384 \text{ torr}$

$P_T = P_{N_2} + P_{O_2} = 296 + 384 =$ **680 torr**

9.43

Oxygen Data	i	f
P	400 torr	? torr
V	50.0 mL	100 mL
T	60°C	50°C

$$\frac{(400 \text{ torr})(50.0 \text{ mL})}{(273 + 60) \text{ K}} = \frac{(? \text{ torr})(100 \text{ mL})}{(273 + 50) \text{ K}}$$

$P_{Oxygen} = ? \text{ torr} = 194 \text{ torr}$

$P_{Nitrogen} = P_{Total} - P_{Oxygen} = 800 \text{ torr} - 194 \text{ torr} = 606 \text{ torr}$

Nitrogen Data	i	f
P	400 torr	606 torr
V	X mL	100 mL
T	40°C	50°C

$$\frac{(400 \text{ torr})(X \text{ mL})}{(273 + 40) \text{ K}} = \frac{(606)(100 \text{ mL})}{(273 + 50) \text{ K}}$$

X mL of Nitrogen = **147 mL**

9.44 $P_{Total} = P_{dry\ gas} + P_{H_2O}$

$700 \text{ torr} = P_{dry\ gas} + 23.8 \text{ torr}$

$P_{dry\ gas} = 676 \text{ torr}$

Dry Gas Data	i	f
P	676 torr	760
V	100 mL	? mL
T	298 K	273 K

$$\frac{(676 \text{ torr})(100 \text{ mL})}{298 \text{ K}} = \frac{(760 \text{ torr})(? \text{ mL})}{273 \text{ K}}$$

? mL = **81.5 mL**

9.45 (a) First find the partial pressure of nitrogen $PV = nRT$

Pressure of N_2 = $\dfrac{(0.0020\text{ mol})(0.0821\text{ L atm mol}^{-1}\text{K}^{-1})(308\text{ K})}{0.200\text{ L}}$

= 0.253 atm or 192 torr

Use $P_A = X_A P_T$ or $X_A = P_A / P_T$ $X_{Nitrogen} = 192/720 = \underline{\mathbf{0.27}}$

(b) **<u>190 torr</u>** (only 2 significant figures)

(c) 720 - 190 = **<u>530 torr</u>** (only 2 significant figures)

(d) $n = PV/RT = \dfrac{(530/760\text{ atm})(0.200\text{ L})}{(0.0821\text{ L atm mol}^{-1}\text{K}^{-1})(308\text{ K})}$ = **<u>0.0055 mol of O_2</u>**

9.46 Use $P_A = X_A P_T$

P_T = 569 torr + 116 torr + 28 torr + 47 torr + 760 torr

mol fraction N_2 = 569 torr /760 torr = **<u>0.749</u>**

mol fraction O_2 = 116 torr /760 torr = **<u>0.153</u>**

mol fraction CO_2 = 28 torr /760 torr = **<u>0.037</u>**

mol fraction H_2O = 47 torr /760 torr = **<u>0.062</u>**

9.47 $P_T = P_{N_2} + P_{CO_2}$ 900 = 800 + ? pressure CO_2

Partial pressure CO_2 = 100 torr at 20°C and 500 mL

CO_2 Data

	i	f
P	700 torr	100 torr
V	? V	500 mL
T	303 K	293 K

$\dfrac{(700\text{ torr})(?\text{ V})}{(303\text{ K})} = \dfrac{(100\text{ torr})(500\text{ mL})}{(293\text{ K})}$

? V = **<u>73.9 mL</u>**

9.48 Partial pressure of O_2 = 740 torr - 21.1 torr = 719 torr

$$V = \frac{nRT}{P} = \frac{0.0244\ g}{32.0\ g/mol} \times (0.0821\ L\ atm\ mol^{-1}K^{-1}) \times 296\ K$$

$$\times \frac{1}{(719/760)\ atm} = 0.0196\ L = \underline{\mathbf{19.6\ mL}}$$

9.49 **(a)** $n_T = \frac{P_T V}{RT} = \frac{(800/760)(10)}{(0.0821)(303)} = \underline{\mathbf{0.42\ mol}}$

(b) First calculate the moles of N_2 present.

$$0.42\ \text{moles total} = \frac{8.0\ g\ CO_2}{44.0\ g\ CO_2/mol} + \frac{6.0\ g\ O_2}{32.0\ g\ O_2/mol} + \text{moles}\ N_2$$

moles N_2 = 0.42 - 0.18 - 0.19 = 0.050

$$\text{mol fraction}\ N_2 = \frac{0.050\ mol\ N_2}{0.42\ mol\ total} = \underline{\mathbf{0.12}}$$

$$\text{mol fraction}\ CO_2 = \frac{0.18\ mol\ CO_2}{0.42\ mol\ total} = \underline{\mathbf{0.43}}$$

$$\text{mol fraction}\ O_2 = \frac{0.19\ mol\ O_2}{0.42\ mol\ total} = \underline{\mathbf{0.45}}$$

(c) partial pressure = mol fraction x total pressure

partial pressure N_2 = 0.12 x 800 torr = **<u>96 torr</u>**

partial pressure CO_2 = 0.43 x 800 torr = **<u>340 torr</u>**

partial pressure O_2 = 0.45 x 800 torr = **<u>360 torr</u>**

(d) $0.050\ mol \times \frac{28\ g}{mol} = \underline{\mathbf{1.4\ g\ N_2}}$

9.50 Data of Dry Gas

	i	f
P	800 - 42	? torr
V	500 mL	250 mL
T	273 + 35	273 + 35

$$\frac{(800 - 42)(500)}{308} = \frac{(? \text{ torr})(250)}{308}$$

? torr = 1,520 torr

1,520 torr + 42 torr = total pressure at final conditions

= 1,562 torr or **1,560 torr**

9.51 Vap. press. of H_2O at 31°C = 33.7 torr

$$n = \frac{PV}{RT} = \frac{(33.7 /760)(1)}{(0.0821)(273 + 31)} = 0.00178 \text{ mol } H_2O$$

$$0.00178 \text{ mol } H_2O \times \frac{18.02 \text{ g } H_2O}{\text{mol } H_2O} = \mathbf{0.0320 \text{ g } H_2O}$$

9.52 V.P. (H_2O) = 17.5 torr at 20°C

Total P on gases = 763 torr - pressure of the column of H_2O

$$\text{Pressure of the column of water} = 28.4 \text{ mm } H_2O \times \frac{1 \text{ mm Hg}}{13.6 \text{ mm } H_2O}$$

= 2.09 mm Hg = 2.1 torr   Total P = 763 - 2.1 = 760.9

Partial pressure of gas = 760.9 torr - 17.5 torr = 743 torr

Data

	i	f
P	743	760
V	280 mL	? mL
T	293 K	273 K

$$\frac{(743)(280)}{293} = \frac{(760)(? \text{ mL})}{273}$$

? mL = **255 mL**

9.53 Gay-Lussac's law states that at a constant volume, the pressure of a given quantity of gas is directly proportional to the absolute temperature. Avogadro's principle states that under conditions of constant temperature and pressure, equal volumes of gas contain equal numbers of molecules.

9.54 (a) $0.200 \text{ mol} \times \frac{22.4 \text{ L (STP)}}{\text{mol}} = \underline{\mathbf{4.48 \text{ L (STP)}}}$

(b) $12.4 \text{ g } Cl_2 \times \frac{1 \text{ mol } Cl_2}{70.9 \text{ g } Cl_2} \times \frac{22.4 \text{ L (STP)}}{\text{mol}} = \underline{\mathbf{3.92 \text{ L (STP)}}}$

(c) $0.150 \text{ mol (total)} \times \frac{22.4 \text{ L}}{\text{mol}} = \underline{\mathbf{3.36 \text{ L (total at STP)}}}$

9.55 $245 \text{ mL (STP) } SO_2 \times \frac{1 \text{ mol}}{22.4 \text{ L (STP)}} \times \frac{1 \text{ L}}{1{,}000 \text{ mL}} \times \frac{64.1 \text{ g } SO_2}{\text{mol}}$

$= \underline{\mathbf{0.701 \text{ g } SO_2}}$

9.56 For C_4H_{10} $\frac{58.1 \text{ g}}{\text{mol}} \times \frac{1 \text{ mol}}{22.4 \text{ L (STP)}} = \underline{\mathbf{2.59 \text{ g/L (STP)}}}$

9.57 $\frac{1.96 \text{ g}}{\text{L (STP)}} \times \frac{22.4 \text{ L (STP)}}{\text{mol}} = \underline{\mathbf{43.9 \text{ g/mol}}}$

9.58 atm liter^2 K^2 /mol

9.59 The units used for pressure and volume determine which R you should use.

9.60 $\frac{0.08206 \text{ L atm}}{\text{mol K}} \times \frac{10^3 \text{ cm}^3}{\text{L}} \times \frac{\text{m}^3}{(100 \text{ cm})^3} \times \frac{1.013 \times 10^5 \text{ Pa}}{\text{atm}}$

$= \underline{\mathbf{8.31 \text{ Pa m}^3 \text{ mol}^{-1}\text{K}^{-1}}}$

9.61 $n = \frac{PV}{RT} = \frac{760 \text{ torr}}{760 \text{ torr/atm}} \times \frac{250 \text{ mL}}{1000 \text{ mL/L}} \times \frac{\text{mol K}}{0.0821 \text{ L atm}} \times \frac{1}{(273 + 25) \text{ K}}$

$= 0.0102 \text{ mol}$

$\frac{0.164 \text{ g}}{0.0102 \text{ mol}} = \underline{\mathbf{16.1 \text{ g/mol}}}$

9.62 $P = \frac{nRT}{V} = 25\ kg \times \frac{1000\ g}{kg} \times \frac{1\ mol\ H_2O}{18.02\ g}$

$\times\ 0.0821\ L\ atm\ mol^{-1}K^{-1} \times (273 + 200)\ K \times \frac{1}{1000\ L}$

$=$ **54 atm** or **41,000 torr**

9.63 $n = \frac{PV}{RT} = \frac{760\ torr}{760\ torr/atm} \times 1\ L \times \frac{1}{0.0821\ L\ atm\ mol^{-1}K^{-1}}$

$\times \frac{1}{(273 + 30)\ K} = 0.0402\ mol$ $\qquad \frac{1.81\ g}{0.0402\ mol} =$ **45.0 g /mol**

9.64 $V = \frac{nRT}{P} = \frac{0.234\ g}{17.03\ g/mol} \times 0.08206\ L\ atm\ mol^{-1}K^{-1}$

$\times\ (273 + 30)\ K \times \frac{1}{0.847\ atm} = 0.403\ L =$ **403 mL**

9.65 (a) For C: $\frac{80.0g}{12.01\ g/mol} = 6.66\ mol$

For H: $\frac{20.0\ g}{1.01\ g/mol} = 19.80\ mol$

Empirical Formula $C_{6.66/6.66}H_{19.80/6.60} =$ **CH_3**

(b) $n = \frac{PV}{RT} = \frac{1\ atm \times .5\ L}{0.0821\ L\ atm\ mol^{-1}K^{-1} \times 273\ K} = 0.0223\ mol$

M.W. $= \frac{0.6695\ g}{0.0223\ mol} =$ **30.0 g /mol**

(c) $CH_3 = 15\ g/mol$ $\qquad$ $30\ g/mol =$ **C_2H_6**

9.66 (a) For C: $0.482 \text{ g } CO_2 \times \frac{1 \text{ mol } CO_2}{44.01 \text{ g}} \times \frac{1 \text{ mol C}}{\text{mol } CO_2} \times \frac{12.01 \text{ g C}}{\text{mol}} = 0.132 \text{ g C}$

$$\% C = \frac{0.132 \text{ g C}}{0.200 \text{ g sample}} \times 100 = \underline{65.8\% \text{ C}}$$

For H: $0.271 \text{ g } H_2O \times \frac{1 \text{ mol } H_2O}{18.02 \text{ g}} \times \frac{2 \text{ mol H}}{\text{mol } H_2O} \times \frac{1.01 \text{ g H}}{\text{mol}} = 0.0304 \text{ g H}$

$$\% H = \frac{0.0304 \text{ g H}}{0.200 \text{ g sample}} \times 100 = \underline{15.2\% \text{ H}}$$

For N: $n = \frac{PV}{RT} = \frac{(755/760)(0.0423)}{(0.0821)(273 + 26.5)} = 0.00171 \text{ mol } N_2$

$$0.00171 \text{ mol } N_2 \times \frac{2 \text{ mol N}}{\text{mol } N_2} \times \frac{14.01 \text{ g N}}{\text{mol N}} = 0.0479 \text{ g N}$$

$$\% N = \frac{0.0479 \text{ g N}}{0.2500 \text{ g sample}} \times 100 = \underline{19.2\% \text{ N}}$$

(b) mol C in 100 g $= \frac{65.8 \text{ g C}}{12.01 \text{ g/mol}} = 5.48 \text{ mol C}$

mol H in 100 g $= \frac{15.2 \text{ g H}}{1.01 \text{ g/mol}} = 15.05 \text{ mol H}$

mol N in 100 g $= \frac{19.2 \text{ g N}}{14.01 \text{ g/mol}} = 1.37 \text{ mol N}$

Empirical Formula: $C_{5.48/1.37}H_{15.05/1.37}N_{1.37/1.37} = \underline{C_4H_{11}N}$

9.67 From the partial pressure of O_2 and the moles and temp. of the O_2, the volume of the flask can be calculated. Once the volume of the flask is known, the mass of N_2 can be calculated.

(9.67 continued)

For O_2: $V = \frac{nRT}{P} = \frac{0.100\ g}{32.0\ g/mol} \times \frac{0.0821\ L\ atm}{mol\ K}$

$\times\ (25 + 273)\ K \times \frac{1}{[(760 - 525)/760]\ atm} = 0.247\ L$

For N_2: $n = \frac{PV}{RT} = (525/760)\ atm \times 0.247\ L$

$\times \frac{1}{0.0821\ L\ atm\ mol^{-1}K^{-1}} \times \frac{1}{298\ K} = 0.00697\ mol\ N_2$

$0.00697\ mol\ N_2 \times \frac{28.02\ g\ N_2}{mol} = \underline{\mathbf{0.195\ g\ N_2}}$

9.68 $1\ L \times 1\ atm \times \frac{101{,}325\ Pa}{atm} \times \frac{1\ N\ m^{-2}}{Pa} \times \frac{1\ J}{1\ N\ m} \times \frac{(0.100000\ m)^3}{L}$

$= \underline{\mathbf{101.325\ J}}$

$R = 0.0821\ L\ atm\ mol^{-1}\ K^{-1} \times 101.325\ J\ L^{-1}\ atm^{-1} = \underline{\mathbf{8.32\ J\ mol^{-1}K^{-1}}}$

$R = 8.32\ J\ mol^{-1}\ K^{-1} \times \frac{1\ cal}{4.184\ J} = \underline{\mathbf{1.99\ cal\ mol^{-1}\ K^{-1}}}$

9.69 $400\ mL\ NH_3 \times \frac{1\ L}{1{,}000\ mL} \times \frac{1.00\ mol\ NH_3}{22.4\ L\ NH_3} \times \frac{1\ mol\ N_2}{2\ mol\ NH_3} \times \frac{22.4\ L\ N_2}{1\ mol\ N_2}$

$\times \frac{1{,}000\ mL\ N_2}{L} = \underline{\mathbf{200\ mL\ N_2}}$

$400\ mL\ NH_3 \times \frac{3\ mL\ H_2}{2\ mL\ NH_3} = \underline{\mathbf{600\ mL\ H_2}}$

9.70 (a) $0.00140 \text{ mol NO} \times \frac{1 \text{ mol } N_2}{2 \text{ mol NO}} \times \frac{22.4 \text{ L}}{\text{mol}} \times \frac{1{,}000 \text{ mL}}{\text{L}}$

$= \underline{\mathbf{15.7 \text{ mL } N_2}}$ (STP)

(b) $1.3 \times 10^{-3} \text{ g } H_2 \times \frac{1 \text{ mol } H_2}{2.02 \text{ g } H_2} \times \frac{1 \text{ mol } N_2}{2 \text{ mol } H_2} \times \frac{22.4 \text{ L}}{\text{mol}} \times \frac{1{,}000 \text{ mL}}{\text{L}}$

$= \underline{\mathbf{7.2 \text{ mL } N_2}}$ (STP)

9.71 $2KClO_3 \longrightarrow 2KCl + 3O_2$

Vapor pressure of water at 30° C = 31.8 torr

(a) $n = \frac{PV}{RT} = \frac{(600 - 32) \text{ atm}}{760} \times \frac{0.150 \text{ L}}{1} \times \frac{1 \text{ mol K}}{0.0821 \text{ L atm}} \times \frac{1}{303 \text{ K}}$

$= 0.004507 \text{ mol } O_2$

$0.004507 \text{ mol} \times 32.0 \text{ g/mol} = \underline{\mathbf{0.144 \text{ g } O_2}}$

(b) $0.004507 \text{ mol } O_2 \times \frac{2 \text{ mol } KClO_3}{3 \text{ mol } O_2} \times \frac{122.5 \text{ g } KClO_3}{\text{mol}} = \underline{\mathbf{0.368 \text{ g } KClO_3}}$

9.72 $10.0 \text{ g } HNO_3 \times \frac{1 \text{ mol } HNO_3}{63.02 \text{ g}} \times \frac{3 \text{ mol } NO_2}{2 \text{ mol } HNO_3} \times \frac{22.4 \text{ L (STP)}}{\text{mol}} \times \frac{760 \text{ torr}}{770 \text{ torr}}$

$\times \frac{298 \text{ K}}{273 \text{ K}} \times \frac{1{,}000 \text{ mL}}{\text{L}} = \underline{\mathbf{5{,}740 \text{ mL } NO_2}}$

9.73 For the initial amount of NH_3

$n = \frac{PV}{RT} = \frac{750 \text{ atm}}{760} \times \frac{0.120 \text{ L}}{1} \times \frac{1 \text{ mol K}}{0.0821 \text{ L atm}} \times \frac{1}{298 \text{ K}}$

$= 0.00484 \text{ mol } NH_3$

(continued)

(9.73 continued)

For the initial amount of O_2

$$n = \frac{PV}{RT} = \frac{635 \text{ atm}}{760} \times \frac{0.165 \text{ L}}{1} \times \frac{1 \text{ mol K}}{0.0821 \text{ L atm}} \times \frac{1}{323 \text{ K}} = 0.00520 \text{ mol } O_2$$

Moles of NH_3 that would react with 0.00520 mol O_2 =

$$0.00520 \text{ mol } O_2 \times \frac{4 \text{ mol } NH_3}{5 \text{ mol } O_2} = 0.00416 \text{ mol } NH_3$$

O_2 is the limiting reactant.

0.00484 mol NH_3 present - 0.00416 mol NH_3 reacted = 0.00068 mol of excess NH_3

Moles of gaseous product =

$$0.00520 \text{ mol } O_2 \times \frac{10 \text{ mol products}}{5 \text{ mol } O_2} = 0.01040 \text{ mol product.}$$

Total number of moles at the end of the reaction is = moles of gaseous products

+ moles of excess NH_3 = 0.01040 mol + 0.00068 = 0.01108 mol.

$$P = \frac{nRT}{V} = 0.01108 \text{ mol} \times \frac{0.0821 \text{ L atm}}{\text{mol K}} \times \frac{423 \text{ K}}{0.300 \text{ L}}$$

= 1.283 atm or **<u>975 torr</u>**

9.74 $2CO + O_2 \longrightarrow 2CO_2$

Moles of CO before reaction $= \frac{PV}{RT} = \frac{760 \text{ atm}}{760} \times \frac{0.500 \text{ L}}{1} \times \frac{1 \text{ mol K}}{0.0821 \text{ L atm}}$

$$\times \frac{1}{288 \text{ K}} = 0.02115 \text{ mol CO}$$

(continued)

(9.74 continued)

Moles of O_2 before reaction =

$$\frac{PV}{RT} = \frac{770 \text{ atm}}{760} \times .500\text{L} \times \frac{1 \text{ mol K}}{0.0821 \text{ L atm}} \times \frac{1}{273 \text{ K}} = 0.02260 \text{ mol } O_2$$

The limiting reactant is CO.

$$\text{Moles } CO_2 = 0.02115 \text{ mol CO} \times \frac{2 \text{ mol } CO_2}{2 \text{ mol CO}} = 0.02115 \text{ mol } CO_2$$

$$\text{Volume } CO_2 = \frac{nRT}{P} = 0.02115 \text{ mol} \times \frac{0.0821 \text{ L atm}}{\text{mol K}} \times 301\text{K}$$

$$\times \frac{760 \text{ atm}}{750} = 0.530 \text{ L or } \underline{\mathbf{530 \text{ mL } CO_2}}$$

9.75 (a) $0.420 \text{ mL } Na_2S_2O_3 \times \frac{0.0100 \text{ mol } Na_2S_2O_3}{\text{L } Na_2S_2O_3} \times \frac{1 \text{ L}}{1{,}000 \text{ mL}}$

$$\times \frac{1 \text{ mol } I_2}{2 \text{ mol } Na_2S_2O_3} = \underline{\mathbf{2.10 \times 10^{-6} \text{ mol } I_2}}$$

(b) $\underline{\mathbf{2.10 \times 10^{-6} \text{ mol } I_2}}$

(c) $2.10 \times 10^{-6} \text{ mol } I_2 \times \frac{1 \text{ mol } O_3}{\text{mol } I_2} = \underline{\mathbf{2.10 \times 10^{-6} \text{ mol } O_3}}$

(d) $2.10 \times 10^{-6} \text{ mol} \times \frac{22.4 \text{ L}}{\text{mol}} \times \frac{1{,}000 \text{ mL}}{\text{L}} = \underline{\mathbf{4.70 \times 10^{-2} \text{ mL}}}$

(e) $\frac{4.70 \times 10^{-2} \text{ mL}}{200{,}000 \text{ L}} \times \frac{1 \text{ L}}{1{,}000 \text{ mL}} \times 10^6 = \underline{\mathbf{0.000235 \text{ ppm}}}$

9.76 The sequence of calculations in this problem are: calculate the moles of NO, convert to moles of O_2, and then calculate the volume of the O_2.

$$\text{moles of NO} = \frac{PV}{RT} = \frac{750 \text{ atm}}{760} \times 100 \text{ L} \times \frac{\text{mol K}}{0.0821 \text{ L atm}} \times \frac{1}{773 \text{ K}}$$

$= 1.55$ moles NO

$$\text{moles } O_2 = 1.55 \text{ mol NO} \times \frac{5 \text{ mol } O_2}{4 \text{ mol NO}} = 1.94 \text{ mol } O_2$$

$$\text{vol. } O_2 = \frac{nRT}{P} = 1.94 \text{ mol} \times \frac{0.0821 \text{ L atm}}{\text{mol K}} \times 298 \text{ K} \times \frac{1}{0.895 \text{ atm}}$$

= <u>53.1 L of O_2</u>

9.77 (a) Vapor pressure of water at 25°C = 23.8 torr.

Partial pressure of oxygen = 745 torr - 23.8 torr = 721 torr.

Moles of oxygen = n = PV /RT.

$$n = \frac{721 \text{ atm}}{760} \times 0.0350 \text{ L} \times \frac{\text{mol K}}{0.0821 \text{ L atm}} \times \frac{1}{298 \text{ K}} = \underline{1.36 \times 10^{-3} \text{ mol } O_2}$$

(b) $$1.36 \times 10^{-3} \text{ mol } O_2 \times \frac{2 \text{ mol } KClO_3}{3 \text{ mol } O_2} \times \frac{122.6 \text{ g } KClO_3}{\text{mol } KClO_3}$$

= <u>0.111 g $KClO_3$</u>

(c) $$\frac{0.111 \text{ g } KClO_3}{0.2500 \text{ g sample}} \times 100 = \underline{44.4\%}$$

9.78 <u>Effusion</u> is the escape of a gas, under pressure, through a very small opening, while <u>diffusion</u> is the spontaneous mixing of two gases placed in the same container.

9.79 Graham's law states that under identical conditions of temperature and pressure the rate of effusion of gases is inversely proportional to the square root of their densities.

9.80 (a) $\frac{V_{He}}{V_{Ne}} = \sqrt{\frac{M_{Ne}}{M_{He}}}$

(b) **He**

(c) $\frac{\text{Rate of effusion of He}}{\text{Rate of effusion of Ne}} = \sqrt{\frac{20.2}{4}} = \underline{\textbf{2.25 times faster}}$

9.81 $\frac{V_a}{V_b} = \sqrt{\frac{M_b}{M_a}}$ Let $a = CO_2$ and $b = CH_4$

$\frac{\text{speed of } CO_2}{1{,}000 \text{ miles /hr}} = \sqrt{\frac{16.05}{44.01}} = 0.6039$

Speed of CO_2 = 0.6039 x 1,000 = **603.9 miles /hr**

(1,000 miles /hr is assumed to have four significant figures)

9.82 $\frac{\text{rate of effusion of unknown}}{\text{rate of effusion of } NH_3} = 2.92 = \sqrt{\frac{\text{M.W. }(NH_3)}{\text{M.W. (unknown)}}}$

$(2.92)^2 = \frac{17}{\text{M.W. (unknown)}}$

$8.526 = \frac{17}{\text{M.W. (unknown)}}$

M.W. of the unknown = **1.99 g mol^{-1}**

9.83 A gas is composed of a large number of infinitesimally small particles that are in rapid random motion, and the average kinetic energy of the gas is directly proportional to the absolute temperature.

9.84 Pressure arises from the impacts of the molecules of the gas with the walls of the container.

9.85 At the same temperature, their average kinetic energies are the same. Since KE $= 1/2\ mv^2$, if the masses of the molecules of one is less than that of the other, the average velocity must be larger, so the product, $1/2\ mv^2$, can be the same for both.

9.86 Raising the temperature increases the average velocity of the molecules and the gas should diffuse more rapidly.

9.87 More molecules are forced into a given volume. This means that each unit area of wall surface has more molecules above it, so there are more molecule-wall collisions per second.

9.88 Raising the temperature tends to increase the pressure because the molecules hit the walls with more force at the higher temperature and more often.

9.89 The transfer of heat energy is from the warm object to the cool one. As the warm object loses heat its temperature decreases as well as the average K.E. of its molecules. The cooler object receiving heat energy begins to warm, increasing its temperature and the average kinetic energy of its molecules. This process will continue until the average kinetic energies of the molecules in both objects become equal.

9.90 See Figure 9.12. The curves are not symmetrical because molecules have a lower limit of speed (zero) but virtually no upper limit.

9.91 Gases that do not obey Boyle's law are said to be nonideal. This is most evident at high pressures and low temperatures.

9.92 As gases expand, the average distance of separation of the molecules increases. Since real molecules in a gas attract each other somewhat, moving the molecules further apart requires an increase in potential energy at the expense of kinetic energy. Thus, the average kinetic energy of the molecules decreases, which leads to a decrease in the temperature of the gas.

9.93 The a is the constant that corrects for the intermolecular attractive forces and b is the constant that corrects for the excluded volume of the molecules.

9.94 Van der Waals subtracted a correction from the value of the measured volume to exclude the volume occupied by the molecules. He added a correction to the measured pressure to correct for the pressure drop in real molecule systems caused by attractions between molecules.

9.95 $$\left(P + \frac{n^2 a}{V^2}\right)(V - nb) = nRT$$

$$\left(P + \frac{1.00^2 \times 0.034}{22.400^2}\right)(22.400 - 1.000 \times 0.0237)$$

$$= (1.000)(0.082057)(273.15)$$

$$(P + 6.776 \times 10^{-5})(22.3763) = 22.414$$

$$P + 6.776 \times 10^{-5} = 22.414 / 22.3763 = 1.0017$$

$P = 1.0017 - 6.776 \times 10^{-5} =$ **1.002 atm**

(This shows that He acts very nearly like an ideal gas.)

9.96 $(P + \frac{n^2a}{V^2})(V - nb) = nRT$

$$(P + \frac{1.000^2 \times 5.489}{22.400^2})(22.400 - 1.000 \times 0.06380)$$

$$= 1.000 \times 0.082057 \times 273.15$$

$(P + 0.0109)(22.336) = 22.414$

$P + 0.0109 = 22.414 / 22.336 = 1.003$

$P = 1.003 - 0.0109 =$ **0.992 atm** (ideal gas would have P = 1 atm)

9.97 $(P + \frac{n^2a}{V^2})(V - nb) = nRT$

For 1 mol this equation becomes

$(P + \frac{a}{V^2})(V - b) = RT$ or

$V - b = \frac{RT}{P + a/V^2}$ or $V = \frac{RT}{P + a/V^2} + b$

The V^2 is part of the pressure term and its effect is small once it has been divided into a. Therefore, one can substitute 22.400 L in for V in the V^2 term and solve for V. This will give an answer slightly different than 22.400. A more precise answer can be obtained by substituting the value obtained for V into the V^2 term and re-solving for V. This should be repeated until the value of V does not change. (continued)

(9.97 continued)

$$V_1 = \frac{(0.082057)\,(273.15)}{(1.0000) + (1.36\,/22.40^2)} + 0.0318$$

= 22.385 (This is one more significant figure than is justified).

$$V_2 = \frac{(0.082057)\,(273.15)}{1.0000 + (1.36\,/22.385^2)} + 0.0318$$

= 22.385 (The value did not change).

Answer: **22.38 L /mol at STP**

The value in Table 9.2 is 22.397.

10 STATES OF MATTER AND INTERMOLECULAR FORCES

10.1

	density	rate of diffusion	compressibility	ability to flow
Solid	high	low	very small	poor
Liquid	medium	medium	very small	good
Gas	low	high	high	good

10.2 density, rate of diffusion, compressibility

10.3 The distance traveled by a molecule between collisions in a liquid is very short compared to a gas. It, therefore, takes a given molecule more time to move a given distance in the liquid.

10.4 At room temperature molecules within solids are very tightly packed and held quite rigidly in place. Therefore, diffusion in solids is virtually nonexistent. At high temperatures the molecules are not as tightly packed and some diffusion can take place.

10.5 It is a measure of the energy needed to increase the surface area of a liquid. They minimize their surface area and, therefore, lower their energy.

10.6 Surface tension keeps the surface area of the liquid from expanding, which would happen if the water overflowed.

10.7 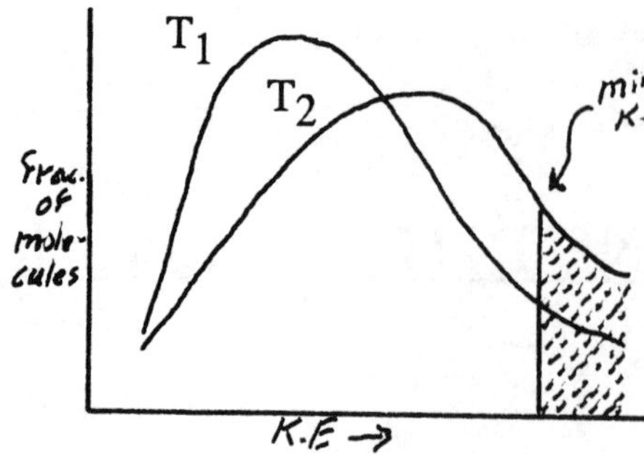

$T_1 < T_2$ It is clear from this diagram that more molecules possess the minimum K.E. for the evaporation at T_2. Therefore, the liquid at T_2 will evaporate faster.

10.8 As the liquid evaporates, the molecules possessing the higher K.E. are leaving, which leads to a lower average K.E. A lower average K.E. means a lower temp.

10.9 On a dry day water evaporates rapidly because there is little water vapor in the air. The rate of return of H_2O to the clothes is slow compared to the rate of evaporation. When the wind is blowing, the air immediately surrounding the clothes does not have a chance to saturate. Thus, evaporation can continue at a rapid rate.

10.10 It sublimes at the low pressures found at high altitudes.

10.11 A greater fraction of molecules in the warm water has enough energy to escape the surface.

10.12 Sublimation

10.13 Increasing the surface area increases the overall rate of evaporation.

10.14 methyl alcohol

10.15 Camphor, naphthalene (mothballs)

10.16 Attractions between the positive end of one dipole and the negative end of another are called dipole-dipole attractions. They are weaker in a gas because the molecules are further apart.

10.17 Hydrogen bonds are extra strong dipole-dipole attractions. They are most important for N-H, O-H, and F-H bonds because N, O, and F are very small and very electronegative.

10.18 Instantaneous dipole-induced dipole attractions.

10.19

	dipole-dipole	hydrogen bonding	London forces
HCl	x		x
Ar			x
CH_4			x
HF		x	x
NO	x		x
CO_2			x
H_2S	x		x
SO_2	x		x

10.20 Hydrogen bonding forces water molecules into a tetrahedral arrangement about each other which leads to a more "open", less dense structure for ice than for the liquid.

10.21 Surface tension, vapor pressure, ΔH_{vap}, boiling point, freezing point, and ΔH_{fus}.

10.22 They should increase.

10.23 Polarizability is the ease of distortion of the electron cloud of an atom, molecule or ion. The greater the polarizability, the stronger the London forces.

10.24 See Figure 10.18.

10.25 The molar heat of vaporization is the amount of energy needed to cause the evaporation of one mole of the liquid. Because we are really only interested in their difference.

10.26 Substance X should have the higher boiling point. Substance Y would be the least likely to hydrogen bond.

10.27 ΔH_{vap} and boiling points increase from CH_4 to $C_{10}H_{22}$ because of increased London forces in the same direction. Long chain-like molecules are attracted to one another in more places than shorter molecules.

10.28 ΔH_{vap} should increase $PH_3 < AsH_3 < SbH_3$

10.29 ΔH_{vap} should increase $H_2S < H_2Se < H_2Te$

10.30 There are more hydrogen bonds in water than in HF because H_2O has 2 hydrogen atoms whereas HF has only one.

10.31 The gasoline evaporates very rapidly, thereby removing heat <u>faster</u> than the evaporation of water.

10.32 The source of energy in a thunderstorm is the heat of vaporization that is liberated when H_2O condenses.

10.33 When steam contacts skin, it condenses to H_2O at 100°C. Heat equal to the heat of vaporization is given off to the skin. Then the skin is further burned by the hot water produced during condensation.

10.34 $\dfrac{\Delta H_{vap}}{B.P.} = \text{const.}$ For CH_4: $\dfrac{9.20 \text{ kJ/mol}}{(273 - 161)\text{K}} \times 10^3 \text{ J/kJ} = \underline{\mathbf{82.1 \text{ J mol}^{-1} \text{ K}^{-1}}}$

For C_2H_6: $\underline{\mathbf{76 \text{ J mol}^{-1} \text{ K}^{-1}}}$ For C_3H_8: $\underline{\mathbf{74.5 \text{ J mol}^{-1} \text{ K}^{-1}}}$

(continued)

(10.34 continued)

For C_4H_{10} : $\underline{\mathbf{81.7\ J\ mol^{-1}\ K^{-1}}}$ For C_6H_{14} : $\underline{\mathbf{83.9\ J\ mol^{-1}\ K^{-1}}}$

For C_8H_{18}: $\underline{\mathbf{85.2\ J\ mol^{-1}\ K^{-1}}}$ For $C_{10}H_{22}$: $\underline{\mathbf{82.7\ J\ mol^{-1}\ K^{-1}}}$

(They all have about the same value since ΔH_{vap} and boiling points increase with increasing molecular weight for nonpolar compounds.)

10.35 $55.0 \text{ g} \times \frac{1 \text{ mol}}{46.08 \text{ g}} \times \frac{38.6 \text{ kJ}}{\text{mol}} = \underline{\mathbf{46.1\ kJ}}$

10.36 $35.0 \text{ g} \times \frac{1 \text{ mol}}{78.12 \text{ g}} \times \frac{2.37 \text{ kcal}}{\text{mol}} \times \frac{4.184 \text{ kJ}}{\text{kcal}} = \underline{\mathbf{4.44\ kJ}}$

10.37 $4.29 \text{ kJ} \times \frac{1}{14.5 \text{ g Hg}} \times \frac{200.6 \text{ g Hg}}{\text{mol Hg}} = \underline{\mathbf{59.3\ kJ\ /mol}}$

$\frac{59.3 \text{ kJ}}{\text{mol}} \times \frac{1 \text{ kcal}}{4.184 \text{ kJ}} = \underline{\mathbf{14.2\ kcal\ /mol}}$

10.38 K.E. = $1/2\ mv^2 = 1/2\ (68.2 \text{ kg})\ (10.0 \text{ mi /hr})^2\ (1 \text{ hr /60 min})^2\ (1 \text{ min /60 s})^2$

$(5280 \text{ ft /mi})^2\ (12 \text{ in. /ft})^2\ (2.54 \text{ cm /in.})^2\ (1 \text{ m /100 cm})^2\ (1 \text{ J s}^2 \text{ /kg m}^2)$

$= 6.81 \times 10^2$ J $\Delta H_{fus.}(H_2O) = 5.98$ kJ /mol (Table 8.3)

$6.81 \times 10^2 \text{ J} \times \frac{1 \text{ mol}}{5.98 \text{ kJ}} \times \frac{1 \text{ kJ}}{1{,}000 \text{ J}} \times \frac{18.02 \text{ g}}{\text{mol}} = \underline{\mathbf{2.05\ g}}$

10.39 Energy change = heat released via condensation plus heat released via cooling.

ΔH_{vap} (H_2O) = 40.6 kJ /mol (Table 10.3) $\Delta H_{cond.}$ (H_2O) = -40.6 kJ /mol

Specific heat (H_2O) = 4.184 J /g °C (from Section 1.5)

Energy change = ($\Delta H_{cond.} \times mol_{H_2O}$) + (sp. heat x g x change in temp.)

(continued)

(10.39 continued)

Energy change = (-40.6 kJ /mol) (1.00 g /18.02 g mol $^{-1}$) (1000 J /kJ) +

(4.184 J /g °C) (1.00 g) (40°C - 100°C) = (-2253 J) + (-251 J) = -2504 J

= **2.50 kJ of energy absorbed**

10.40 Energy absorbed by the benzene = $\Delta H_{fus.}$ x $mol_{benzene}$

= 2.37 kcal /mol x 10.0 g /(78.06 g /mol) = 0.304 kcal

0.304 kcal = energy also released by the H_2O = sp. heat x g x change in temp.

0.304 kcal = (1.00 cal /g °C) x (50.0 g) x (30.0 - ?)°C

6.08 = (30.0 - ?) ? = **23.9°C**

10.41 Heat gained by less energetic body = (-1) x heat lost by the more energetic body.

($\Delta H_{fus.}$ x mol_{ice}) + (sp. $heat_{(\ell)}$ x $mass_{ice}$ x change temp.) =

(-1) [(ΔH_{cond} x mol_{steam}) + (sp. $heat_{(\ell)}$ x mass steam x change temp.)

(1430 cal /mol x 50.0 g /18.02 g mol $^{-1}$) + [1 cal /g °C x 50.0 g x (X - 0.00)°C]

= (-1) {(-9710 cal /mol x 10.0 g /18.02 g mol $^{-1}$) + [1 cal /g °C x 10.0 g x

(X - 100.0°C)]} or 3968 + 50.0 X = -1(-5,388 + 10.0 X - 1,000)

60.0 X = 2420 X = 40.3 or **40.3°C**

10.42 The "equilibrium vapor pressure" is the pressure exerted by the gaseous molecules of a substance above a liquid in a closed system at equilibrium.

10.43 The nature of the attractive forces in the liquid phase and the temperature are the two principal factors that determine the magnitude of the vapor pressure.

10.44 Ethyl alcohol

10.45 The vapor pressure of a liquid increases with increasing temperature because at higher temperatures a larger fraction of molecules in the liquid state have sufficient kinetic energy to leave the liquid state. The greater the number evaporating, the greater the vapor pressure.

10.46 The equilibrium vapor pressure depends on the rate of evaporation of the liquid, which is determined by the fraction of molecules having enough K.E. to escape. If the attractive forces are large, this fraction is small.

10.47 Decreasing the volume of a container will simply force more vapor molecules to condense into the liquid leaving the V.P. constant. See Figure 10.16.

10.48 Vapor pressure is the equilibrium pressure of the gas in the equilibrium, liquid $\rightleftharpoons$ gas. The value of the equilibrium gas pressure is independent of volume of liquid or gas. Increased surface area of the liquid will increase the rate at which equilibrium can be attained but not the value at equilibrium.

10.49 If the beverage is cold enough, water in the air immediately surrounding the glass will be cooled sufficiently to condense it on the vessel.

10.50 A humidity of 100% implies air saturated with H_2O vapor, which exerts a partial pressure equal to the vapor pressure of water at that temperature. Vapor pressure increases with temperature; therefore, the amount of water in a given volume of saturated air also increases.

10.51 As the warm moist air rises, the temperature begins to fall. The decrease in temperature brings about a lowering of the average K.E., rendering more molecules capable of condensing. This increased condensation is in the form of rain.

10.52 The critical temperature is that temperature above which the substance can no longer exist as a liquid regardless of the pressure. The critical pressure is that pressure required to liquefy a substance at its critical temperature.

10.53 It disappears.

10.54 Below its critical temperature, -267.8°C (Table 10.2)

10.55 On a cool day the CO_2 is below its critical temperature (31°C, or 88°F) and a separate liquid phase exists.

10.56 The water is able to evaporate more quickly and this cools the coffee.

10.57 Le Chatelier's principle states that when a system in a state of dynamic equilibrium is disturbed by some outside influence that upsets the equilibrium, the system responds by undergoing a change in a direction that reduces the disturbance and, if possible, brings the system back to equilibrium.

10.58 **(a)** Increasing the temperature will cause a shift to the right.

(b) Increases in temperature will cause a shift to the right.

10.59 It will shift the equilibrium to the left.

10.60 That temperature at which the vapor pressure of a liquid is equal to the atmospheric pressure is known as the boiling point of the liquid. The boiling point of a liquid at one standard atmosphere, 760 torr, is referred to as its standard or normal boiling point.

10.61 **~88°C**

10.62 (From Figure 10.15) **~73°C** (From Table 9.1) **between 73 and 75°C**

10.63 The stronger the intermolecular attractive forces, the more difficult it is for molecules to break away from the liquid and enter the gaseous state.

10.64 Crystalline solids have highly regular, symmetrical shapes. They possess faces that intersect each other at characteristic interfacial angles.

10.65 An amorphous solid has particles arranged in a chaotic fashion. Amorphous solids do not have the characteristic faces and angles of crystals.

10.66 A lattice is a regular or repetitive pattern of points or particles. A unit cell is the smallest grouping of particles that is repeated throughout the solid that can generate the entire lattice. We can create an infinite number of chemical structures by simply varying the chemical environment about each point in a lattice.

10.67 With the use of the Bragg equation, $2d \sin \theta = n\lambda$, we can find the spacing between the successive layers of particles in a crystal: d is the spacing between successive layers, θ is the angle at which X rays enter and leave, λ is the wavelengths of the X rays and n is an integer.

10.68 The quantities a, b & c, corresponding to the edge lengths of the cell and α, β & γ, corresponding to the angles at which the edges intersect one another, describe a particular lattice.

10.69 See Figure 10.27 (a), (b), and (c).

10.70 (a) Its lattice arrangement is a face-centered cubic arrangement of chloride ions with sodium ions at the center of each edge and in the center of the unit cell.

(10.70 continued)

(b) Cl^- 8 corners x 1/8 Cl^- per corner = 1 Cl^-

6 faces x 1/2 Cl^- per face = 3 Cl^-

Total = 4 Cl^-

Na^+ 12 edges x 1/4 Na^+ per edge = 3 Na^+

1 center x 1 Na^+ per center = 1 Na^+

4 Na^+

Na_4Cl_4 or **4 Formula Unit per Unit Cell**

(c) **No.** It needs to have a mono-charged anion if all the corners and faces are to be occupied.

10.71 (a) $2d \sin\theta = n\lambda$ $n = 1$

$2 \times 1{,}000 \times \sin\theta = 1 \times 229$ $\sin\theta = 229/2{,}000 = 0.1145$ $\theta = 6.57°$

(b) $2 \times 200 \times \sin\theta = 1 \times 229$ $\sin\theta = 229/400 = 0.5725$ $\theta = 34.9°$

10.72 $2d \sin\theta = n\lambda$ $n = 1$ $\lambda = 141$ pm

(a) $2d \sin 20.0° = 1 \times 141$

$2 \times d \times 0.342 = 141$ $d = 141/0.684 =$ **206 pm**

(b) $2d \sin 27.4° = 1 \times 141$ $d = 141/0.920 =$ **153 pm**

(c) $2d \sin 35.8° = 1 \times 141$ $d = 141/1.170 =$ **121 pm**

10.73 If $n = 1$, $2 \times 200 \sin\theta = 1 \times 141$, $\theta = 20.6°$

If $n = 2$, $2 \times 200 \sin\theta = 2 \times 141$, $\theta = 44.8°$

If $n = 3$, $2 \times 200 \sin\theta = 3 \times 141$, $\theta > 90°$

Answers: **20.5°** and **44.8°**

10.74 (Draw a picture of the unit cell). In the body-centered cubic unit cell there is a sphere at each corner and in the very center. The corner spheres each touch the center sphere but they do not touch each other. The distance from one corner to the corner diagonally through the unit cell is 4 radii or 4 r. From the unit cell two right triangles can be constructed. The first involves 2 edges (E) and the diagonal across the face (DF). The other involves the unit cell diagonal (DC), an edge (E), and the diagonal across the face (DF). In the first triangle we can use the known edge length (E) to calculate the length of the diagonal across the face of the unit cell (DF). Then in the second triangle we can use the now known length of the diagonal across the face (DF) and the edge length (E) to calculate the unit cell diagonal (DC). Knowing the unit cell diagonal (DC) is 4r, we then have the radius of the atom. First Triangle $(E)^2 + (E)^2 = (DF)^2$

$(288.4)^2 + (288.4)^2 = (DF)^2$ DF = 407.86 pm

Second Triangle $(E)^2 + (DF)^2 = (DC)^2$

$(288.4)^2 + (407.86)^2 = (DC)^2$ $249{,}500 = (DC)^2$

DC = 499.5 pm 4r = 499.5 pm

r = 124.9 pm

10.75 Body-centered unit cell = 2 atoms /unit cell

Vol. of the unit cell = $(288.4\text{ pm})^3 = 23{,}990{,}000\text{ pm}^3 = 2.399 \times 10^{-23}\text{ cm}^3$

$$\frac{51.996\text{ g Cr}}{1\text{ mol Cr}} \times \frac{\text{cm}^3}{7.19\text{ g}} \times \frac{1\text{ unit cell}}{2.399 \times 10^{-23}\text{ cm}^3} \times \frac{2\text{ atoms}}{\text{unit cell}} =$$

6.03×10^{23} atoms /mole

10.76 A diagonal (DF) drawn across the face of the unit cell forms a right triangle with 2 edges (E). The diagonal (DF) is 4 radii.

$(DF)^2 = (E)^2 + (E)^2 = (407.86)^2 + (407.86)^2$

$DF = 576.80 = 4r \qquad \underline{r = 144.20 \text{ pm}}$

10.77 (See the discussion with Problem 10.76)

$(4r)^2 = (DF)^2 = (E)^2 + (E)^2 \qquad (4 \times 143)^2 = 2(E)^2$

$E^2 = 163{,}600 \qquad E = \text{Edge} = \underline{404 \text{ pm}}$

10.78 (See the discussion with Problem 10.74)

$(E)^2 + (E)^2 = (DF)^2 \qquad (412.3)^2 + 412.3)^2 = DF^2$

$DF = 583.1 \qquad (E)^2 + (DF)^2 = (DC)^2$

$(412.3)^2 + (583.1)^2 = (DC)^2 \qquad DC = 714.1$

$DC = 2r\ (Cs^+) + 2r\ (Cl^-)$

$714.1 = 2r\ (Cs^+) + (2 \times 181 \text{ pm}) \qquad r\ (Cs^+) = \underline{176 \text{ pm}}$

10.79 Unit cell edge length = 658 pm

$658 \text{ pm} = 2r\ (Rb^+) + 2r\ (Cl^-) \qquad 658 \text{ pm} = 2r(Rb^+) + (2 \times 181)$

$r\ (Rb^+) = 148 \text{ pm} \qquad$ <u>148 pm or 1.48 angstroms</u>

10.80 For a discussion of the body-centered unit cell, see the solution to Problem 10.74. For a discussion of the face-centered unit cell, see the solution to Problem 10.76. For the simple cubic E = 2 radii or 2r. The body-centered unit cell has 2 atoms per unit cell (See problem 10.75). The face-centered unit cell

(continued)

(10.80 continued)

has 4 atoms per unit cell (See Problem 10.70). The simple cubic unit cell has 1 atom per unit cell.

(a) Volume = $(E)^3 = (2r)^3 = (2 \times 144)^3 = 2.39 \times 10^7\ pm^3$

$$\frac{107.9\ g\ Ag}{mol} \times \frac{1\ mol}{6.022 \times 10^{23}\ atoms} \times \frac{1\ atom}{unit\ cell} \times \frac{1\ unit\ cell}{2.39 \times 10^7 pm^3} \times \frac{(10^{10}\ pm)^3}{cm^3} = \underline{7.50\ g/cm^3}$$

(b) $(E)^2 + (E)^2 = (DF)^2$ and $(E)^2 + (DF)^2 = (DC)^2$

$$(DC)^2 = (4r)^2 = (4 \times 144\ pm)^2 = 3.32 \times 10^5\ pm^2$$

$3.32 \times 10^5\ pm^2 = (E)^2 + (E)^2 + (E)^2$ $\quad$ E = 333 pm

Volume = $E^3 = (333)^3 = 3.68 \times 10^7\ pm^3$

$$\frac{107.9\ g\ Ag}{mol} \times \frac{1\ mol}{6.022 \times 10^{23}\ atoms} \times \frac{2\ atoms}{unit\ cell} \times \frac{1\ unit\ cell}{3.68 \times 10^7\ pm^3} \times \frac{(10^{10}\ pm)^3}{cm^3} = \underline{9.74\ g/cm^3}$$

(c) $(E)^2 + (E)^2 = (DF)^2 = (4r)^2$ $\quad$ $2(E)^2 = (4 \times 144)^2$

E = 407 pm $\quad$ Volume = $(E)^3 = 6.76 \times 10^7\ pm^3$

$$\frac{107.9\ g\ Ag}{mol} \times \frac{1\ mol}{6.022 \times 10^{23}\ atoms} \times \frac{4\ atoms}{unit\ cell} \times \frac{1\ unit\ cell}{6.76 \times 10^7\ pm^3} \times \frac{(10^{10}\ pm)^3}{cm^3} = \underline{10.6\ g/cm^3}$$

The density calculated for the **face-centered cubic** structure is closest to the actual density.

10.81 AY = YB = 1/2 nλ; AY + YB = nλ; XY = d

$\sin\theta = YB/XY = YB/d$

$d\sin\theta = 1/2\, n\lambda$ **$2d\sin\theta = n\lambda$**

10.82 Volume of sphere = $4/3\,\pi r^3 = 4/3\,\pi(50\text{ pm})^3 = 5.236 \times 10^5\text{ pm}^3$

(a) volume of primitive cubic unit cell (See Problem 10.80).

$v = (2r)^3 = (2 \times 50\text{ pm})^3 = 1.0 \times 10^6\text{ pm}^3$

Vacant space = $1.0 \times 10^6\text{ pm} - 5.23 \times 10^5\text{ pm}^3 = 4.8 \times 10^5\text{ pm}^3$

$\frac{4.8 \times 10^5}{1.00 \times 10^6} \times 100 =$ **48% vacant**

(b) For a discussion of the body-centered cubic unit cell see Problem 10.74.

$(4r)^2 = (DC)^2 = (E)^2 + (E)^2 + (E)^2$ $(4 \times 50\text{ pm})^2 = 3(E)^2$

$E = 116\text{ pm}$ $V = (116\text{ pm})^3 = 1.56 \times 10^6\text{ pm}^3$ (2 spheres per unit cell)

Vacant space = $1.56 \times 10^6\text{ pm}^3 - (2 \times 5.23 \times 10^5\text{ pm}^3) = 5.1 \times 10^5\text{ pm}^3$

$\frac{5.1 \times 10^5}{1.56 \times 10^6} \times 100 =$ **33% vacant**

(c) For a discussion of the face-centered cubic unit cell see Problem 10.76.

$(4r)^2 = (DF)^2 = (E)^2 + (E)^2$ $(4 \times 50)^2 = 2(E)^2$

$E = 141\text{ pm}$

$V = (141\text{ pm})^3 = 2.80 \times 10^6\text{ pm}^3$ (Four spheres per unit cell)

Vacant space = $2.80 \times 10^6 - (4 \times 5.23 \times 10^5) = 7.1 \times 10^5\text{ pm}^3$

$\frac{7.1 \times 10^5}{2.80 \times 10^6} \times 100 =$ **26% vacant**

10.83 The Br^- forms a face-centered cubic unit cell. (See Problem 10.76).

$(4r)^2 = (DF)^2 = (E)^2 + (E)^2$ $\qquad (4r)^2 = (550\text{ pm})^2 + (550\text{ pm})^2$

$r = \underline{\textbf{194 pm = radius of Br}^-}$

Edge = (2 x radius of Br^-) + (2 x radius Li^+)

$550\text{ pm} = 2 \times 194\text{ pm} + 2r(Li^+)$ $\qquad r = \underline{\textbf{81.0 pm}}$

The 80.5 pm represents the maximum radius of the Li^+. If it is smaller, it simply will not fill all the available space between the bromide ions.

10.84 Volume of the cube = $(412.3\text{ pm})^3 = 7.009 \times 10^7\text{ pm}^3$

Atoms per unit cell: if face-centered = 4CsCl (See 10.74)

if body-centered = 2CsCl (See 10.75)

Calculated density of the face-centered unit cell =

$$\frac{4\text{ formula units CsCl}}{7.009 \times 10^7\text{pm}^3} \times \frac{168.4\text{ g}}{\text{mole}} \times \frac{1\text{ mole}}{6.022 \times 10^{23}\text{ form. units}} \times \frac{(10^{10}\text{ pm})^3}{\text{cm}^3} =$$

15.96 g /cm³ **Not very close to the known value of 3.99 g / cm³**

Calculated density of the body-centered unit cell =

$$\frac{2\text{ formula unit CsCl}}{7.009 \times 10^7\text{pm}^3} \times \frac{168.4\text{ g}}{\text{mole}} \times \frac{1\text{ mole}}{6.022\times 10^{23}\text{ form. units}} \times \frac{(10^{10}\text{ pm})^3}{\text{cm}^3}$$

= **7.979 g /cm³** **Not very close to the known value of 3.99 g /cm³**

10.85
$$\frac{2\text{ Na atoms}}{\text{unit cell}} \times \frac{22.99\text{ g Na}}{\text{mol}} \times \frac{1\text{ mol}}{6.022 \times 10^{23}\text{ atoms}} \times \frac{1\text{ cm}^3}{0.97\text{ g}} = \frac{7.871 \times 10^{-23}\text{ cm}^3}{\text{unit cell}}$$

Edge $= (7.871 \times 10^{-23}\text{ cm}^3)^{1/3} = 4.3 \times 10^{-8}\text{ cm}$ or **0.43 nm**

10.86 vol./unit cell = [546.26 pm x (10^{-10} cm /pm)]^3 = 1.6300×10^{-22} cm^3

$$\frac{1.6300 \times 10^{-22}\ \text{cm}^3}{\text{unit cell}} \times \frac{3.180\ \text{g}}{\text{cm}^3} \times \frac{1\ \text{mol}}{78.08\ \text{g}} \times \frac{6.022 \times 10^{23}\ \text{form. units}}{\text{mol}}$$

= **3.998 formula units /unit cell**

10.87 (See the solution to Problem 10.70)

$$\frac{\text{vol}}{\text{unit cell}} = \frac{4\ \text{formula units}}{\text{unit cell}} \times \frac{58.44\ \text{g}}{\text{mol}} \times \frac{1\ \text{mol}}{6.022 \times 10^{23}\ \text{form. units}}$$

$$\times \frac{1\ \text{cm}^3}{2.165\ \text{g}} \times \frac{(10^{10}\ \text{pm})^3}{\text{cm}^3} = \frac{1.793 \times 10^8\ \text{pm}^3}{\text{unit cell}}$$

Edge length = (1.793×10^8 pm^3)$^{1/3}$ = 563.9 pm

Edge length = 2 x radius Cl^- + 2 x radius Na^+

563.9 = 2 x 181 + 2 radius Na^+

radius Na^+ = **101 pm**

10.88 Please see Table 10.5.

10.89 (a) molecular (b) molecular (c) metallic (d) ionic

(e) covalent (f) ionic (g) molecular

10.90 (a) molecular (b) ionic (c) ionic (d) metallic

(e) covalent (f) molecular (g) ionic

10.91 molecular

10.92 covalent

10.93 molecular

10.94 molecular

10.95 ionic

10.96 Liquid crystals are certain substances, in a range of temperatures just above their melting points, that exhibit properties charactristic of both liquids and crystals. They are fluid, like liquids, but are highly ordered like crystals.

10.97 Nematic, smectic, and cholesteric. They differ in the way the rodlike molecules are packed.

10.98 The color is produced by constructive and destructive interference of light waves reflected from layers in the cholesteric liquid crystal. The particular color observed depends on the distance between the layers, which changes with temperature.

10.99 nematic liquid crystals

10.100 The equilibrium between solid and liquid exists at the melting point.

10.101 The only difference in freezing point and melting point depends on whether you imagine approaching it from high or low temperatures.

10.102 Fusion is the process of melting.

10.103 The difference is the direction of flow of energy as indicated by the positive sign on molar heat of fusion (endothermic) and the negative sign on the molar heat of crystallization (exothermic).

10.104 From solid —> liquid only small changes in separation take place and only small increases in P.E. occur. When a liquid evaporates, large changes in intermolecular distances occur with correspondingly larger P.E. changes.

10.105

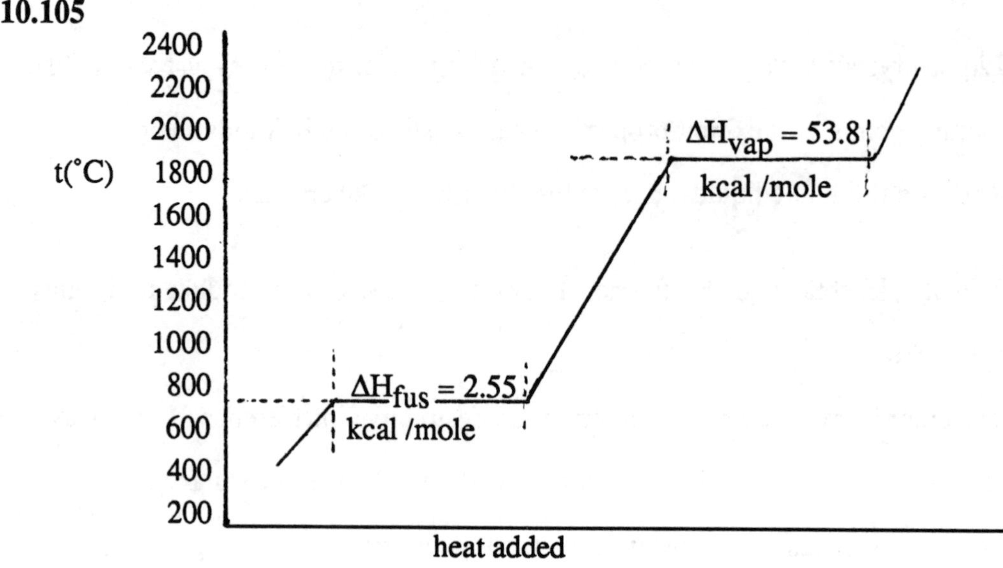

10.106 The temperature cannot rise above the melting point as long as there is liquid in contact with solid.

10.107 Glass is an amorphous solid. The disorientation of the molecules gives rise to a melting point range.

10.108 When water is cooled, it reaches 32°F (0°C) where it is present as <u>liquid</u> water until further heat is extracted. Then freezing will begin. The answer to the question is yes.

10.109 All the heat that is added is used to increase the kinetic energy of the molecules being converted to the gas phase. Therefore, the average kinetic energy and the temperature of the remaining molecules remain constant.

10.110

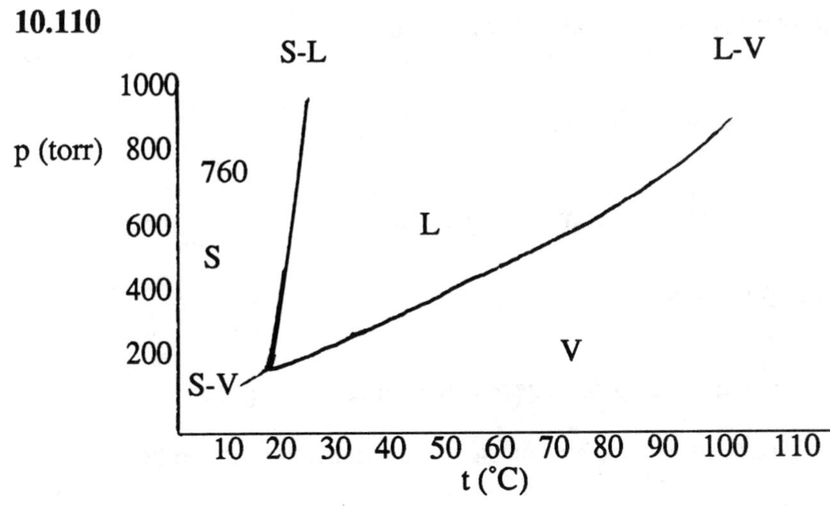

10.111

At 22°C

State	Pressure (torr)
vapor	up to 160
vapor-liquid	160
liquid	160 to 250
solid-liquid	250
solid	250 to 1,000

At 10°C

State	Pressure (torr)
vapor	up to 75
solid-vapor	75
solid	75 to 1,000

10.112

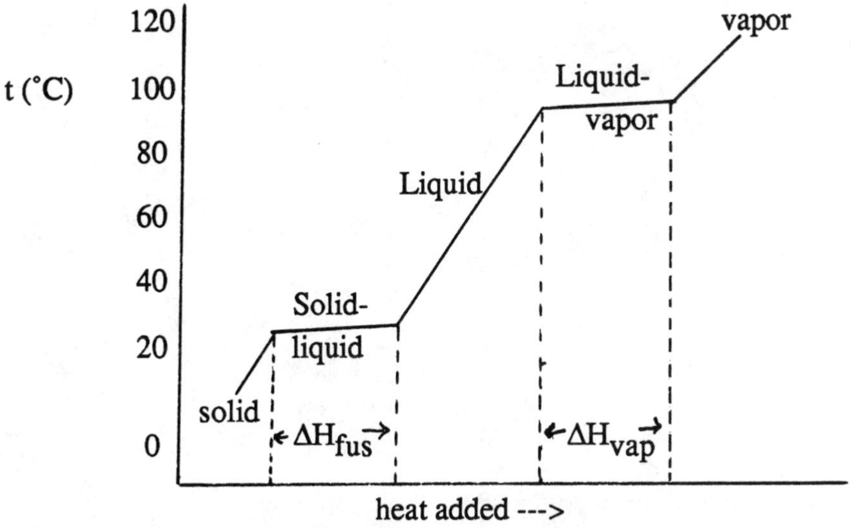

t (°C)
120
100
80
60
40
20
0
vapor
Liquid-
vapor
Liquid
Solid-
liquid
solid
$\leftarrow \Delta H_{fus} \rightarrow$
$\leftarrow \Delta H_{vap} \rightarrow$
heat added --->

10.113 The density of the solid is greater than that of the liquid.

10.114 Solid, vapor, solid, vapor, solid, liquid.

10.115 The triple point of I_2 occurs at a relatively high temperature and at a pressure above atmospheric pressure.

10.116 Increases in pressure lead to the production of the more dense phase. **(a)**Therefore, increases in pressure will cause the production of more liquid in the case of H_2O. **(b)** Increases in pressure will cause the production of more solid in the case of CO_2.

11 PHYSICAL PROPERTIES OF SOLUTIONS AND COLLOIDS

11.1 Pure substances, unlike mixtures, have constant composition.

11.2 Suspensions have dispersed particles of greater than 1,000 nm in size. Fine sand suspended in water and snow being blown about through the air are two examples of suspensions.

11.3 **From 1nm to 1,000 nm**

(a) **1×10^{-6} mm to 1×10^{-3} mm**

(b) **3.9×10^{-8} in. to 3.9×10^{-5} in.**

11.4 Filtration, centrifugation, and settling under the influence of gravity.

11.5 By spinning the sample, the centrifugal force thus produced behaves as a very powerful artificial gravity and drives the suspended particles to the bottom of the container.

11.6 The scattering of light by colloidal dispersions allows one to view from the side a focused beam of light as it passes through the dispersions. The scattering of light by colloidal dispersions is known as the Tyndall effect. Only colloidal dispersions show the Tyndall effect because the dispersed particles in solution are too small to deflect light and the dispersed particles in suspensions will not deflect the light but will instead block out the light.

11.7

	Dispersing phase	Dispersed phase	Kind of colloid
(**a**) styrofoam	solid	gas	solid foam
(**b**) cream	liquid	liquid	emulsion
(**c**) lard	solid	liquid	solid emulsion
(**d**) jelly	liquid	solid	gel, sol
(**e**) liq. rubber cement	liquid	solid	sol, gel

11.8 Emulsifying agents stabilize emulsions by preventing the dispersed particles from sticking to each other when they collide.

11.9 Test for the Tyndall effect.

11.10 An electrical charge on the surface of dispersed particles in a colloidal dispersion will stabilize the dispersion. A colloid stabilized in this way can be coagulated by removal or neutralization of the electrical charge.

11.11 First AgCl forms and begins to form dispersed particles. The excess Cl^- adsorbs on the AgCl particles and acts to prevent them from growing too large to remain suspended. As more Ag^+ is added, the electrical charge is neutralized by the formation of more AgCl and the particles grow in size and will settle out of solution.

11.12 A gas dispersed in a gas. Because gases will mix on the molecular level.

11.13 Solid, liquid and gaseous solutions are possible.

11.14 The dispersed particles in a solution are smaller than those of colloidal dispersions or suspensions.

11.15 Substitutional solid solutions - exist when atoms, molecules, or ions of the solute replace particles of the solvent in the crystalline lattice. Brass is an example.

11.16 Interstitial solid solutions - exist when solute particles fit into spaces between "solute" particles in the host lattice. Tungsten carbide is an example.

11.17 Interstitial solid solution.

11.18 Mole fraction = moles solute /total moles of all species in the solution.

Mole percent = 100 x mole fraction.

Weight fraction = weight of a particular solute /total weights of all components.

Weight percent = 100 x weight fraction.

Molarity = moles solute /volume of solution (in liters).

Molality = moles solute /kilograms of solvent.

11.19 They are ratios (fractions).

11.20 45.0 g $C_3H_5(OH)_3$ = 45.0 g / 92.1 g /mol = 0.489 mol $C_3H_5(OH)_3$

100.0 g H_2O = 100.0 g /18.02 g /mol = 5.549 mol H_2O

$$X_{glycerin} = \frac{0.489 \text{ mol}}{0.489 \text{ mol} + 5.549 \text{ mol}} = \underline{0.0810}$$

$$w_{glycerin} = \frac{45.0 \text{ g}}{45.0 \text{ g} + 100.0 \text{ g}} = \underline{0.310}$$

weight % glycerin = 0.310 x 100 = **31.0%**

$$m_{glycerin} = \frac{0.489 \text{ mol glycerin}}{0.100 \text{ kg } H_2O} = \underline{4.89 \text{ m}}$$

11.21 45.0 g of benzene = 45.0 g /78.06 g /mol = 0.576 mol benzene

80.0 g of toluene = 80.0 g /92.15 g /mol = 0.868 mol toluene

(a) weight % toluene = $\frac{80.0\text{ g}}{80.0\text{ g} + 45.0\text{ g}}$ x 100 = **64.0% toluene**

weight % benzene = $\frac{45.0\text{ g}}{80.0\text{ g} + 45.0\text{ g}}$ x 100 = **36.0% benzene**

(b) $X_{toluene} = \frac{0.868\text{ mol toluene}}{0.868\text{ mol} + 0.576\text{ mol}}$ = **0.601**

$X_{benzene} = \frac{0.576\text{ mol benzene}}{0.868\text{ mol} + 0.576\text{ mol}}$ = **0.399**

(c) $m = \frac{0.576\text{ mol benzene}}{0.0800\text{ kg toluene}}$ = **7.20 m**

11.22 Weight of 1 L soln. = $\frac{1.107\text{ g}}{\text{mL}}$ x $\frac{1{,}000\text{ mL}}{\text{L}}$ = 1,107 g /L

Weight of water in 1 L soln. = 1,107 g - 121.8 g = 985 g H_2O

Moles of $Zn(NO_3)_2$ in 1 L soln. = 121.8 g /189.4 g /mol = 0.6431 mol

(a) Weight % $Zn(NO_3)_2$ = $\frac{121.8\text{ g}}{1{,}107\text{ g}}$ x 100 = **11.00%**

(b) m = 0.6431 mol /0.985 kg H_2O = **0.653 m**

(c) X of $Zn(NO_3)_2$ = $\frac{0.6431\text{ mol}}{0.6431\text{ mol} + (985\text{ g}/18.02\text{ g/mol})}$ = **0.0116**

(d) M = 0.6431 mol /1 L soln. = **0.6431 M**

11.23 40.0 mol of H_2O = 40.0 mol x 18.02 g /mol or 721 g

0.30 mol of $CuCl_2$ = 0.30 mol x 134.5 g /mol or 40 g

(a) X of $CuCl_2$ = 0.30 /(0.30 + 40.0) = **0.0074**

X of H_2O = 40.0 /(0.30 + 40.0) = **0.993**

(b) m of $CuCl_2$ = 0.30 mol /0.721 kg H_2O = **0.42 m**

(c) weight % $CuCl_2$ = [40 g /(40 + 721) g] x 100 = **5.3%**

weight % H_2O = [721 g /(40 + 721) g] x 100 = **94.7%**

11.24 Calculate the weight in grams of $CHCl_3$ in one kilogram of solution.

$$1.00 \text{ kg soln.} \times \frac{1{,}000 \text{ g}}{\text{kg}} \times \frac{12.4 \text{ g } CHCl_3}{10^6 \text{ g soln}} = 1.24 \times 10^{-2} \text{ g } CHCl_3$$

(a) Weight % $CHCl_3$ = $(1.24 \times 10^{-2}$ g /1,000 g) x 100 = **1.24×10^{-3}%**

(b) For a very dilute solution like the one in this problem, its density will be 1.00 g /mL. Therefore, 1.00 kg of solution will occupy 1.00 L.

$$\text{m of } CHCl_3 = \frac{1.24 \times 10^{-2} \text{ g} / 119.5 \text{ g mol}^{-1}}{1.00 \text{ L}} = \mathbf{1.04 \times 10^{-4}\ M}$$

11.25 $$X_{alcohol} = 0.250 = \frac{0.250 \text{ mol alc.}}{0.250 \text{ mol alc.} + ? \text{ mol } H_2O}$$? mol H_2O = 0.750 mol

$$\text{wt. \% alc.} = \frac{0.250 \text{ mol} \times 60.1 \text{ g mol}^{-1}}{(0.250 \text{ mol} \times 60.1 \text{ g mol}^{-1}) + (0.750 \text{ mol} \times 18.02 \text{ g mol}^{-1})} \times 100$$

$$= \frac{15.02 \text{ g}}{28.54 \text{ g}} \times 100 = \mathbf{52.6\%} \qquad \text{m (alc.)} = \frac{0.250 \text{ mol alc.}}{0.01352 \text{ kg } H_2O} = \mathbf{18.5\ m}$$

11.26 $9.6\text{ g NaHCO}_3 = 9.6\text{ g}/84.01\text{ g mol}^{-1} = 0.11\text{ mol}$

$100\text{ g H}_2\text{O} = 100\text{ g}/18.02\text{ g mol}^{-1} = 5.55\text{ mol}$

$$X(\text{NaHCO}_3) = \frac{0.11}{0.11 + 5.55} = \underline{\mathbf{0.019}} \qquad m(\text{NaHCO}_3) = \frac{0.11\text{ mol}}{0.100\text{ kg}} = \underline{\mathbf{1.1\ m}}$$

11.27 $$6.25\text{ m} = \frac{6.25\text{ mol NaCl}}{1.000\text{ kg H}_2\text{O}}$$

$$X_{\text{NaCl}} = \frac{6.25\text{ mol NaCl}}{6.25\text{ mol NaCl} + (1{,}000\text{ g H}_2\text{O}/18.02\text{ g mol}^{-1})}$$

$$= \frac{6.25}{6.25 + 55.49} = \underline{\mathbf{0.101}}$$

$$w_{\text{NaCl}} = \frac{6.25\text{ mol NaCl} \times 58.44\text{ g mol}^{-1}}{(6.25\text{ mol NaCl} \times 58.44\text{ g mol}^{-1}) + 1{,}000\text{ g H}_2\text{O}}$$

$$= \frac{365\text{ g}}{365\text{ g} + 1{,}000\text{ g}} = \underline{\mathbf{0.268}}$$

11.28 $$14.0\%\ \text{Na}_2\text{CO}_3 = \frac{14.0\text{ g Na}_2\text{CO}_3}{14.0\text{ g Na}_2\text{CO}_3 + (100 - 14.0)\text{ g H}_2\text{O}}$$

$$X\text{ of Na}_2\text{CO}_3 = \frac{14.0\text{ g Na}_2\text{CO}_3/106\text{ g mol}^{-1}}{(14.0\text{ g Na}_2\text{CO}_3/106\text{ g mol}^{-1})+(86.0\text{ g H}_2\text{O}/18.02\text{ g mol}^{-1})}$$

$$= \frac{0.1321}{0.132 + 4.77} = \underline{\mathbf{0.0269}}$$

$$m\text{ of Na}_2\text{CO}_3\text{ soln.} = \frac{0.1321\text{ mol Na}_2\text{CO}_3}{0.0860\text{ kg H}_2\text{O}} = \underline{\mathbf{1.54\ m}}$$

11.29 **(a)** $M = \dfrac{150 \times 10^{-3}\ g / 24.3\ g\ mol^{-1}}{1.00\ L} = \underline{\mathbf{0.00617\ M\ Mg^{2+}}}$

(b) $m = \dfrac{150 \times 10^{-3}\ g / 24.3\ g\ mol^{-1}}{(1\ kg - 150 \times 10^{-6}\ kg)} = \dfrac{6.173 \times 10^{-3}\ mol}{0.99985\ kg} = \underline{\mathbf{0.00617\ m\ Mg^{2+}}}$

Note: For very dilute solutions molarity and molality are equal to 2 or 3 sign. figs.

11.30 $m = \dfrac{96.0\ g / 98.1\ g\ mol^{-1}}{4.00\ g\ H_2O \times 1\ kg / 1{,}000\ g} = \underline{\mathbf{245\ m\ H_2SO_4}}$

$X_{sulfuric\ acid} = \dfrac{96.0\ g / 98.1\ g\ mol^{-1}}{(96.0\ g / 98.1\ g\ mol^{-1}) + (4.00\ g / 18.02\ g\ mol^{-1})}$

$= \dfrac{0.9786}{0.9786 + 0.2220} = \underline{\mathbf{0.815}}$ $\qquad X_{H2O} = \dfrac{0.2220}{0.9786 + 0.2220} = \underline{\mathbf{0.185}}$

11.31 $2.25\ m\ NH_4NO_3\ soln. = \dfrac{2.25\ mol\ NH_4NO_3}{1.00\ kg\ H_2O}$

$\text{Weight \% } NH_4NO_3 = \dfrac{2.25\ mol\ NH_4NO_3 \times 80.06\ g\ mol^{-1}}{2.25\ mol \times 80.06\ g\ mol^{-1} + 1{,}000\ g\ H_2O} \times 100$

$= \dfrac{180.1}{180.1 + 1{,}000} = \underline{\mathbf{15.3\%\ NH_4NO_3}}$

$X\ (NH_4NO_3) = \dfrac{2.25\ mol\ NH_4NO_3}{2.25\ mol\ NH_4NO_3 + 1{,}000\ g\ H_2O / 18.02\ g\ mol^{-1}}$

$= \dfrac{2.25}{2.25 + 55.49} = \underline{\mathbf{0.0390}}$ $\qquad X_{H2O} = \dfrac{55.5}{2.25 + 55.5} = \underline{\mathbf{0.961}}$

11.32 $X_{benzene} = 0.240$ $\qquad X_{chloroform} = 1 - 0.240 = 0.760$

(a) mole percent $CHCl_3 = 0.760 \times 100 =$ **<u>76.0 mol %</u>**

(11.32 continued)

(b) $m\ (C_6H_6) = \dfrac{0.240\text{ mol } C_6H_6}{0.760\text{ mol } CHCl_3 \times 119.4\text{ g mol}^{-1} \times 1\text{ kg}/1{,}000\text{ g}}$

$= 2.645\text{ mol kg}^{-1} = \underline{\mathbf{2.64\ m\ C_6H_6}}$

(c) $m\ (CHCl_3) = \dfrac{0.760\text{ mol } CHCl_3}{0.240\text{ mol } C_6H_6 \times 78.12\text{ g mol}^{-1} \times 1\text{ kg}/1{,}000\text{ g}}$

$= 40.5\text{ mol/kg} = \underline{\mathbf{40.5\ m\ CHCl_3}}$

(d) Weight % C_6H_6

$= \dfrac{0.240\text{ mol} \times 78.12\text{ g/mol}}{(0.240\text{ mol} \times 78.12\text{ g/mol}) + (0.760\text{ mol} \times 119.3\text{ g/mol}) \times 100}$

$= \dfrac{18.749}{18.749 + 90.668} \times 100 = \underline{\mathbf{17.1\%}}$

11.33 $m = \dfrac{222.6\text{ g}/62.08\text{ g mol}^{-1}}{0.200\text{ kg } H_2O} = \underline{\mathbf{17.9\ m}}$

$M = \dfrac{222.6\text{ g}/62.08\text{ g mol}^{-1}}{(200\text{ g} + 222.6\text{ g})(1\text{ mL}/1.072\text{ g})(1\text{ L}/1{,}000\text{ mL})} = 9.096\ \dfrac{\text{mol}}{\text{L}} = \underline{\mathbf{9.10\ M}}$

11.34 4.03 M ethylene glycol is 4.03 mol ethylene glycol in 1.000 L of solution. The 1.000 L of solution weighs 1.045 g /mL x 1000 mL or 1045 g. Of the 1045 grams of solution, 4.03 mol ethylene glycol x 62.08 g mol^{-1} (or 250 g) would be ethylene glycol and 1045 - 250 (or 795) grams would be water.

$w_{\text{ethylene glycol}} = \dfrac{250}{1045} \times 100 = \underline{\mathbf{23.9\%}}$

$X_{\text{ethylene glycol}} = \dfrac{4.03\text{ mol ethylene glycol}}{4.03\text{ mol} + (795\text{ g } H_2O/18.02\text{ g mol}^{-1})} = \underline{\mathbf{0.0837}}$

$m = \dfrac{4.03\text{ mol}}{0.795\text{ kg}} = \underline{\mathbf{5.07\ m}}$

11.35 1 kg of H_2O will contain the number of moles of the ions listed in the table.

That number of moles will weigh: (0.566 mol x 35.45 g mol^{-1}) + (0.486 mol x 22.99 g mol^{-1}) + (0.055 mol x 24.31 g mol^{-1}) + (0.029 mol x 96.1 g mol^{-1}) + (0.011 mol x 40.1 g mol^{-1}) + (0.011 mol x 39.10 g mol^{-1}) + (0.002 mol x 61.0 g mol^{-1}) = 36.36 g of salts

$$\text{Weight of } Cl^- = \frac{0.566 \text{ mol } Cl^-}{1 \text{ kg } H_2O} \times \frac{35.45 \text{ g } Cl^-}{\text{mol}} \times \frac{1 \text{ kg } H_2O}{(1{,}000 \text{ g } H_2O + 36.36 \text{ g salts})}$$

$$\times \frac{1024 \text{ g soln.}}{\text{L}} \times 3.78 \text{ L soln} = \underline{74.9 \text{ g } Cl^-}$$

$$\text{Weight of } Na^+ = \frac{0.486 \text{ mol } Na^+}{1 \text{ kg } H_2O} \times \frac{22.99 \text{ g } Na^+}{\text{mol}} \times \frac{1 \text{ kg } H_2O}{(1{,}000 \text{ g} H_2O + 36.36 \text{ g salts})}$$

$$\times \frac{1024 \text{ g soln.}}{\text{L}} \times 3.78 \text{ L soln.} = \underline{41.7 \text{ g } Na^+}$$

Weight of Mg^+ = 0.055 x 24.3 x 3.735 = **5.0 g Mg^+**

Weight of SO_4^{2-} = 0.029 x 96.06 x 3.735 = **10 g SO_4^{2-}**

Weight of Ca^{2+} = 0.011 x 40.08 x 3.735 = **1.6 g Ca^{2+}**

Weight of K^+ = 0.011 x 39.1 x 3.735 = **1.6 g K^+**

Weight of HCO_3^- = 0.002 x 61 x 3.735 = **0.5 g HCO_3^-**

Total Mass of salts = **135.3 g** or **135 g**

11.36

$$50.0 \text{ g soln.} \times \frac{10.0 \text{ g } Na_2CO_3}{100 \text{ g soln.}} \times \frac{286.2 \text{ g } Na_2CO_3 \cdot 10H_2O}{106.0 \text{ g } Na_2CO_3}$$

$$= \underline{13.5 \text{ g } Na_2CO_3 \cdot 10H_2O}$$

11.37 Because the strength of the solute-solvent interactions formed is very much less than the solvent-solvent interactions that must be replaced.

11.38 Because ammonia can form solute-solvent forces of attraction with water that are comparable to the strength of the solvent-solvent force in water. H_2 and O_2 are incapable of forming such strong solute-solvent forces of attraction with water.

11.39 NH_3. Because it is capable of forming hydrogen bonding with the water.

11.40 Substances that exhibit similar intermolecular attractive forces tend to be soluble in one another.

11.41 The salt increases the effective polarity of the solvent and, therefore, decreases the solubility of solutes that are not as polar.

11.42 Methyl alcohol is polar enough to dissolve water and, at the same time, non-polar enough to be dissolved into the gasoline.

11.43 The ion is said to be hydrated when it is surrounded by water molecules. When the solute particle becomes surrounded by molecules of the solvent it is referred to as being solvated; hydration is a special case of solvation.

11.44 When dissolving an ionic compound the water molecules surround the ions.

11.45 Micelles are collections of fatty acid anions which are colloidal in size. Soaps are fatty acid salts which when dissolved become separated fatty acid anions and metal cations. The hydrophobic end of the fatty acid anion will dissolve in grease or oil forming micelles with the hydrophilic part of the fatty acid anion pointing toward the solvent, this makes the oil more soluble in water and allows it to be carried away with the water.

11.46 They do not form precipitates with the cations found in hard water.

11.47 The amount of energy that is absorbed or released when a substance enters solution is called the heat of solution. A negative ΔH_{sol} values means the solution temperature will increase.

11.48 Positive

11.49 In an ideal gas there are no intermolecular attractions. An ideal solution is one in which the solute-solute, solute-solvent and solvent-solvent interactions are all the same (but they are not zero).

11.50 The heat of solution is equal to the difference between the lattice energy and the hydration energy. If the lattice energy is greater, a net input of energy is required; therefore, the solution process is endothermic.

11.51 (a) Na^+ (b) F^- (c) Ca^{2+} (d) Fe^{3+} (e) S^{2-}

11.52 The dominant energy effect when gases dissolve in a liquid is caused by the solvation of the gas molecules, which is exothermic.

11.53 $AlCl_3$ either has a small value for its lattice energy or a large value for its hydration energy.

11.54 Lattice energy

11.55 Since trends in the strengths of lattice energy and hydration energy tend to vary in a very similar way, it is usually not practical to attempt to predict heats of solutions.

11.56 $\Delta H_{soln.}(AlCl_3) = -321\ kJ/mol$

$$\frac{-321\ kJ}{mol} \times 10.0\ g \times \frac{1\ mol}{133.3\ g} = -24.1\ kJ \text{ or } \mathbf{24.1\ kJ\ liberated}$$

11.57 $\Delta H_{soln.}(NH_4NO_3) = 26 \text{ kJ/mol}$

$$\frac{26 \text{ kJ}}{\text{mol}} \times 115 \text{ g} \times \frac{1 \text{ mol}}{80.1 \text{ g}} \times \frac{10^3 \text{ J}}{\text{kJ}} \times \frac{1 \text{ cal}}{4.184 \text{ J}} = \underline{8900 \text{ cal or } 8.9 \text{ kcal}}$$

11.58 KI would become more soluble with an increase in temperature. Addition of heat favors an endothermic process.

11.59 In fractional crystallization, an impure product is dissolved in a small amount of hot solvent, which is then cooled. As the solution cools, the pure product separates from the mixture, leaving the impurities behind.

11.60 KBr @ 70°C, KNO_3 will crystallize first @ 20°C.

11.61 From Figure 11.15, solubility of $NaNO_3$ at 70°C is ~137 g /100 g soln. and at 25°C is ~93 g /100 g soln.

$$\frac{137 \text{ g}}{100 \text{ g}} \times 200 \text{ g} = 274 \text{ g of } NaNO_3 \text{ in soln. at } 70°C$$

$$\frac{93 \text{ g}}{100 \text{ g}} \times 200 \text{ g} = 186 \text{ g of } NaNO_3 \text{ in soln. at } 25°C$$

Amount of precipitate = 274 g - 186 g = **88 g**

11.62 Solubility of NaBr at 80°C is 118 g NaBr /100 g H_2O (See Figure 11.15)

$$\frac{118 \text{ g NaBr}}{100 \text{ g } H_2O} \times ?\text{ g } H_2O = 35.0 \text{ g} \qquad ?\text{ g } H_2O = \frac{35.0 \times 100}{118} = \underline{29.7 \text{ g } H_2O}$$

11.63 Since the solution process for a gas in a liquid is nearly always exothermic, gases are less soluble as the temperature is raised.

11.64 Increasing the pressure will increase the rate at which molecules leave the gas and enter the solution. This will continue until equilibrium is reestablished, at which time the concentration of the solute in the solution will have increased.

11.65 Pressure only has an appreciable effect on equilibria where sizable volume changes occur. When a liquid or solid dissolves in a liquid, only very small changes in volume occur.

11.66 $\frac{5.00 \times 10^{-2}\ g / 30.0\ g/mol}{6.56 \times 10^{-2}\ g / 30.0\ g/mol}$ = mole ratio $\qquad \frac{C_1}{P_1} = \frac{C_2}{P_2}$

$P_{ethane} = 751\ torr \times \frac{5.00 \times 10^{-2}\ g}{6.56 \times 10^{-2}\ g} = \underline{\mathbf{572\ torr}}$

11.67 $p_g = C_g / k_g = 0.0478\ g\ L^{-1} / 6.50 \times 10^{-5}\ g\ L^{-1}\ torr^{-1} = 735\ torr$

$P_{total} = p_g + P_{water} = 735 + 23.8 = \underline{\mathbf{759\ torr}}$

11.68 $C_1 = k \times p_1$ or $k = C_1 / p_1$ = constant

$k = (2.09 \times 10^{-4} / 0.968)\ g\ L^{-1}\ atm^{-1} = 2.16 \times 10^{-4}\ g\ L^{-1}\ atm^{-1}$

$C_2 = k \times p_2 = 2.16 \times 10^{-4}\ g\ L^{-1}\ atm^{-1} \times 1{,}000\ atm = \underline{\mathbf{0.216\ g/L}}$

11.69 $C = 5.34 \times 10^{-5}\ g\ L^{-1}\ atm^{-1} \times 760\ torr \times 0.20 = 8.12 \times 10^{-3}\ g/L$

$8.12 \times 10^{-3}\ g/L \times 1\ L = \underline{\mathbf{8.1 \times 10^{-3}\ g}}$

11.70 The vapor pressure of a solvent depends on the fraction of the total number of molecules at the surface of the solution that are solvent molecules; i.e., the mole fraction of the solvent.

11.71 When the vapor pressure of a mixture is greater than that predicted, it is said to exhibit a positive deviation from Raoult's law; conversely, when a solution gives a lower vapor than we would expect from Raoult's law, it is said to show a negative deviation.

11.72 ΔH_{sol} for positive deviations is endothermic; whereas, ΔH_{sol} for negative deviations is exothermic.

11.73 Raoult's Law states that $P_{soln} = X_{solvent}\ P^{\circ}_{solvent}$

$P^{\circ}_{solvent} = 93.4$ torr

$$X_{solvent} = \frac{1{,}000 \text{ g benzene } / 78.06 \text{ g mol}^{-1}}{(1{,}000 \text{ g benz. } / 78.06 \text{ g mol}^{-1}) + (56.4 \text{ g } C_{20}H_{42} / 283 \text{ g mol}^{-1})}$$

$$= \frac{12.81}{13.01} = 0.985$$

$P_{soln} = 0.985 \text{ x } 93.4 \text{ torr} =$ **92.0 torr**

11.74 $P_{soln.} = X_{solvent}\ P^{\circ}_{solvent}$ $\qquad 130 = X_{solvent} \bullet 160$

$X_{solvent} = 0.813$ $\qquad X_{glycerol} = 1 - 0.813 =$ **0.187**

11.75 $P_T = X_A P^{\circ}_A + X_B P^{\circ}_B$

$$P_T = \frac{25.0 \text{ g} / 100.1 \text{ g mol}^{-1}}{(25.0 \text{ g} / 100.1 \text{ g mol}^{-1}) + (35.0 \text{ g} / 114.1 \text{ g mol}^{-1})} \text{ x } 791 \text{ torr}$$

$$+ \frac{35.0 \text{ g} / 114.1 \text{ g mol}^{-1}}{(25.0 \text{ g} / 100.1 \text{ g mol}^{-1}) + (35.0 \text{ g} / 114.1 \text{ g mol}^{-1})} \text{ x } 352 \text{ torr}$$

$$= \frac{0.250}{0.250 + 0.307} \text{ x } 791 \text{ torr} + \frac{0.307}{0.250 + 0.307} \text{ x } 352 \text{ torr}$$

$= (0.449 \text{ x } 791 \text{ torr}) + (0.551 \text{ x } 352 \text{ torr}) =$ **549 torr**

11.76 60.0 g benzene x 1 mol /78.1 g = 0.768 mol benzene

40.0 g toluene x 1 mol /92.1 g = 0.434 mol benzene

$P_{soln} = X_A P^{\circ}_A + X_B P^{\circ}_B$ = [0.768 /(0.768 + 0.434) x 93.4 torr] +[0.434/(0.434 + 0.768) x 26.9 torr] = (0.639 x 93.4 torr) + (0.361 x 26.9 torr) = **69.4 torr**

11.77 $P_{soln.} = X_A P^\circ_A + X_B P^\circ_B$

$$137 \text{ torr} = \frac{400 \text{ g}/154 \text{ g mol}^{-1}}{(400 \text{ g}/154 \text{ g mol}^{-1}) + (43.3 \text{ g}/? \text{ g mol}^{-1})} \times 143 \text{ torr}$$

$$+ \frac{43.3 \text{ g}/? \text{ g mol}^{-1}}{(400 \text{ g}/154 \text{ g mol}^{-1}) + (43.3 \text{ g}/? \text{ g mol}^{-1})} \times 85 \text{ torr}$$

$$137 = \frac{(2.597)(143)}{2.597 + 43.3/?} + \frac{(43.3/?)(85)}{2.597 + 43.3/?}$$

$$2.597 + 43.3/? = \frac{371.4}{137} + \frac{3681/?}{137} \qquad 43.3/? - \frac{3681/?}{137} = 0.1139$$

$$5{,}932/? - 3{,}681/? = 15.604 \qquad ? = \mathbf{144 \text{ g/mol}}$$

11.78 (a) $511 \text{ torr} = X_{chloroform} \times 526 \text{ torr}$

$X_{chloroform} = 0.971$ $\qquad X_{unkn.} = 1 - 0.971 = \mathbf{0.029} = X_{solute}$

(b) $$X_{solute} = \frac{\text{moles solute}}{\text{moles solute} + \text{moles } CHCl_3} \qquad 0.029 = \frac{x}{x+1}$$

$0.029x + 0.029 = x$ $\qquad x = \mathbf{0.030 \text{ mol solute}}$

(c) $0.030 \text{ mol} = 8.3 \text{ g}/? \text{ M.W.}$ $\qquad$ M.W. = **277** or **280 (2 sign. figs.)**

11.79 $$X_{water} = \frac{100 \text{ g}/18.02 \text{ g mol}^{-1}}{(100 \text{ g}/18.02 \text{ g mol}^{-1}) + (150 \text{ g}/92.11 \text{ g mol}^{-1})} = 0.773$$

$91.1 \text{ torr} = 0.773 P^\circ_{water}$ $\qquad P^\circ_{water} = 118 \text{ torr}$

118 torr = **55°C** (From Table 9.1)

11.80 When a mixture of two liquids is boiled, the vapor is always richer in the more volatile component. Successive condensations and boilings produce fractions ever richer in the more volatile component.

11.81 Approximately three times.

11.82

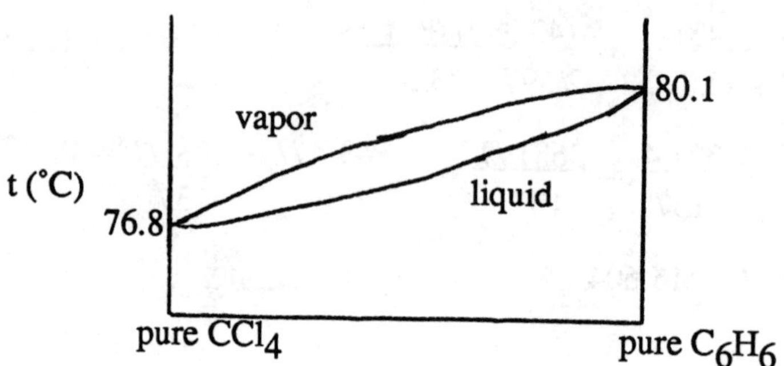

11.83

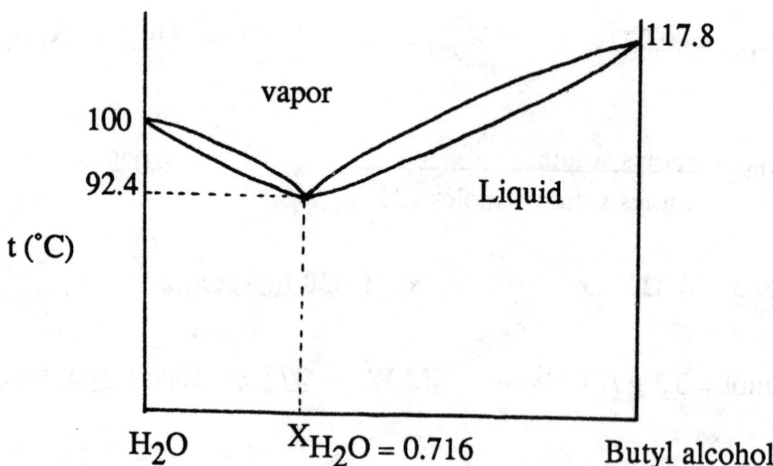

Positive deviation from identity

11.84 Colligative properties are properties that depend on the number of particles of solute in a solution instead of on their specific chemical nature.

11.85 In the presence of a solute the rate of freezing at a particular temperature is decreased because fewer solvent particles are in contact with the solid. The rate of melting, however, is the same since no solute is incorporated in the solid solvent. The temperature must be lowered to reestablish equilibrium where the solvent freezes faster from the solution and the solvent melts more slowly from the solid.

11.86 $\Delta T_b = K_b\,m$ $\quad$ $B.P._{soln.} - 100.0°C = (0.51°C\,m^{-1})\,\dfrac{(55.0\text{ g}/92.11\text{ g mol}^{-1})}{0.250\text{ kg } H_2O}$

$B.P._{soln.} - 100.0°C = (0.51)(2.388) = 1.22°C$ $\quad$ $B.P._{soln} =$ **101.2°C**

$\Delta T_f = K_f\,m = (1.86°C\,m^{-1})(2.388\text{ m}) = 4.44°C$

F.P. = 0.00°C - 4.44°C = **-4.44°C**

11.87 $\Delta T_f = K_f\,m$ $\quad$ $0.307°\text{ C} = (5.12°C\,m^{-1})\,\dfrac{(3.84\text{ g }/M.W.)}{0.500\text{ kg benzene}}$

MW = **128** Empirical formula calculated from % comp. = C_4H_2N

Therefore the molecular formula based upon calculated MW is: **$C_8H_4N_2$**

11.88 $\Delta T_f = K_f\,m$ $\quad$ $0.744°C = (1.86°C\,m^{-1})\,\dfrac{(16.9\text{ g }/M.W.)}{0.250\text{ kg } H_2O}$

0.1000 = 16.9 /M.W. $\quad$ M.W. = 169.0

moles C = 169 g x (57.2% /100) x (1 mol /12.01 g) = 8.05 mol

moles H = 169 g x (4.77% /100) x (1 mol /1.01 g) = 7.98 mol

moles O = 169 g x (38.1% /100) x (1 mol /16.0 g) = 4.02 mol

Emp. Form. = C_2H_2O Emp. F. W. = 42 Therefore, Mol. Form. = **$C_8H_8O_4$**

11.89 $\Delta T_f = K_f m$ $\qquad 0.750°\,C = (1.86°C\,m^{-1}) \dfrac{(X\,g/180.2\,g\,mol^{-1})}{0.150\,kg\,H_2O}$

X = **10.9 g** added

$\Delta T_b = K_b m = (0.51°C\,m^{-1}) \dfrac{(10.9\,g/180.2\,g\,mol^{-1})}{0.150\,kg} = 0.21°C$

B.P. = 100.00 + 0.21 = **100.21°C**

11.90 $\Delta T_f = K_f m$ $\qquad 2.47°C = (1.86°C\,m^{-1})\,(X\,m)$

$X\,m = 1.328\,m$, $\Delta T_b = K_b m$, $\Delta T_b = (0.51°C\,m^{-1})\,(1.328\,m)$

$\Delta T_b = 0.68°C$ $\qquad$ B.P. = 100.00 + 0.68 = **100.68°C**

11.91 0.075 = fraction dissociated, $\qquad$ 1.000 - 0.075 = fraction undissociated

Total = [(1.000 - 0.075) x 0.100 m] + [(2 x 0.075) x 0.100 m] = 0.1075 m

$\Delta T_f = (1.86°C\,m^{-1})\,(0.1075\,m) = 0.200°C$

F.P. = 0.000°C - 0.200°C = **-0.200°C**

11.92 If we select a volume of 1.00 L of each, we have: 1.000 $L_{ethyl.}$ x 1.113 g /mL x 1,000 mL /L x 1 mol /62.08 g = 17.93 mol ethylene glycol and 1.000 L H_2O x 1 g /mL x 1,000 mL /L x 1 kg /1,000 g = 1.000 kg water.

$\Delta T_f = K_f m$ $\qquad \Delta T_f = (1.86°C\,m^{-1})\,(17.93\,mol/1.00\,kg) = 33.3°C$

F.P. = 0.0°C - 33.3°C = **-33.3°C**

°F = (9/5)°C + 32.0 = [(9/5) (-33.3)] + 32.0 = **-28.0°F** This is the temperature at which the first crystals will form. At -34°C all the solution might not be solidified; therefore, this solution might give some protection to -34°C but its protection at that temperature would be minimal.

11.93 $\Delta T_f = K_f m$ $\qquad 0.500° C = (1.86°C\ m^{-1})\ X$

$X = 0.269\ m$ = effective molality

$0.269\ m = (0.25\ m - X\ m) + 2(X\ m)$

$X\ m = 0.019\ m,$ $\qquad$ % dissociation $= \frac{0.019}{0.25} \times 100 = \underline{7.6\ \%}$

11.94 In dialysis small ions, small molecules, and solvent are allowed to pass through a membrane, but in osmosis only solvent is allowed through the membrane.

11.95 A semipermeable membrane is a film that restricts the passage of solute through it.

11.96 Solutions that have the same osmotic pressure are called isotonic solutions. During intravenous feeding, the solute concentration must be carefully controlled to prevent excessive movement of fluid in to or out of the cells.

11.97 $\pi = MRT$

$$\pi = \frac{(5.0\ g / 342\ g\ mol^{-1})}{1\ L} (0.0821\ L\ atm\ mol^{-1}\ K^{-1})\ (298\ K)\ (760\ torr\ atm^{-1})$$

$\pi =$ **270 torr** (2 sign. figures)

11.98 $\pi = MRT$

$$3.74\ torr / 760\ torr\ atm^{-1} = \frac{(0.40\ g / M.W.)}{1L}(0.0821\ L\ atm\ mol^{-1}\ K^{-1})(300\ K)$$

M.W. = **2,000** (2 sign. figures)

11.99 $\Delta T_f = m K_f = 0.10\ m\ MgSO_4 \times \frac{2\ m\ ions}{1\ m\ salt} \times 1.86°C\ m^{-1} = 0.372°C$

F.P. = 0.00°C - 0.372°C = **-0.37°C** (if completely dissociated)

11.100 $\Delta T_f = m K_f = 0.10 \text{ m } CaCl_2 \times \frac{3 \text{ m ions}}{1 \text{ m salt}} \times 1.86°C\ m^{-1} = 0.558°C$

F.P. = 0.00°C - 0.558 = **-0.56°C** (if completely dissociated)

11.101 It suggests that there is less than one mole of particles in the solution for each mole expected to have been present in the solution.

11.102 $\pi = MRT = 2 \times 0.010 \text{ M} \times (0.0821 \text{ atm } M^{-1}\ °K^{-1})\ (298°K)\ (760 \text{ torr /atm})$

= **370 torr** (2 sign. figures)

11.103 $i = \frac{(\Delta T_f) \text{ measured}}{(\Delta T_f) \text{ calc. as non-electrolyte}} = \frac{-1.91}{-1.86} = \mathbf{1.03}$

11.104 From Problem 11.35: total m = 1.160 m. For a dilute solution m ≈ M. Therefore, we will use 1.160 M for this soln.

$\pi = 1.160 \text{ M} \times 0.0821 \text{ atm } M^{-1}\ °K^{-1} \times 298°K = 28.38 \text{ atm} = \mathbf{28.4\ atm}$

Greater than 28.4 atm

11.105 $\pi_{\text{sugar soln.}} = (0.1000 \text{ M})\ (0.0821 \text{ atm } M^{-1}\ °K)\ (298°K)\ (760 \text{ torr atm}^{-1})$

= 1,859.4 torr

$\pi_{\text{acetic acid, calc}} = (0.1000 \text{ M})(0.0821 \text{ atm } M^{-1}\ °K)(298°K)(760 \text{ torr atm}^{-1})$

= 1,859.4 torr

$\pi_{\text{acetic acid, measured}} = 1{,}859.4 + 24.9 = 1{,}884.3 \text{ torr}$

$$M = \frac{\pi}{RT} = \frac{1{,}884.3 \text{ torr}}{(0.0821 \text{ atm } M^{-1}\ °K)\ (298°K)\ (760 \text{ torr atm}^{-1})} = 0.1013 \text{ M}$$

0.1013 M = (0.1000 + X) M , X = 0.0013 M

fraction dissociated = 0.0013 /0.1000 = 0.013 **1.3% dissociated**

11.106 $\Delta T_f = m K_f$

$\Delta T_f = (0.10 \text{ m}) (1.86°\text{C m}^{-1}) = 0.19°\text{C (calculated)}$

$i = \frac{(\Delta T_f) \text{ measured}}{(\Delta T_f) \text{ calculated}}$ $\quad$ i = 1.21 (from Table 11.7)

$1.21 = \frac{(\Delta T_f) \text{ measured}}{0.19}$

$\Delta T_f = 0.23°\text{C}$

F.P. = 0.00 - 0.23 = **-0.23°C**

11.107 $MgSO_4$. The greater the degree of attraction between ions, the less it dissociates.

11.108 A nonelectrolyte that has formed a dimer or polymer might give an i factor less than one.

11.109 $Al_2(SO_4)_3$

11.110 KCl, i factor = **2**; $NiCl_2$, i factor = **3**; $Al_2(SO_4)_3$, i factor = **5**.

12 CHEMICAL THERMODYNAMICS

12.1 **Thermo** - heat, **dynamics** - movement or change

12.2 **System &Surroundings** - By **system** we mean that particular portion of the universe upon which we wish to focus our attention. Everything else we call the **surroundings.**

Isothermal change - change occurring at constant temperature.

Adiabatic change - a change that occurs without heat transfer between system and surroundings.

State function - a quantity whose value for a system in a particular state is independent of the system's prior history.

Heat capacity - heat needed to raise the temperature of a substance by 1°C.

Molar heat capacity - heat needed to raise the temperature of 1 mol of a substance by 1°C.

Specific heat - heat needed to raise the temperature of one gram of a substance by 1°C.

12.3 An equation that relates state variables (e.g., P, V, T).

12.4 Pressure - Volume and electrical.

12.5 A **spontaneous change** is one that will take place by itself, without outside aid.

12.6 **A reversible process** is one that can be made to reverse its direction by an infinitesimal change in pressure, temperature, or whatever opposes the change.

12.7 Isothermal: immerse the system in a vat of water kept at a constant temperature by a thermostat. Adiabatic: keep the system in an insulated container.

12.8 $\Delta E = q - w$

12.9 The ΔE is the difference between the heat that is added to the system as it passes from the initial to the final state and the work done by the system upon its surroundings. E represents all of the energies, KE + PE; whereas, ΔE represents $E_{final} - E_{initial}$. ΔE, therefore, is only dependent on the energy the molecules have finally minus what they had initially, regardless of the path.

12.10 A "perpetual motion machine" is a device that could run forever without a net consumption of energy. Such a machine is not possible because it would have to create energy.

12.11 Because of the very nature of E, which represents the KE as well as the PE. For instance, because there is no stationary reference point in the universe, we cannot measure absolute velocity; therefore, we cannot know KE.

12.12 **(a)** There would be no change in temperature. There are no attractive forces between the molecules in an ideal gas, so there would be no change in PE when the molecules move further apart.

(b) Since gases cool on expansion, the average kinetic energy of the molecules must decrease. Therefore, ΔE is positive, q is positive, w = 0. Heat would have to be supplied to keep the temperature of the system constant (isothermal).

12.13 Because during an isothermal expansion or compression there is no change in the KE or PE of the material. KE remains constant because T remains constant. PE is zero because in an ideal gas there are no intermolecular attractive forces.

12.14 It can't just disappear. It shows up as an increase in the heat of reaction.

12.15 $P\Delta V$ has the units Joules, when P is in pascals and ΔV is in m^3, which is in energy units rather than other units.

12.16 ΔE is the heat of reaction at constant volume, whereas ΔH is the heat of reaction at constant pressure. Most reactions that are of interest to us take place at constant P, not constant V.

12.17 First step: $\Delta V = V_2 - 10.0\text{ L}$

$$V_2 = 10.0\text{ L} \times \frac{15.0\text{ atm}}{7.50\text{ atm}} = 20.0\text{ L}$$

$$\Delta V = 20.0\text{ L} - 10.0\text{ L} = 10.0\text{ L}$$

$$w = P\Delta V = 7.50\text{ atm} \times (20.0\text{ L} - 10.0\text{ L}) = 75.0\text{ L atm}$$

$$\mathbf{\Delta T = 0,\ \Delta E_{system} = 0,\ \Delta E_{surroundings} = 0,\ q = w = 75.0\ L\ atm}$$

Second Step: $\Delta V = V_3 - 20.0\text{ L}$

$$V_3 = 20.0\text{ L} \times \frac{7.50\text{ atm}}{1.00\text{ atm}} = 150\text{ L}$$

$$\Delta V = 150\text{ L} - 20.0\text{ L} = 130\text{ L}$$

$$w = P\Delta V = 1.00\text{ atm} \times 130\text{ L} = 130\text{ L atm}$$

$$\mathbf{\Delta T = 0,\ \Delta E_{system} = 0,\ \Delta E_{surroundings} = 0,\ q = w = 130\ L\ atm}$$

12.18 $w = P\Delta V$ $V_2 = 50.0\ m^3 \times \frac{\underline{200\ kPa}}{100\ kPa} = 100\ m^3$

$w = 100\ kPa \times (100\ m^3 - 50.0\ m^3) = 5{,}000\ kPa\ m^3 = 5.0 \times 10^3\ kJ$

$w = q = \underline{\mathbf{5.0 \times 10^3\ kJ}}$

12.19 $w = 3.00\ atm\ (0.250\ L - 0.500\ L) = -0.750\ atm\ L$

$w = -0.750\ atm\ L \times \frac{24.2\ cal}{atm\ L} \times \frac{1\ kcal}{1{,}000\ cal} = \underline{\mathbf{-0.0182\ kcal}}$

$q = \underline{\mathbf{3.00\ kcal}}$

$\Delta E_{system} = q - w = 3.00\ kcal - (-0.0182\ kcal) = \underline{\mathbf{3.02\ kcal}}$

$\Delta E_{surr.} = \underline{\mathbf{-3.02\ kcal}}$

12.20 **(a)** $q = \underline{\mathbf{35\ J}}$, $w = \underline{\mathbf{-40\ J}}$, $\Delta E_{system} = q - w = 35\ J - (-40J) = \underline{\mathbf{75\ J}}$

(b) $q_{surr.} = \underline{\mathbf{-35\ J}}$, $w_{surr.} = \underline{\mathbf{40\ J}}$, $\Delta E_{surr.} = \underline{\mathbf{-75\ J}}$

12.21 A calorimeter is an apparatus for measuring quantities of heat energy absorbed or evolved during a chemical or physical change. It includes an insulated container filled with water surrounding a reaction vessel.

12.22 A heavy metal container (in which a reaction can be carried out) that is immersed in a large insulated container filled with water. Its purpose is to measure heats of reaction at constant volume.

12.23 **(a)** $q = \text{heat cap.} \times \Delta T = \Delta E$

$1{,}347\ J = \text{heat cap.} \times (26.135°C - 25.000°C)$, **heat cap.** $= \underline{\mathbf{1{,}187\ J\ °C^{-1}}}$

(b) heat cap. $= 1{,}187\ J\ °C^{-1} \times 1\ cal / 4.18\ J = \underline{\mathbf{284.0\ cal\ °C^{-1}}}$

12.24 $q = \text{heat cap.} \times \Delta T = \Delta E$

$14{,}300\ J = [1.78 \times 10^4\ J/°C] \times (T_f - 25.000)°C$

$T_f - 25.000°C = 0.803°C$

$T_f =$ **25.803°C**

12.25 $\Delta E = q_V$ because $P\Delta V = 0$.

$\Delta H = q_p$ because $\Delta H = (q - P\Delta V) + P\Delta V$

12.26 (a) $\Delta E = q = \text{heat cap.} \times \Delta T = 97.1 \times 10^3\ J\ °C^{-1}\ (27.282°C - 25.000°C)$

$=$ **2.22×10^5 J**

(b) $\Delta E = -2.22 \times 10^5\ J/0.100\ mol = -2.22 \times 10^6\ J\ mol^{-1}$

$=$ **-2.22×10^3 kJ mol^{-1}**

12.27 $\Delta H = -162\ kJ/0.500\ mol =$ **-324 kJ mol^{-1}**

12.28 $\Delta H = 4.18\ J\ g^{-1}\ °C^{-1} \times 350\ mL \times 1\ g\ mL^{-1} \times (30.00°C - 25.00°C)$

$= 7315$ J or 7.315 kJ for the reaction of $0.150\ L \times 1.00\ mol\ L^{-1}$ HCl

(HCl is the limiting reactant)

$\Delta H = 7.315\ kJ/0.150\ mol =$ **48.8 kJ/mol**

12.29 $\Delta E = q_v = (45.06\ kJ/°C)(1.413°C)(1/1.500\ g)(92.15\ g/mol)$

$\Delta E =$ **-3911 kJ/mol C_7H_8**

12.30 Reactions that involve only liquids and/or solids. ΔE and ΔH rarely differ very much, even when gases are reacted or produced.

12.31 $\Delta H = \Delta E + \Delta(PV)$ $\Delta(PV) = \Delta nRT$

$\Delta n = 3 - (1 + 5)$ $= (-3 \text{ mol})(8.3144 \text{ J mol}^{-1} \text{ K}^{-1})(300.3 \text{ K})$

$= -7.490 \text{ kJ}$

$\Delta H = -2.22 \times 10^3 \text{ kJ} + (-7.490 \text{ kJ}) =$ **-2230 kJ**

12.32 $\Delta H =$ **-15.6 kcal** $\Delta E = \Delta H - \Delta(PV)$

$\Delta(PV) = P\Delta V = 1.00$ atm [volume of 1 mol of $Ca(OH)_2$ - the volume of the sum of 1 mol of CaO and 1 mol of H_2O]

$P\Delta V = 1.00 \text{ atm } [(74.1 \text{ g mol}^{-1} \times 1 \text{ mol} \times 1 \text{ mL}/2.24 \text{ g}) - (56.08 \text{ g mol}^{-1} \times 1 \text{ mol} \times 1 \text{ mL}/3.25 \text{ g}) - (18.02 \text{ g mol}^{-1} \times 1 \text{ mol} \times 1 \text{ mL}/0.997 \text{ g})]$

$= 1 \text{ atm } (33.08 \text{ mL} - 17.26 \text{ mL} - 18.07 \text{ mL}) = -2.25 \text{ atm mL}$

$P\Delta V = -2.25 \text{ atm mL} \times (1\text{L}/1{,}000 \text{ mL}) \times (24.2 \text{ cal/L atm})$

$\times 1.000 \text{ kcal}/1{,}000 \text{ cal} = -5.45 \times 10^{-5} \text{ kcal}$

$\Delta E = \Delta H - P\Delta V = -15.6 \text{ kcal} - (-5.45 \times 10^{-5} \text{ kcal})$

= **-15.6 kcal**

The difference between ΔH and ΔE is very much less than the uncertainty of the larger value (ΔH). Therefore, for solids and liquids ΔH and ΔE are considered to be equal. The change in volume is insignificant; therefore, the change from ΔE to ΔH is insignificant.

12.33 H_2 (g) + 1/2 O_2 (g) —> H_2O (ℓ), Δn = -1.5 mol (for gaseous species)

$\Delta E_f°(H_2O) = \Delta H_f° - P\Delta V$ = (-286 kJ /mol) - Δn (RT)

= (-286 kJ /mol) - (-1.5 mol x 8.314 x 10^{-3} kJ mol^{-1} K^{-1} x 298 K) /mol H_2O

= -282 kJ /mol

-282 kJ mol^{-1}= calorimeter constant x 0.880°C x 1 /0.200 mol

calorimeter constant = -64.1 kJ $°C^{-1}$

ΔE = 64.1 kJ $°C^{-1}$ x 0.615°C x 1 /0.0100 mol = **-3940 kJ**

12.34 $\Delta E = \Delta H - w$

w = $P\Delta V = \Delta n(RT)$ = - 2 x 1.987 x 10^{-3} kcal mol^{-1} K^{-1}x 298 K

w = **-1.18 kcal /mol**

ΔH = q = **-214.3 kcal /mol**

ΔE = (-214.3 kcal /mol) - (-1.18 kcal /mol) = **-213.1 kcal /mol**

12.35 $\Delta E = \Delta H - w$ w = $P\Delta V = \Delta n(RT)$

w = 1 x 1.987 x 10^{-3} kcal mol^{-1} K^{-1} x 298 K = **0.592 kcal /mol**

ΔH = q = **10.5 kcal /mol**

ΔE = (10.5 kcal /mol) - (0.592 kcal /mol) = **9.9 kcal /mol**

12.36 $\Delta H°$ (reaction) = $\Delta H_f°$ (NO(g)) + $\Delta H_f°$ (O(g)) - $\Delta H_f°$ (NO_2(g))

= 90.4 kJ + 249 kJ - 34 kJ = 305.4 kJ

$\Delta E = \Delta H - (\Delta n)RT$ = 305.4 kJ - (1 mol)(8.314 x 10^{-3} kJ mol^{-1} K^{-1})(298 K)

= 303 kJ per mol of reaction

(continued)

(12.36 continued)

$$\nu = \Delta E / h = (303 \times 10^3 \text{ J mol}^{-1} / 6.6262 \times 10^{-34} \text{ J s}) \times \frac{1 \text{ mole}}{6.022 \times 10^{23} \text{ molecules}}$$

$$= 7.59 \times 10^{14} \text{ cycles /sec (per molecule)}$$

$$\lambda = \frac{c}{\nu} = (3.00 \times 10^8 \text{ m s}^{-1})(1 \text{ nm} / 10^{-9} \text{ m}) / 7.59 \times 10^{14} \text{ s}^{-1} = \underline{395 \text{ nm}}$$

12.37 Hess's law of heat summation states that the ΔH of an overall process is merely the sum of all of the enthalpy changes that take place along the way. Conditions of 25°C and one atmosphere pressure are taken to be the standard state of a substance.

12.38 No; only $\Delta H°$ for the second reaction should be labeled $\Delta H_f°$ because only in that reaction is SO_3 formed from its elements.

12.39 The second reaction (because the additional heat is released when gas is condensed to liquid).

12.40

Reaction	$\Delta H°$
(1) $7C(s) + 4H_2(g) \longrightarrow C_7H_8(\ell)$	?
(2) $7CO_2(g) + 4H_2O(\ell) \longrightarrow C_7H_8(\ell) + 9O_2(g)$ (reverse of the reaction in Problem 12.33)	3940 kJ
(3) $7C(s) + 7O_2(g) \longrightarrow 7CO_2$	$7 \times \Delta H_f° = -2758$ kJ
(4) $4H_2(g) + 2O_2(g) \longrightarrow 4H_2O(\ell)$	$4 \times \Delta H_f° = -1144$ kJ

Reactions (2)+(3)+(4)= reaction (1); therefore, 3940 kJ - 2758 kJ - 1144 kJ =?

$\Delta H_f°(C_7H_8(\ell)) = \underline{38 \text{ kJ}}$

12.41

Reaction	ΔH
(1) $2C(s) + 3H_2(g) + 1/2O_2(g) \longrightarrow C_2H_5OH(\ell)$	?
(2) $2CO_2(g) + 3H_3O(\ell) \longrightarrow C_2H_5OH(\ell) + 3O_2(g)$	1.37×10^3 kJ
(3) $2C(s) + 2O_2(g) \longrightarrow 2CO_2(g)$	2 (-394 kJ)
(4) $3H_2(g) + 3/2O_2(g) \longrightarrow 3H_2O(\ell)$	3 (-286 kJ)

Reaction (2) + (3) + (4) = Reaction 1 = -276 kJ

$\Delta H_f°$ (C_2H_5OH) = <u>-276 kJ /mol</u>

12.42

Reaction	ΔH
(1) $3C(s) + 4H_2(g) \longrightarrow C_3H_8(g)$	?
(2) $3CO_2(g) + 4H_2O(\ell) \longrightarrow C_3H_8(g) + 5O_2(g)$	2220 kJ
(3) $3C(s) + 3O_2(g) \longrightarrow 3CO_2(g)$	3 (-394 kJ)
(4) $4H_2(g) + 2O_2(g) \longrightarrow 4H_2O(\ell)$	4 (-286 kJ)

? =(1) = (2) + (3) + (4) = -106 kJ

$\Delta H_f°$ (C_3H_8) = <u>-106 kJ /mol</u>

12.43 ΔH° = (sum $\Delta H_f°$ products) - (sum $\Delta H_f°$ reactants)

(a) ΔH° = [(-1676) + 0] - [0 + (-822.2)] = **<u>-854 kJ</u>**

(b) ΔH° = [(-910.0 + 2(-242)] - [(+33) + 0] = **<u>-1427 kJ</u>**

(c) ΔH° = [-1433] - [(-635.5) + (-396)] = **<u>-402 kJ</u>**

(d) ΔH° = [(0) + (-242)] - (-155) + 0] = **<u>-87 kJ</u>**

(e) ΔH° = [-84.5] - [(+51.9) + 0] = **<u>-136 kJ</u>**

(continued)

(12.43 continued)

The method used in this problem was not, in a strict sense, Hess's Law. One can also construct a series of reactions involving formation of the compounds from the elements and their heats of formations so that the summation of each series will give the answer to each of the above questions.

12.44 ΔH° = (sum ΔH_f° products) - (sum ΔH_f° reactants)

(a) ΔH° = (+12.4) - [(+54.2) + (0)] = **-41.8 kcal**

(b) ΔH° = (-194.5) - [(-94.6) + (-68.3)] = **-31.6 kcal**

(c) ΔH° = (-306.0) - [(-221.0) + (2 x -22.1)] = **-40.8 kcal**

(d) ΔH° = [(-26.4) + (-57.8)] - [(-94.1) + (0)] = **9.9 kcal**

(e) ΔH° = [(10 x 0) + (3 x -94.1) + (4 x -57.8)] - [(10 x +19.5) + (1 x -24.8)] = **-684 kcal**

Each value is in kcal per equation expressed in mole quantities.

12.45

	Reaction	ΔH
(1)	$O_3 + Cl \longrightarrow O_2 + ClO$	-126 kJ
(2)	$ClO + O \longrightarrow Cl + O_2$	- 268 kJ
(3)	$O_3 + O \longrightarrow 2\,O_2$	? ΔH°

ΔH° = sum of Step 1 plus Step 2 = -126 kJ + (-268 kJ) = **-394 kJ**

12.46

Reaction	ΔH
(1) $2N_2(g) + 5O_2(g) \longrightarrow 2N_2O_5(g)$	?
(2) $2N_2(g) + 6O_2(g) + 2H_2(g) \longrightarrow 4HNO_3(\ell)$	4 (-41.6 kcal)
(3) $4HNO_3(\ell) \longrightarrow 2N_2O_5(g) + 2H_2O(\ell)$	- 2 (-18.3 kcal)
(4) $2H_2O(\ell) \longrightarrow 2H_2(g) + O_2(g)$	-1 (-136.6 kcal)

(2) + (3) + (4) = (1) ? = 4 (-41.6) + {-2(-18.3)} + {-1(-136.6)}

ΔH° = 6.8 kcal

12.47

Reaction	ΔH
(1) $FeO(s) + CO(g) \longrightarrow Fe(s) + CO_2(g)$	?
(2) $FeO(s) + 1/3\ CO_2(g) \longrightarrow 1/3\ Fe_3O_4(s) + 1/3\ CO(g)$	-1/3(+38 kJ)
(3) $1/3\ Fe_3O_4(s) + 1/6\ CO_2(g) \longrightarrow 1/2\ Fe_2O_3(s) + 1/6\ CO(g)$	- 1/6(-59kJ)
(4) $1/2Fe_2O_3(s) + 3/2CO(g) \longrightarrow Fe(s) + 3/2CO_2(g)$	1/2(-28 kJ)

(2)+(3)+(4) = (1) $\underline{\Delta H^\circ}$ = -1/3 (+38) + [-1/6(-59)] + [1/2(-28)] = **-17 kJ**

12.48 ΔH° = (sum ΔH_f° products) - (sum ΔH_f° reactants)

$FeO(s) + CO(g) \longrightarrow Fe(s) + CO_2(g)$ $\quad$ ΔH = -17kJ

ΔH° (reaction) = [ΔH_f° (Fe) + ΔH_f° (CO_2)] - [ΔH_f° (FeO) + ΔH_f° (CO)]

-17 kJ = [0 + (-394)] - [ΔH_f° (FeO) + (-110)]

ΔH_f° (FeO(s)) = **-267 kJ /mol** or -267kJ /mol x 1 kcal /4.184 kJ =

-63.6 kcal mol^{-1}

12.49

Reaction	ΔH
(1) $2C(s) + H_2(g) \longrightarrow C_2H_2(g)$	?
(2) $CaC_2 + 2H_2O \longrightarrow Ca(OH)_2 + C_2H_2$	-30.0 kcal
(3) $CaO + 3C \longrightarrow CaC_2 + CO$	+ 110.5 kcal
(4) $Ca(OH)_2 \longrightarrow CaO + H_2O$	-1(-15.6 kcal)
(5) $CO \longrightarrow C + 1/2\ O_2$	-1/2 (-52.8 kcal)
(6) $H_2 + 1/2\ O_2 \longrightarrow H_2O$	-1/2 (+136.6 kcal)

(2)+(3)+(4)+(5)+(6) =(1) Check it very carefully! If the reactions can be added to give the desired reaction, then the energies can be added to obtain ΔH for the desired reaction. ΔH = **54.2 kcal mol^{-1}** or **227 kJ mol^{-1}**

12.50 ΔH° (reaction) = (sum ΔH_f° products) - (sum ΔH_f° reactants)

ΔH° (per mol) = 1 (-2020 kJ)-[1(-1573 kJ)+(3/2)(-286 kJ)] = **-18.0 kJ mol^{-1}**

12.51 $2NO + O_2 \longrightarrow 2NO_2$ ΔH° (reaction) = [2 (+34)] - [2(+90.4) + (0)] = **-113 kJ**

$NO_2 \longrightarrow NO + O$ ΔH° (reaction) = [(+90.4) + (249)] - (34) = **305 kJ**

$O_2 + O \longrightarrow O_3$ ΔH° (reaction) = [+143] - [0 + (249)] = **-106 kJ**

12.52 $C_2H_5OH + 1/2\ O_2 \longrightarrow CH_3CHO + H_2O(\ell)$ [Liq. H_2O at Std. Temp.]

ΔH° (reaction) = [(-167) + (-286)] -[(-278) + 1/2 (O)] = **-175 kJ**

$CH_3CHO + 1/2\ O_2 \longrightarrow HC_2H_3O_2$

ΔH° (reaction) = [-487.0] - [(-167) + 1/2 (O)] = **-320 kJ**

$HC_2H_3O_2 + 2O_2 \longrightarrow 2CO_2 + 2H_2O(\ell)$

ΔH° (reaction) = [2(-394) + 2 (-286)] - [(-487.0) + 2(0)] = **-873 kJ**

Net equation: $C_2H_5OH + 3O_2 \longrightarrow 2CO_2 + 3H_2O$

ΔH° (reaction) = [2 (-394) + 3 (-286)] - [(-278) + 3(0)] = **-1368 kJ**

The answer could also have been obtained by adding ΔH's for the 3 steps.

12.53 $C_2H_6 + 7/2\ O_2 \longrightarrow 2CO_2 + 3H_2O(g)$

ΔH° (reaction as written, expressed in moles)

= [2(-94.1 kcal) + 3(-57.8 kcal)] - [1(-20.2 kcal) + 7/2(O)]

= -341.4 kcal mol^{-1}

45.0 g x 1 mol /30.08 g = 1.496 mol

341.4 kcal mol^{-1} x 1.496 mol x 10^3 cal /kcal = **5.11×10^5 cal**

12.54 (1 g /4 kcal) x (2,000 kcal) = **500 g**

12.55 $H_2O(\ell) \longrightarrow H_2O(g)$ ΔH° (reaction) = ΔH° (vap.)

$\Delta H_{vap} = (-242) - (-286) = +44 \text{ kJ mol}^{-1}$

(44 kJ mol^{-1}) (10 g H_2O) (1 mol /18.02 g) = **24 kJ**

12.56 $C_8H_{18}(\ell) + 25/2\ O_2(g) \longrightarrow 8CO_2(g) + 9H_2O(\ell)$

$\Delta H = [8 \times (-394) + 9 \times (-286)] - [1 \times (-208.4) + 25/2 \times (0)]$

$= -5517.6 \text{ kJ mol}^{-1}$ or $-5518 \text{ kJ mol}^{-1}$

moles of C_8H_{18} = ?

$$3.79 \text{ L } C_8H_{18} \times \frac{1{,}000 \text{ mL}}{\text{L}} \times \frac{0.703 \text{ g}}{\text{mL}} \times \frac{1 \text{ mol}}{114.3 \text{ g}} = 23.3 \text{ mol}$$

23.3 mol x 5518 kJ mol^{-1} = **1.29×10^5 kJ liberated**

$H_2 + 1/2\ O_2 \longrightarrow H_2O(\ell)$ $\Delta H = -286 \text{ kJ mol}^{-1}$ (H_2 or H_2O)

1.29×10^5 kJ /286 kJ mol^{-1} (H_2) = 4.51×10^2 mol H_2

4.51×10^2 mol H_2 x 2.02 g mol^{-1} = **911 g H_2**

PV = nRT (170 atm) V = (4.51×10^2) (0.0821) (298) V = **64.9 L**

64.9 L /3.79 L gal^{-1} = **17.1 gal of H_2**

H_2 would require 17 times as much space for storage as would octane.

12.57 $H_2O(\ell) \longrightarrow H_2O(g)$ $\Delta H = (-242) - (-286) = 44 \text{ kJ mol}^{-1}$

[5,900 kJ /(44. kJ mol^{-1})] x 18.02 g /mol = **2,400 g H_2O**

12.58 Total energy x 60% = 5,900 kJ Total energy = 9,830 kJ

[9,830 kJ /(2820 kJ mol^{-1})] x 180.2 g mol^{-1} = **630 g**

12.59 Energy required to warm 250 mL or 250 grams of water from 20°C to 100°C:

250 g x 1.00 cal g^{-1} $°C^{-1}$ x 80°C x 1 kcal /10^3 cal = 20 kcal

Energy required to convert the water to steam at 100°C:

250 g x 9.71 kcal mol^{-1} x 1 mol /18.02 g = 135 kcal

Total amount of energy required = 20 kcal + 135 kcal = 155 kcal

Energy available from, $CH_4 + O_2 \longrightarrow CO_2 + 2H_2O(g)$ is:

ΔH = [1 (-94.1 + 2 (-57.8)] - [1 (-17.9)] = -191.8 kcal mol^{-1}

Amount required to warm and convert the water to steam: 155 kcal /(191.8 kcal mol^{-1}) = 0.808 moles. **Volume** occupied by the 0.808 mol of gas:

PV = nRT (1 atm) (V) = (0.808 mol) (0.0821) (298 k) V = **19.8 L**

12.60

Reaction	ΔH
(1) $NaCl(s) \longrightarrow Na^+(g) + Cl^-(g)$	?
(2) ionization $Na(g) \longrightarrow Na^+(g) + e^-$	494.1 kJ
(3) electron affinity $Cl(g) + e^- \longrightarrow Cl^-(g)$	-351 kJ
(4) form. of gas. atoms $Na(s) \longrightarrow Na(g)$	108 kJ
(5) form. of gas. atoms $1/2\ Cl_2(g) \longrightarrow Cl(g)$	121 kJ
(6) $-\Delta H_f$ (NaCl) $NaCl(s) \longrightarrow Na(s) + 1/2\ Cl_2(g)$	-1 (-413) kJ
(2) +(3) +(4) + (5) + (6) = (1) =	**785 kJ mol^{-1}**

12.61 Atomization energy is the sum of all the bond energies in the molecule.

$H_2O(g) \longrightarrow 2H(g) + O(g)$ $\Delta H = \Delta H_{atomization}$

12.62 The calculated ΔH_f° is usually from average bond energies.

12.63 $H_2(g) + 2C(s) \longrightarrow C_2H_2(g)$

$H_2(g) \longrightarrow 2H(g)$ ΔH_1
$2C(s) \longrightarrow 2C(g)$ ΔH_2
$2H(g) + 2C(g) \longrightarrow C_2H_4(g)$ ΔH_3

$\Delta H_f^\circ = \Delta H_1 + \Delta H_2 + \Delta H_3$

$= 2\,(218\ kJ) + 2\,(715\ kJ) + [2\,(-415\ kJ) + (-833\ kJ)]$ = **203 kJ /mol**

12.64 $3H_2(g) + 6C(s) \longrightarrow C_6H_6(g)$

$3H_2(g) \longrightarrow 6\ H(g)$ ΔH_1
$6C(s) \longrightarrow 6C(g)$ ΔH_2
$6H + 6C \longrightarrow C_6H_6(g)$ ΔH_3
ΔH_3 = formation of 3 (C=C), 3(C-C), and 6(H-C) bonds.

$\Delta H_f^\circ = \Delta H_1 + \Delta H_2 + \Delta H_3$

$= 6(218\ kJ) + 6(715\ kJ) + [3(-607\ kJ) + 3(-348\ kJ) + 6(-415\ kJ)]$ = **243 kJ /mol**

Resonance energy = 243 kJ -82.8 kJ = **160 kJ** Compounds that have resonance structures are much more stable than predicted by non-resonance structures.

12.65 $3C(s) + 3H_2(g) \longrightarrow CH_3CHCH_2$ $\Delta H_f^\circ = ?$

$3H_2(g) \longrightarrow 6H(g)$ ΔH_1
$3C(s) \longrightarrow 3C(g)$ ΔH_2
$6H(g) + 3C(g) \longrightarrow CH_3CHCH_2$ ΔH_3

ΔH_3 = formation of 6 (C-H), 1 (C-C), and 1 (C=C) bond.

$\Delta H_f^\circ = \Delta H_1 + \Delta H_2 + \Delta H_3$

$= 6(218\ kJ) + 3(715\ kJ) + [6(-415\ kJ) + 1(-348\ kJ) + 1(-607\ kJ)]$ = **8 kJ /mol**

12.66 $3C(s) + 4H_2(g) \longrightarrow CH_3CH_2CH_3$ $\Delta H_f^\circ = ?$

$4H_2(g) \longrightarrow 8H(g)$ ΔH_1 (Table 12.2)
$3C(s) \longrightarrow 3C(g)$ ΔH_2 (Table 12.2)
$8H(g) + 3C(g) \longrightarrow CH_3CH_2CH_3$ ΔH_3

ΔH_3 = formation of 8 (C-H) and 2 (C-C) bonds. (Table 12.3)

$\Delta H_f^\circ = \Delta H_1 + \Delta H_2 + \Delta H_3$

$= 8\,(218\text{ kJ}) + 3\,(715\text{ kJ}) + [8\,(-415\text{ kJ}) + 2\,(-348\text{ kJ})] =$ **$-\underline{127\text{ kJ mol}^{-1}}$**

Value in Table 12.1 = -104 kJ mol^{-1}

12.67 Many spontaneous reactions give off energy. However, there are many instances where energy is absorbed during a spontaneous reaction. Both the change in energy (heat content) and in degree of randomness (entropy) must be considered when discussing the likelihood of a reaction being spontaneous.

12.68 In any process there is a natural tendency or drive toward increased randomness because a highly random distribution of particles represents a condition of higher statistical probability than an ordered one. A system's entropy is proportional to its statistical probability.

12.69 ΔS must be positive and the product of $T\Delta S$ must be greater than ΔH.

12.70 energy /temperature; e.g., J /K or cal /K

12.71 (a), (b), and (d)

12.72 (a) negative (b) positive (c) positive (d) negative (e) negative (f) negative

12.73 (a) positive (b) negative (c) positive (d) positive (e) negative

12.74 (a) ≈ zero (b) positive (c) negative (d) positive (e) negative

12.75 During any spontaneous change, the entropy of the universe increases.

12.76 ΔG must be negative which means ΔH must be negative and ΔS must be positive.

12.77 Because of the amount of energy required to reverse the spontaneous distribution of the pollutants.

12.78 $\Delta G = \Delta H - T\Delta S$ (Note the temperature in the equation).

12.79 Between 10,000 and 20,000 atm; no.

12.80 The third law of thermodynamics states that the entropy of any pure crystalline substance at absolute zero is equal to zero.

12.81 There is perfect order (zero randomness) in a pure crystalline substance at absolute zero. A mixture would have a positive entropy at 0 K because of the random distribution of particles throughout the mixture.

12.82 For both a and b, $\Delta n = -0.5$ moles. Both reactions involve only gases, etc. Therefore, one can not predict the extent of change of ΔS in either reaction without performing some calculations.

(a) $\Delta S = (1 \text{ mol} \times 61.3 \text{ cal mol}^{-1} \text{ K}^{-1}) - (1/2 \text{ mol} \times 49.0 \text{ cal mol}^{-1} \text{ K}^{-1})$

$- (1 \text{ mol} \times 59.3 \text{ cal mol}^{-1} \text{ K}^{-1}) = \underline{\mathbf{-22.5 \text{ cal K}^{-1}}}$

(b) $\Delta S = (1 \text{ mol} \times 51.06 \text{ cal mol}^{-1} \text{ K}^{-1}) - (1 \text{ mol} \times 47.30 \text{ cal mol}^{-1} \text{ K}^{-1})$

$- (0.5 \text{ mol} \times 49.0 \text{ cal mol}^{-1} \text{ K}^{-1}) = \underline{\mathbf{-20.7 \text{ cal K}^{-1}}}$

Therefore, reaction (a) is accompanied by the greater entropy change.

12.83 (a) $C(s)$ (graphite) + $2Cl_2(g) \longrightarrow CCl_4(\ell)$

$\Delta S = (214.4\ J\ K^{-1}) - [5.69\ J\ K^{-1} + (2 \times 223.0)\ J\ K^{-1}]$

$\Delta S_f^\circ = \underline{\mathbf{-237.3\ J\ K^{-1}}}$

(b) $Mg(s) + O_2(g) + H_2(g) \longrightarrow Mg(OH)_2(s)$

$\Delta S = (63.1\ J\ K^{-1}) - [32.5\ kJ\ K^{-1} + 205.0\ kJ\ K^{-1} + 130.6\ kJ\ K^{-1}]$

$\Delta S_f^\circ = \underline{\mathbf{-305.0\ J\ K^{-1}}}$

(c) $Pb(s) + S(s) + 2O_2(g) \longrightarrow PbSO_4$ $\Delta S_f^\circ = \underline{\mathbf{-358\ J\ K^{-1}}}$

(d) $Na(s) + 1/2\ H_2(g) + C(s) + 3/2\ O_2(g) \longrightarrow NaHCO_3(s)$

$\Delta S_f^\circ = \underline{\mathbf{-274\ J\ K^{-1}}}$

(e) $1/2\ N_2(g) + 3/2\ H_2(g) \longrightarrow NH_3(g)$ $\Delta S_f^\circ = \underline{\mathbf{-99.2\ J\ K^{-1}}}$

12.84 $\Delta S^\circ = \frac{\Delta H^\circ - \Delta G^\circ}{T^\circ}$ or $\frac{\Delta H^\circ - \Delta G^\circ}{273\ K} = \Delta S^\circ$ in joules per degree

(a) $\Delta S^\circ = \frac{-854\ kJ - (-836\ kJ)}{273\ K} \times (1000\ J/kJ) = \underline{\mathbf{-65.9\ J\ K^{-1}}}$

(b) $\Delta S^\circ = \frac{-1427\ kJ - (-1364\ kJ)}{273\ K} \times (1000\ J/kJ) = \underline{\mathbf{-231\ J\ K^{-1}}}$

(c) $\Delta S^\circ = \frac{-402\ kJ - (-346\ kJ)}{273\ K} \times (1000\ J/kJ) = \underline{\mathbf{-205\ J\ K^{-1}}}$

(d) $\Delta S^\circ = \frac{-87\ kJ - (-101\ kJ)}{273\ K} \times (1000\ J/kJ) = \underline{\mathbf{+51\ J\ K^{-1}}}$

(e) $\Delta S^\circ = \frac{-136\ kJ - (-101\ kJ)}{273\ K} \times (1000\ J/kJ) = \underline{\mathbf{-128\ J\ K^{-1}}}$

12.85 Because entropy values have a reference point and enthalpy values do not.

12.86 ΔG° = sum of ΔG_f's of products - sum of ΔG_f's of reactants

(a) $2Al(s) + Fe_2O_3(s) \longrightarrow Al_2O_3(s) + 2Fe(s)$

$$\Delta G^\circ = [1 \text{ mol} \times \frac{(-1577 \text{ kJ})}{\text{mol}} + 2 \text{ mol } (0)] - [2 \text{ mol } (0) + 1 \text{ mol} \times \frac{(-741.0 \text{ kJ})}{\text{mol}}]$$

$$= -1577 \text{ kJ} + 741.0 \text{ kJ} = \underline{\mathbf{-836 \text{ kJ}}}$$

(b) $SiH_4\ (g) + 2O_2(g) \longrightarrow SiO_2(s) + 2H_2O(g)$

$$\Delta G^\circ = [1\ (-856 \text{ kJ}) + 2\ (-228 \text{ kJ})] - [1\ (+52.3) + 2\ (0)] = \underline{\mathbf{-1364 \text{ kJ}}}$$

(c) $CaO(s) + SO_3(g) \longrightarrow CaSO_4(s)$ $\quad \Delta G^\circ = \underline{\mathbf{-346 \text{ kJ}}}$

(d) $CuO(s) + H_2(g) \longrightarrow Cu(s) + H_2O(g)$ $\quad \Delta G^\circ = \underline{\mathbf{-101 \text{ kJ}}}$

(e) $C_2H_4(g) + H_2(g) \longrightarrow C_2H_6(g)$ $\quad \Delta G^\circ = \underline{\mathbf{-101 \text{ kJ}}}$

12.87 $\Delta G^\circ = [6 \times \Delta G_f^\circ(CO_2) + 6 \times \Delta G_f^\circ(H_2O)] - [1 \times \Delta G_f^\circ(\text{glu}) + 6 \times \Delta G_f^\circ(O_2)]$

$$= [6 \times (-395 \text{ kJ}) + 6 \times (-237 \text{ kJ})] - [1 \times (-910.2 \text{ kJ}) + 6 \times (0)] = \underline{\mathbf{-2880 \text{ kJ}}}$$

12.88 (a) $Pb(s) + PbO_2(s) + 2H_2SO_4(\ell) \longrightarrow 2PbSO_4(s) + 2H_2O(\ell)$

$$\Delta G^\circ = [2(-811.3 \text{ kJ}) + 2(-237 \text{ kJ})] - [1(0) + 1(-219 \text{ kJ}) + 2(-689.9 \text{ kJ}) = \underline{\mathbf{-498 \text{ kJ}}}$$

(b) $CH_4(g) + 4Cl_2(g) \longrightarrow CCl_4\ (\ell) + 4HCl(g)$

$$\Delta G^\circ = [1(-65.3) + 4(-95.4)] - [1(-50.6) + 4(0)] = \underline{\mathbf{-396 \text{ kJ}}}$$

(c) $10N_2O(g) + C_3H_8(g) \longrightarrow 10N_2(g) + 3CO_2(g) + 4H_2O(g)$

$$\Delta G^\circ = [10(0) + 3(-395) + 4(-228)] - [10(104) + 1(-23)] = \underline{\mathbf{-3.11 \times 10^3 \text{ kJ}}}$$

12.89 Advantage - maximum work is obtained.

Disadvantage - the change takes forever to occur.

12.90 Maximum amount of useful work at Standard Temperature (25°C) and Standard Pressure (1 atm) = $\Delta G°$.

For $C_3H_8(g) + 5O_2(g) \longrightarrow 3CO_2(g) + 4H_2O(g)$

$\Delta G° = [3 \times \Delta G_f°(CO_2) + 4 \times \Delta G_f°(H_2O)] - [1 \times \Delta G_f°(C_3H_8) + 5 \times \Delta G_f°(O_2)]$

$= [3 \times (-395\ kJ) + 4 \times (-228\ kJ)] - [1 \times (-23) + 5 \times (0)] =$ **-2074 kJ**

The maximum useful work is the work that would be available under ideal, reversible conditions. A real process can only approach these ideal conditions. Therefore, we always get less than this maximum amount of work in any real process that uses the above reaction.

12.91 See Figure 12.13 (c) The position of the equilibrium favors products.

12.92 Refer to Figure 12.12. Once a minimum free energy has been achieved by the system, the composition of the system can no longer change, since such a change involves going "uphill" on the free energy curve. At the minimum, both reactants and products possess the same free energy and, therefore, $\Delta G = 0$.

12.93 At constant pressure, $\Delta S = \frac{q_{rev}}{T} = \frac{\Delta H}{T}$

$\Delta S_{vap} = 9720\ cal\ mol^{-1} / 373\ K =$ **$26.1\ cal\ mol^{-1}\ K^{-1}$**

$\Delta S_{fus} = 1440\ cal\ mol^{-1} / 273\ K =$ **$5.27\ cal\ mol^{-1}\ K^{-1}$**

Both should be positive since both processes increase the randomness of the system. One would expect vaporization to have a greater increase in randomness than does melting and the above values verify that expectation.

12.94 $Br_2(\ell) \rightleftharpoons Br_2(g)$ $\Delta H = +30.9 - (0) = +30.9$ kJ

$\Delta S = 245.4 - 152.2 = +93.2$ J K^{-1} $T\Delta S = \Delta H$ (constant pressure)

$T = \Delta H / \Delta S = 30{,}900$ J $/93.2$ J K^{-1} = <u>332 K</u> or 332-273 = <u>59°C</u>

12.95 $\Delta G°$ determines the position of equilibrium between reactants and products. Whether we start with pure reactants or pure products, some reaction will occur (accompanied by a free energy decrease) until equilibrium is reached.

12.96 The sign and magnitude of $\Delta G°$ tells us where the reaction is going, in the sense that it relates to the position of equilibrium.

12.97 There is none.

12.98 Whether the reaction is spontaneous or not, and how fast the reaction occurs.

12.99 See Figure 12.13.

12.100 (a) $1/2\ N_2(g) + O_2(g) \longrightarrow NO_2(g)$ $\Delta G° =$ <u>+51.9 kJ</u> (No)

(b) $2HNO_3(\ell) + Ag(s) \longrightarrow AgNO_3(s) + NO_2(g) + H_2O(\ell)$

$\Delta G° =$ <u>-57 kJ</u> (Yes)

(c) $2NH_3(g) + 3O_2(g) \longrightarrow NO_2(g) + NO(g) + 3H_2O(g)$

$\Delta G° =$ <u>-511 kJ</u> (Yes)

(d) $CuO(s) + NO(g) \longrightarrow NO_2(g) + Cu(s)$ $\Delta G° =$ <u>+92 kJ</u> (No)

(e) $NO(g) + 1/2\ O_2(g) \longrightarrow NO_2(g)$ $\Delta G° =$ <u>-34 kJ</u> (Yes)

(f) $9H_2O(g) + 7N_2O(g) \longrightarrow 6NH_3(g) + 8NO_2(g)$

$\Delta G° =$ <u>1637 kJ /8 mol NO_2</u> (No)

13 CHEMICAL KINETICS: THE STUDY OF THE RATES OF REACTION

13.1 (a) the nature of reactants and products (b) concentration of reacting species

(c) temperature (d) influence of outside agents (catalysts)

13.2 The smaller the particle size (i.e., the larger the surface area), the faster the reaction.

13.3 Methods must be fast, accurate and not interfere with the normal course of the reaction system.

13.4 Some common examples:

(a) combustion of gas (rapid)

(b) explosion of gasoline vapor in auto engine (very fast)

(c) digestion of food (moderately slow)

(d) iron rusting (slow)

(e) decay of leaves (slow)

13.5 It is simply because some substances react rapidly with one another because of their chemical composition, while others react more slowly. In other words, even under conditions of equal concentrations and temperature, different chemical reactions progress at different rates.

13.6 (a) magnesium (b) zinc in 1.00 M HCl (c) powdered zinc

(d) iron nail at 40°C

13.7 Reaction rate = the speed at which reactants are consumed or the products are formed. It is the ratio of the change in concentration to the change in time.

units = mol liter^{-1} s^{-1}

13.8 (a) $\text{Rate} = \frac{-\Delta[H_2]}{\Delta t} = \frac{-2\Delta[O_2]}{\Delta t} = \frac{\Delta[H_2O]}{\Delta t}$

(b) $\text{Rate} = \frac{-\Delta[NOCl]}{\Delta t} = \frac{\Delta[NO]}{\Delta t} = \frac{2\Delta[Cl_2]}{\Delta t}$

(c) $\text{Rate} = \frac{-\Delta[NO]}{\Delta t} = \frac{-\Delta[O_3]}{\Delta t} = \frac{\Delta[NO_2]}{\Delta t} = \frac{\Delta[O_2]}{\Delta t}$

(d) $\text{Rate} = \frac{-\Delta[H_2O_2]}{\Delta t} = \frac{-\Delta[H_2]}{\Delta t} = 1/2\ \frac{\Delta[H_2O]}{\Delta t}$

(a) H_2 disappears twice as fast as O_2, and at the same rate that H_2O appears.

(b) NOCl disappears at the same rate as NO appears and twice as fast as Cl_2 appears.

(c) As NO and O_3 disappear, NO_2 and O_2 appear at the same rate.

(d) H_2O_2 and H_2 disappear half as fast as H_2O appears.

13.9 $CH_4 + 2O_2 \longrightarrow CO_2 + 2H_2O$

rate (for CO_2) = $\frac{0.16 \text{ mol } CH_4}{L \times s} \times \frac{1 \text{ mol } CO_2}{1 \text{ mol } CH_4} = \mathbf{0.16\ mol\ CO_2\ L^{-1}\ s^{-1}}$

rate (for H_2O) = $\frac{0.16 \text{ mol } CH_4}{L \times s} \times \frac{2 \text{ mol } H_2O}{1 \text{ mol } CH_4} = \mathbf{0.32\ mol\ H_2O\ L^{-1} s^{-1}}$

13.10 $4NH_3 + 3O_2 \longrightarrow 2N_2 + 6H_2O$

(a) rate for water being formed =

$$\frac{0.68 \text{ mol } N_2}{L \times s} \times \frac{6 \text{ mol } H_2O}{2 \text{ mol } N_2} = \underline{\mathbf{2.0 \text{ mol } H_2O \ L^{-1} \ s^{-1}}}$$

(b) rate for NH_3 reacting =

$$\frac{-0.68 \text{ mol } N_2}{L \times s} \times \frac{4 \text{ mol } NH_3}{2 \text{ mol } N_2} = \underline{\mathbf{-1.4 \text{ mol } NH_3 \ L^{-1} s^{-1}}}$$

(c) rate for O_2 being consumed =

$$\frac{-0.68 \text{ mol } N_2}{L \times s} \times \frac{3 \text{ mol } O_2}{2 \text{ mol } N_2} = \underline{\mathbf{-1.0 \text{ mol } O_2 \ L^{-1} s^{-1}}}$$

13.11 $2A \longrightarrow 4B + C$

From your graph, slope of the disappearance of A at 25 min =

$\frac{\Delta[A]}{\Delta t} \approx$ $\underline{\mathbf{-9.6 \times 10^{-3} \text{ mol A } L^{-1} \text{ min}^{-1}}}$ (or $- 1.6 \times 10^{-4}$ mol L^{-1} sec^{-1})

The slope for the rate of formation B at 25 min =

$\frac{\Delta[B]}{\Delta t} \approx$ $\underline{\mathbf{1.9 \times 10^{-2} \text{ mol B } L^{-1} \text{ min}^{-1}}}$ (or 3.2×10^{-4} mol L^{-1} sec^{-1})

The slope of the disappearance of A at 40 min =

$\frac{\Delta[A]}{\Delta t} \approx$ $\underline{\mathbf{-6.4 \times 10^{-3} \text{ mol A } L^{-1} \text{ min}^{-1}}}$ (or $- 1.1 \times 10^{-4}$ mol L^{-1} sec^{-1})

The slope of the formation of B at 40 min =

$\frac{\Delta[B]}{\Delta t} \approx$ $\underline{\mathbf{1.3 \times 10^{-2} \text{ mol B } L^{-1} \text{ min}^{-1}}}$ (or 2.2×10^{-4} mol L^{-1} sec^{-1})

(continued)

(13.11 continued)

Rate of B = -2 x rate of A

$\frac{\Delta[C]}{\Delta t}$ at 25 min ≈ **5.0 x 10^{-3} mol C mol^{-1} L^{-1}**

$\frac{\Delta[C]}{\Delta t}$ at 40 min ≈ **3.2 x 10^{-3} mol C L^{-1} min^{-1}**

13.12 An experimentally determined relationship between the rate of reaction and the concentrations of the reactants. Temperature and catalysts affect the value of k.

13.13 The sum of exponents on the concentrations in the rate law.

13.14 (a) s^{-1} (b) liter mol^{-1} s^{-1} (c) $liter^2$ mol^{-2} s^{-1}

13.15 As the concentration of CO varies, the rate at which it is removed remains constant (no concentration dependence); therefore, it appears to be a zero-order reaction.

13.16 (a) First order with respect to A and B, overall order is two.

(b) Second order with respect to E, overall order is two.

(c) Second order with respect to G and H, overall order is four.

13.17 (a) liter /mol s (b) liter /mol s (c) $liter^3$ /mol^3 s

13.18 (a) rate doubled (b) rate increased fourfold

(c) rate increased eightfold (d) rate increased sixteenfold

(e) rate increased by a factor of $2^{1/2}$ = 1.44

(f) rate decreased by a factor of 4 (2^{-2} = 1/4)

13.19 -1; i.e., Rate = $k[A]^{-1}$

13.20 rate = 1.63×10^{-1} L $mol^{-1}s^{-1}$ x [ICl] [H_2]

(a) rate = (1.63×10^{-1} L $mol^{-1}s^{-1}$) (0.25 mol L^{-1}) (0.25 mol L^{-1})

= **$\underline{1.0 \times 10^{-2}\ mol\ L^{-1}\ s^{-1}}$**

(b) rate = **$\underline{2.0 \times 10^{-2}\ mol\ L^{-1}\ s^{-1}}$** (c) rate = **$\underline{4.1 \times 10^{-2}\ mol\ L^{-1}\ s^{-1}}$**

13.21 (a) **rate** = (2.35×10^{-6} L^2 mol^{-2} s^{-1}) (1.00 mol L^{-1})^2 (1.00 mol L^{-1})

= **$\underline{2.35 \times 10^{-6}\ mol\ L^{-1}\ s^{-1}}$**

(b) **rate** = (2.35×10^{-6} L^2 mol^{-2} s^{-1}) (0.250 mol L^{-1})^2 (1.30 mol L^{-1})

= **$\underline{1.91 \times 10^{-7}\ mol\ L^{-1}\ s^{-1}}$**

13.22

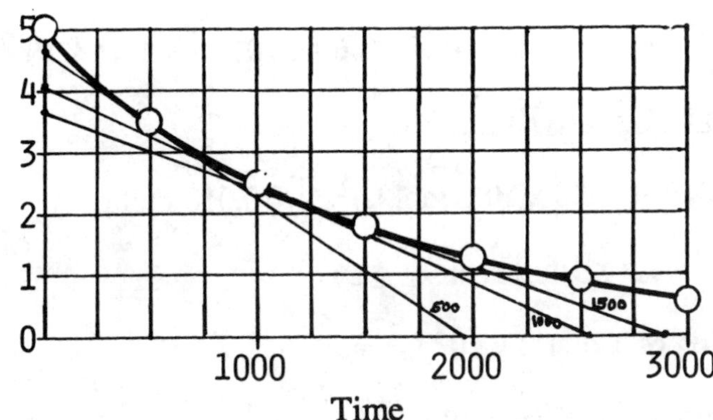

rate = k N_2O_5 $k_{500} = \frac{2.5 \times 10^{-3}}{3.52} = 7.1 \times 10^{-4}$

$k_{1000} = \frac{1.6 \times 10^{-3}}{2.48} = 6.5 \times 10^{-4}$

$k_{1500} = \frac{1.3 \times 10^{-3}}{1.75} = 7.4 \times 10^{-4}$ **$k_{average} = 7.0 \times 10^{-4}$**

13.23 (a) rate = $k[NO_2]^x [O_3]^y$ In the first and second experiments, the initial NO_2 concentration is constant, the initial concentration of O_3 is doubled, and the rate is doubled. Therefore, the value of y must be 1. In the second and third experiments, the initial concentration of O_3 is constant, the initial concentration of NO_2 is halved, and the rate is halved. Therefore, the value of x must be 1. **Rate = $\underline{k[NO_2][O_3]}$**

(b) **k** = Rate /$[NO_2][O_3]$ = 0.022 mol L^{-1} s^{-1}/[(5.0 x 10^{-5} mol L^{-1}) (1.0 x 10^{-5} mol L^{-1})] = **$\underline{4.4 \times 10^{7}\ L\ mol^{-1}\ s^{-1}}$**

13.24 (a) Rate = $k[A]^x[B]^y$ From experiments 1 and 2, x = 1

From experiments 3 and 4, y = 2. That is $(3.60 \times 10^{-3})^2 = 1.44 \times 10^{-2}$

$\underline{\text{Rate of formation of C} = k[A][B]^2}$

(b) **k** = Rate /$[A][B]^2$ = 1.20 x 10^{-3} mol $L^{-1}s^{-1}$/[(0.010 mol L^{-1}) $(0.010\ mol\ L^{-1})^2$] = **$\underline{1.2 \times 10^{3}\ L^{2}\ mol^{-2}\ s^{-1}}$**

(c) Rate of formation of C = 1.2 x 10^3 L^2 mol^{-2} s^{-1} x

$(0.020\ mol\ L^{-1})\ (0.060\ mol\ L^{-1})^2 = 8.6 \times 10^{-2}\ mol\ L^{-1}\ s^{-1}$

$$\frac{8.6 \times 10^{-2}\ mol}{L \times s} \times \frac{2\ mol\ D}{mol\ C} = \underline{\mathbf{1.7 \times 10^{-1}\ mol\ D\ L^{-1}\ s^{-1}}}$$

13.25 (a) Rate = $k[NOCl]^x$ When the concentration was doubled, the rate changed by a factor of 1.44 x 10^{-8} /3.60 x 10^{-9} or 4.00. Therefore, x must be 2.

Rate = $k[NOCl]^2$

(continued)

(13.25 continued)

(b) k = Rate /$[NOCl]^2$ = 3.60×10^{-9} mol L^{-1} s^{-1} /$(0.30 \text{ mol } L^{-1})^2$

= **4.0×10^{-8} L mol^{-1} s^{-1}**

(c) $(0.45 / 0.30)^2$ = **2.2 times faster**

13.26 **(a)** Rate = $k[NO]^x[Cl_2]^y$

From experiments 1 and 2, one can see that when [NO] is held constant while the $[Cl_2]$ is doubled, the rate also doubles. Therefore, y = 1. From experiments 1 and 3, one can see that when the $[Cl_2]$ is held constant while the [NO] is doubled, the rate quadruples. Therefore, x = 2.

Rate = $k[NO]^2[Cl_2]$

(b) k = rate /$[NO]^2[Cl_2]$ = 2.53×10^{-6} mol L^{-1} s^{-1}

/ $(0.10 \text{ mol } L^{-1})^2$ $(0.10 \text{ mol } L^{-1})$ = **2.5×10^{-3} L^2 mol^{-2} s^{-1}**

13.27 A graph of the data in Exercise 13.11 shows that a plot of log[A] versus time is a curved line while a plot of 1/[A] against time gives a straight line. Therefore, the reaction is **second order.**

k = 2.5×10^{-2} L $mol^{-1}$$min^{-1}$

13.28 The time required for the concentration of a given reactant to be decreasd by a factor of 2.

13.29 It is unaffected by the initial concentration.

13.30 See Figure 13.3.

13.31 **(a)** $\ln \frac{[A]_o}{[A]_t} = kt$

$$\ln \frac{(4.50 \times 10^{-3})}{[A]_t} = (1.46 \times 10^{-1}\ s^{-1})\ (20.0\ s)$$

$$\ln \frac{(4.50 \times 10^{-3})}{[A]_t} = 2.92$$

$$\frac{(4.50 \times 10^{-3})}{[A]_t} = 18.54$$

$[A]_t$ **= 2.43 x 10^{-4} mol /L**

(b) $t_{1/2} = \frac{0.693}{k} = \frac{0.693}{1.46 \times 10^{-1}\ s^{-1}} =$ **4.75 s**

(c) $(4.50 \times 10^{-3}\ M)\ (1/2)^3 = 4.50 \times 10^{-3}\ M \times 1/8 =$ **5.62 x 10^{-4} M**

13.32 $t_{1/2} = \frac{1}{k[B]_o}$

$2.11\ min = \frac{1}{k(0.10\ M)}$ $\quad$ $k = 1/(0.10\ M)\ (2.11\ min)$

$k = 4.74\ M^{-1}\ min^{-1}$

$t_{1/2} = \frac{1}{(4.74\ M^{-1} min^{-1})\ (0.010\ M)} =$ **21 min**

13.33 (See 13.32) $k = 4.74\ M^{-1}\ min^{-1} \times \frac{M}{mol\ L^{-1}} \times \frac{min}{60\ s}$

= **7.90 x 10^{-2} L mol^{-1} s^{-1}**

13.34 **(a)** $t_{1/2} = 0.693/k = 0.693 / 3.2 \times 10^{-2}\ s^{-1} = \underline{21\ s}$

(b) $\ln \dfrac{[A]_0}{[A]_t} = kt$

$\ln \dfrac{[A]_0}{(0.010\ M)} = (3.2 \times 10^{-2}\ s^{-1})(60\ s) = 1.92$

$\dfrac{[A]_0}{0.010\ M} = 6.8$

$[A]_0 = 6.8 \times 10^{-2}$ M or **0.068 M**

13.35 The rate of a reaction is proportional to the number of collisions per second between reacting molecules. As the number of molecules is increased (increased in concentration), the number of collisions is increased by the same factor.

13.36 An overall chemical reaction represents the net chemical change. This does not mean that all the reactants come together simultaneously. To predict the rate law, a reaction mechanism must be known.

13.37 A reaction mechanism is a series of elementary processes that lead to the formation of the products.

13.38 A one-step mechanism would involve the simultaneous collision of six molecules, five of which would have to be O_2. This is very improbable.

13.39 **(a)** Rate = $k[NO][Br_2]$

(b) $2NO + Br_2 \longrightarrow 2NOBr$ Rate = $k[NO]^2[Br_2]$

(c) Step 2 must be rate determining (i.e., the slow step)

(continued)

(13.39 continued)

(d) This is a termolecular collision, which is very unlikely for a fairly rapid reaction.

(e) No. A mechanism is only theory, and more information can support it or prove it wrong, but the actual path can never be known with complete certainty.

13.40 The rate law is Rate = $k[NO_2]^2$. CO does not appear in the rate-determining step (slow step), and, therefore, does not affect the rate.

13.41 $(CH_3)_3CBr \longrightarrow (CH_3)_3C^+ + Br^-$ slow

$(CH_3)_3C^+ + OH^- \longrightarrow (CH_3)_3COH$ fast

for which Rate = $k[(CH_3)_3CBr]$

13.42 (a) $2A + B \longrightarrow C + 2D$ (b) Rate = $k[A]^2$

(c) Rate = $k[A]^2[B]$

13.43 $NO_2 + O_3 \longrightarrow NO_3 + O_2$ slow

$NO_3 + NO_2 \longrightarrow N_2O_5$ fast

13.44 The observed rate of reaction is much smaller (approx. 5×10^{12}) than what is expected if all the collisions were effective. A minimum amount of energy is required to cause a reaction to occur, and the molecules must collide with the proper orientation.

13.45 When two molecules collide, the collision can occur so that products are obtained that are the same as the reactants, or no chemical change occurs at all. Only proper orientation produces effective collisions.

13.46 $Cl{-}N(=O){-}O + Cl \longrightarrow [Cl{-}N(=O){-}O\cdots Cl] \longrightarrow Cl{-}N(=O){-}O + Cl$

---> <---   <--- --->

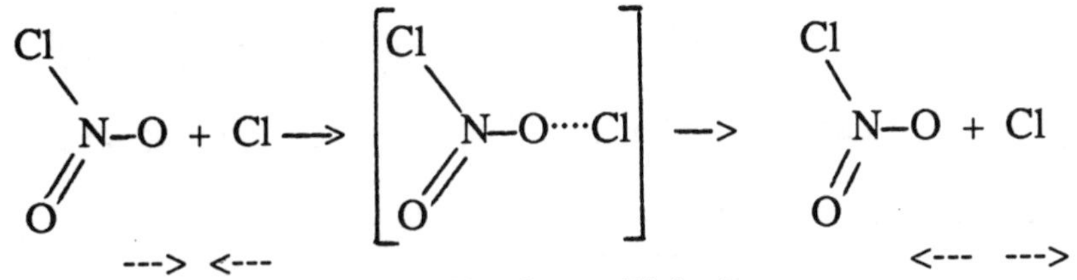

(not an effective collision)

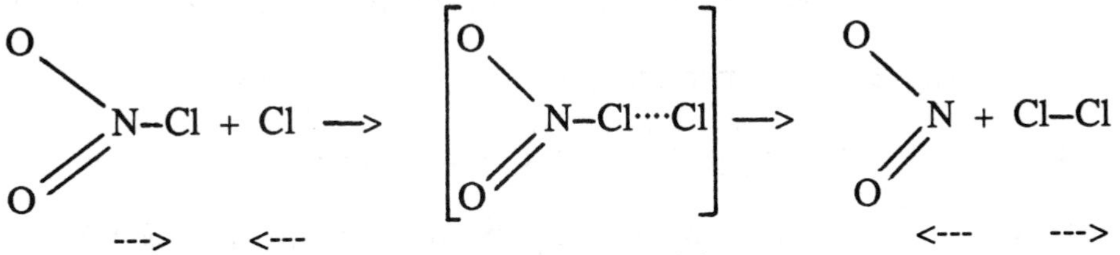

$O{-}N(=O){-}Cl + Cl \longrightarrow [O{-}N(=O){-}Cl\cdots Cl] \longrightarrow O{-}N(=O) + Cl{-}Cl$

---> <---   <--- --->

(an effective collision)

13.47 $NO + O_2 \rightleftharpoons NO_3$ fast

$NO_3 + NO \longrightarrow 2NO_2$ slow

13.48

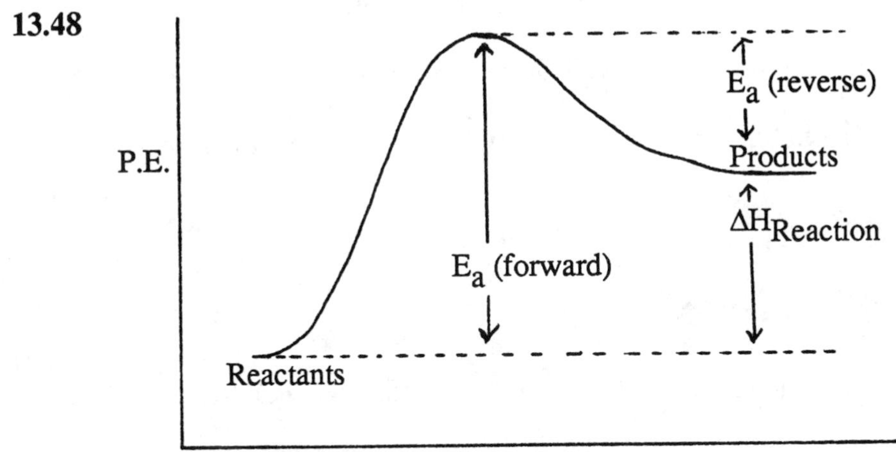

13.49 The activated complex is the intermediate species that is highly unstable, transient and very reactive. The activated complex exists in a transition state between products and reactants. The transition state is on the hump (high potential energy) of the potential energy curve.

13.50 The **activation energy** represents the energy required to bring the reactants to the point where they can react to form products. It is the minimum energy that must be available in a collision.

13.51 Activation energy is the minimum energy required for reaction. As T is increased, more molecules have greater kinetic energy, i.e., a larger fraction of molecules have the minimum energy required for reaction.

13.52 Reactions, including biochemical ones, slow down at low temperatures primarily because a smaller fraction of molecules possesses the required activation energy.

13.53 $\ln (k_1/k_2) = \frac{Ea}{R} (1/T_2 - 1/T_1)$

$$\ln (0.163 / 0.348) = \frac{Ea}{8.314 \text{ J mol}^{-1}\text{K}^{-1}} \left[\frac{1}{513 \text{ K}} - \frac{1}{503 \text{ K}}\right]$$

$$-0.7585 = (Ea / 8.314 \text{ J mol}^{-1}) (0.001949 - 0.001988)$$

$$\frac{0.7585 \times 8.314 \text{ J mol}^{-1}}{3.90 \times 10^{-5}} = Ea = 1.62 \times 10^{5} \text{ J mol}^{-1} = \underline{162 \text{ kJ/mol}}$$

$$k = Ae^{-Ea/RT}$$

$$A = k / e^{-Ea/RT} = ke^{Ea/RT}$$

$$A = 0.163 \text{ L mol}^{-1} \text{ s}^{-1} \times e^{1.627 \times 10^{5} \text{ J mol}^{-1} / (8.314 \text{ J mol}^{-1} \text{ K}^{-1}) (503 \text{ K})}$$

$$= 0.163 \text{ L mol}^{-1} \text{ s}^{-1} e^{38.91} = 0.163 \text{ L mol}^{-1} \text{ s}^{-1} \times 7.88 \times 10^{16}$$

$$A = \underline{1.28 \times 10^{16} \text{ L mol}^{-1} \text{ s}^{-1}}$$

13.54 (See Problem 13.53)

$$\ln(k_1/k_2) = \frac{Ea}{R}(1/T_2 - 1/T_1)$$

$$\ln(1.32 \times 10^{-2}\ /1.64) = (Ea\ /8.314\ J\ mol^{-1}K^{-1})\ (1\ /548\ K - 1\ /473\ K)$$

$$-4.822 = (Ea\ /8.314\ J\ mol^{-1}\ K^{-1})\ (0.001825 - 0.002114)$$

$$Ea = (-4.822)\ (8.314\ J\ mol)\ /(-0.000289)$$

$$\mathbf{Ea} = 1.387 \times 10^5\ J\ mol^{-1} = \underline{\mathbf{139\ kJ\ mol^{-1}}}$$

$$k = Ae^{-Ea/RT} \qquad A = k\ /e^{-Ea/RT} = ke^{Ea/RT}$$

$$A = (1.32 \times 10^{-2}\ L\ mol^{-1}\ s^{-1})\ e^{1.39 \times 10^5\ J\ mol^{-1}/(8.314\ J\ mol^{-1}\ K^{-1})(473\ K)}$$

$$A = (1.32 \times 10^{-2}\ L\ mol^{-1}\ s^{-1})\ (e^{35.346}) = \underline{2.96 \times 10^{13}\ L\ mol^{-1}\ s^{-1}}$$

13.55 $\ln(k_1/k_2) = \frac{Ea}{R}(1/T_2 - 1/T_1)$

$$\ln(1.57 \times 10^{-3}\ L\ mol^{-1}\ s^{-1}/k_2) = \frac{182 \times 10^3\ J\ mol^{-1}}{8.314\ J\ mol^{-1}\ K}\ (1/873\ K - 1/973\ K)$$

$$\ln(1.57 \times 10^{-3}\ L\ mol^{-1}\ s^{-1}/k_2) = 2.577$$

$$\frac{1.57 \times 10^{-3}\ L\ mol^{-1}\ s^{-1}}{k_2} = e^{2.577} = 13.16$$

$$\mathbf{k_2} = \frac{1.57 \times 10^{-3}\ L\ mol^{-1}\ s^{-1}}{13.16} = \underline{\mathbf{1.19 \times 10^{-4}\ L\ mol^{-1}\ s^{-1}}}$$

13.56 $\ln (k_1/k_2) = \frac{Ea}{R}(1/T_2 - 1/T_1)$

$$\ln (1.32 \times 10^{-2}\ L\ mol^{-1}\ s^{-1}/k_2) = \frac{33.1 \times 10^3\ cal\ mol^{-1}}{1.987\ cal\ mol^{-1}\ K^{-1}}(1/573\ K - 1/473\ K)$$

$$\ln (1.32 \times 10^{-2}\ L\ mol^{-1}\ s^{-1}/k_2) = -6.146$$

$$\frac{1.32 \times 10^{-2}\ L\ mol^{-1}\ s^{-1}}{k_2} = e^{-6.146} = 0.00214$$

$k_2 =$ **$\underline{6.16\ L\ mol^{-1}\ s^{-1}}$**

13.57 $\ln (k_1/k_2) = \frac{Ea}{R}(1/T_2 - 1/T_1)$ $\qquad k_1/k_2 = 1/4$

$$\ln (1/4) = \frac{Ea}{8.314\ J\ mol^{-1}\ K^{-1}}(1/373\ K - 1/303\ K)$$

Ea $= 1.86 \times 10^4\ J\ mol^{-1} =$ **$\underline{18.6\ kJ\ mol^{-1}}$**

13.58 $\ln (k_1/k_2) = \frac{Ea}{R}(1/T_2 - 1/T_1)$

$$\ln (3.2 \times 10^{-2} / 9.3 \times 10^{-2}) = \frac{Ea}{8.314\ J\ mol^{-1}\ K^{-1}}(1/848\ K - 1/823\ K)$$

$$\frac{(-1.0669)\ (8.314\ J\ mol^{-1})}{(0.001179 - 0.001215)} = Ea = 2.48 \times 10^5\ J\ mol^{-1} = \mathbf{\underline{248\ kJ\ mol^{-1}}}$$

13.59 Recall the equation: $\ln k = \ln A - Ea/RT$ and its rearranged form

$$-\ln k = -\ln A + \frac{Ea}{R}\left(\frac{1}{T}\right)$$

If one plots $-\ln k$ vs. $1/T$, the slope will be equal to Ea/R. Don't forget to use degrees Kelvin! The value of Ea was determined to be **$\underline{1.6 \times 10^2\ kJ}$** by this method.

13.60 (See Problem 13.59)

$$-\ln k = -\ln A + \frac{Ea}{R}\left(\frac{1}{T}\right)$$ k is proportional to 1/time, therefore:

$$-\ln (1/t) = -\ln A + \frac{Ea}{R}\left(\frac{1}{T}\right)$$

Plot $-\ln (1/t)$ vs. $1/T$ (T = degrees Kelvin)

$$\text{Slope} = \frac{Ea}{R}$$ **Ea = <u>64 kJ mol⁻¹</u>**

Estimated by extrapolation, when $1/T = 1/288 = 3.47 \times 10^{-3}$, $-\ln 1/t = -2.64$.

Therefore, it was estimated that **time = ~<u>14 min.</u>**

13.61 $$\ln (k_1/k_2) = \frac{Ea}{R}(1/T_2 - 1/T_1)$$

T_1 = boiling point of water at 760 torr = 100°C

T_2 = boiling point of water at 355 torr = 80°C (See Table 9.1)

k is proportional to 1/time

$$\ln [(1/t_1 / 1/t_2)] = \frac{418 \times 10^3 \text{ J mol}^{-1}}{8.314 \text{ J mol}^{-1} \text{ K}^{-1}} (1/353 \text{ K} - 1/ 373 \text{ K})$$

$$\ln (t_2 /3.0 \text{ min}) = 7.64$$

$t_2 = 6.2 \times 10^3$ min or over **<u>100 hours</u>**

13.62 A homogeneous catalyst is in the same phase as the reactants while a heterogeneous catalyst is in a different phase (e.g., a catalytic surface in contact with reacting gases).

13.63 (a) A **heterogenous catalyst** is a substance that provides a low energy pathway (Ea) to products, but is not in the same phase as the reactants. These catalysts appear to adsorb reactant molecules and certain bonds within reactants are weakened or broken.

(b) An **inhibitor** interferes with the effectiveness of a catalyst by interfering with adsorption.

13.64 The catalyst lowers the activation energy by giving the reactants a different pathway (mechanism) through a chemical reaction. This path has a lower Ea, thereby increasing the number of effective collisions.

13.65 (a) no effect (b) no effect

(c) lowers activation energy by changing the nature of the transition state.

13.66 Free radicals are atoms or groups of atoms that possess unpaired electrons. They are formed either thermally or by absorption of photons of appropriate frequencies.

13.67 Recall $E = \frac{hc}{\lambda}$ $h = 6.63 \times 10^{-34}$ J s, $c = 3.00 \times 10^{8}$ m s^{-1}, 1nm = 10^{-9} m

$$\lambda = \frac{hc}{E} = \frac{(6.63 \times 10^{-34}\ \text{J s})(3.00 \times 10^{8}\ \text{m s}^{-1})(10^{9}\ \text{nm m}^{-1})}{348{,}000\ \text{J mol}^{-1} \times (1\ \text{mol}/6.022 \times 10^{23}\ \text{molecules})} = \mathbf{344\ nm}$$

13.68 Free radicals are dangerous in living organisms because they are reactive.

13.69 In chain reactions a single reactive intermediate is produced (radical) which produces many product molecules before termination. Therefore, products are produced at a rate faster than the initiation step alone.

13.70 (a) initiation step 1 (b) propagation steps 3, 4, 5, 6 (c) termination step 2

14 CHEMICAL EQUILIBRIUM

14.1 Products are constantly changing to reactants and reactants are constantly changing to products but the overall effect is no apparent change - equilibrium.

14.2 (a) $\frac{[NO]^2}{[N_2][O_2]}$ (b) $\frac{[NO_2]^2}{[NO]^2[O_2]}$ (c) $\frac{[H_2S]^2}{[H_2]^2[S_2]}$ (d) $\frac{[NO_2]^4[O_2]}{[N_2O_5]^2}$

(e) $\frac{[POCl_3]^{10}}{[P_4O_{10}][PCl_5]^6}$

14.3 (a) $\frac{p^2_{NO}}{p_{N_2}\,p_{O_2}}$ (b) $\frac{p^2_{NO_2}}{p^2_{NO}\,p_{O_2}}$ (c) $\frac{p^2_{H_2S}}{p^2_{H_2}\,p_{S_2}}$ (d) $\frac{p^4_{NO_2}\,p_{O_2}}{p^2_{N_2O_5}}$

(e) $\frac{p^{10}_{POCl_3}}{p_{P_4O_{10}}\,p^6_{PCl_5}}$

14.4 (a) $K_p = \frac{p_{CH_3OH}}{p_{CO}\,p^2_{H_2}}$, $K_c = \frac{[CH_3OH]}{[CO][H_2]^2}$

(b) $K_p = \frac{p_{CO_2}\,p_{H_2}}{p_{CO}\,p_{H_2O}}$, $K_c = \frac{[CO_2]]H_2]}{[CO][H_2O]}$

(c) $K_p = \frac{p_{PCl_5}}{p_{PCl_3}\,p_{Cl_2}}$, $K_c = \frac{[PCl_5]}{[PCl_3][Cl_2]}$

(14.4 continued)

(d) $K_p = \dfrac{p_{N2}\, p^4_{H2O}}{p^2_{NO2}\, p^4_{H2}}$, $K_c = \dfrac{[N_2][H_2O]^4}{[NO_2]^2[H_2]^4}$

(e) $K_p = \dfrac{p^2_{H2O}\, p^2_{SO2}}{p^2_{H2S}\, p^3_{O2}}$, $K_c = \dfrac{[H_2O]^2[SO_2]^2}{[H_2S]^2[O_2]^3}$

14.5 (a) $\dfrac{[HCl]^2}{[H_2][Cl_2]}$ (b) $\dfrac{[HCl]}{[H_2]^{1/2}[Cl_2]^{1/2}}$ K_b would be the square root of K_a.

14.6 By convention. This simplifies tabulation of equilibrium constants by removing ambiguity.

14.7 Exp. 1 $K_c = (0.23)\ (0.055)\ /0.0023 = 5.5$

Exp. 2 $K_c = (0.15)\ (0.37)\ /0.010 = 5.6$

Exp. 3 $K_c = (0.99)\ (0.47)\ /0.085 = 5.5$

Exp. 4 $K_c = (3.66)\ (1.50)\ /1.00 = 5.5$

For all of these, K_c (average) = **5.5** (This is within experimental precision)

14.8 By looking at the size of the equilibrium constant, you can determine whether the reaction favors the forward or reverse reaction. If the number is greater than one, the reaction will tend to proceed far toward completion. If, however, the K is less than one, only small amounts of products will be present at equilibrium.

14.9 From the magnitude of K we can say that the tendency to proceed toward completion increases in the order (b) < (c) < (d) < (a).

14.10 ΔG° would equal **zero**

14.11 In Section 14.3 it is stated that for gases, the equilibrium constant calculated from $\Delta G°$ is K_p.

14.12 Eq. 12.11 $\Delta G = \Delta H - T\Delta S$ or $\Delta G° = \Delta H° - T\Delta S°$

Eq. 14.5 $\Delta G° = -2.303\ RT \log K_P$

$\Delta H° - T\Delta S° = -2.303\ RT \log K_P$

$$\log K_P = \frac{T\Delta S° - \Delta H°}{2.303\ RT} = \frac{T\Delta S°}{2.303\ RT} - \frac{\Delta H°}{2.303\ RT}$$

$$\log K_P = \frac{\Delta S°}{2.303\ R} - \frac{\Delta H°}{2.303\ R} \times \frac{1}{T}$$

(This is in the form y = b + mx, where log K_p corresponds to y and 1/T corresponds to x.)

Slope = m = **$-\Delta H° / 2.303\ R$** y intercept = **$\Delta S° / 2.303\ R$**

14.13 $\Delta G = -RT \ln K_P$ or $\Delta G° = -R(298\ K) \ln K_P$

$\Delta G°$ = sum of $\Delta G_f°$ products - sum of $\Delta G_f°$ reactants

(From Table 12.5) $\Delta G°$ = [2 mol (-273 kJ /mol) + 1 (0)] - [2 mol (-95.4 kJ /mol) + 1 (0)] = -355 kJ

-355×10^3 J (per mol) = $-(8.314\ J\ mol^{-1}\ K^{-1})(298\ K) \ln K_P$

K_P = **1.82×10^{62}**

14.14 $\Delta G° = -R\ (298\ K)\ \ln K_P$

$\Delta G°$ = sum of $\Delta G_f°$ products - sum of $\Delta G_f°$ reactants

$\Delta G° = [1\ (86.8\ kJ\ /mol) + 1\ (-370\ kJ\ /mol)] - [1\ (-300\ kJ\ /mol) +$
$1\ (+51.9\ kJ\ /mol)] = -35.1\ kJ$

$-35.1 \times 10^3\ J\ (per\ mol) = -(8.3144\ J\ mol^{-1}K^{-1})\ (298\ K)\ \ln K_P$

$14.17 = \ln K_P \qquad K_P =$ **$\underline{1.4 \times 10^6}$**

14.15 **(a)** $\Delta G° = [1(-184.9\ kcal\ /mol) + 6(-54.6\ kcal\ /mol)] - [1(-531.0\ kcal\ /mol)]$

$=$ **$\underline{18.5\ kcal}$**

(b) $\Delta G° = -RT \ln K_P$

$18.5 \times 10^3\ cal\ (per\ mol) = -(1.987\ cal\ mol^{-1}\ K^{-1})\ (298K)\ \ln K_P$

$-31.24 = \ln K_P \qquad$ **$K_P = \underline{2.71 \times 10^{-14}}$**

14.16 $\Delta G = -RT \ln K_P$

$-3.22 \times 10^3\ cal\ (per\ mol) = -(1.987\ cal\ mol^{-1}\ K^{-1})\ (700\ K)\ \ln K_P$

$2.315 = \ln K_P \qquad$ **$K_P = \underline{10.1}$**

14.17 $395°C = 668\ K \qquad \Delta G = -RT \ln K_P \qquad K_P = 4.56 \times 10^{-2}$

$\Delta G = -(8.314\ J\ mol^{-1}\ K^{-1})\ (668\ K)\ \ln (4.56 \times 10^{-2})$

$\Delta G = 1.71 \times 10^4\ J =$ **$\underline{17.1\ kJ}$**

14.18 $527°C = 800\ K \qquad \Delta G = -RT \ln K_P$

$\Delta G = -(8.314\ J\ mol^{-1}\ K^{-1})\ (800\ K)\ \ln 5.10$

$\Delta G = -1.08 \times 10^4\ J =$ **$\underline{-10.8\ kJ}$**

14.19 $\Delta H^\circ = [0 + 0] - [2\text{ mol}(-92.5\text{ kJ /mol})] = +\ 185\text{ kJ}$

$\Delta S^\circ = [1(130.6\text{ J mol}^{-1}\text{ K}^{-1}) + 1(223.0\text{ J mol}^{-1}\text{ K}^{-1})] - [2(186.7\text{ J mol}^{-1}\text{ K}^{-1})]$

$= -\ 19.80\text{ J K}^{-1}$

$\Delta G = \Delta H - T\Delta S = 185{,}000\text{ J} - (773\text{ K})(-19.80\text{ J K}^{-1})$

$= \mathbf{2.00 \times 10^5\ J} = 2.0 \times 10^2\text{ kJ}$

$\Delta G = -RT \ln K_P$

$2.00 \times 10^5\text{ J} = -(8.314\text{ J mol}^{-1}\text{ K}^{-1})(773\text{ K}) \ln K_P$

$-31.1 = \ln K_P$

$\mathbf{K_P = \underline{3.11 \times 10^{-14}}}$

14.20 $\Delta H^\circ = [1(-84.5\text{ kJ mol}^{-1})] - [1(51.9\text{ kJ mol}^{-1}) + 1(0)] = -136.4\text{ kJ}$

$\Delta S^\circ = [1(230\text{ J mol}^{-1}\text{ K}^{-1})] - [1(220\text{ J mol}^{-1}\text{ K}^{-1}) + 1(130.6\text{ J mol}^{-1}\text{ K}^{-1})]$

$= -120.6\text{ J K}^{-1}$

$\Delta G = -RT \ln K_P = \Delta H - T\Delta S$

$\Delta H = T\Delta S - RT \ln K_P = T(\Delta S - R \ln K_P)$

$$\frac{\Delta H}{\Delta S - R \ln K_P} = T$$

$$\frac{-136.4 \times 10^3\text{ J}}{(-120.6\text{ J K}^{-1}) - (8.314\text{ J mol}^{-1}\text{ K}^{-1})(\ln 1)} = T$$

$$T = \frac{136.4 \times 10^3\text{ K}}{120.6 + 0} = \underline{\mathbf{1.13 \times 10^3\ K}} \text{ or } 860^\circ\text{C}$$

14.21 Eq 14.4 is $\Delta G = \Delta G^\circ + RT \ln Q$

$$Q = \frac{3. \times 10^{-6} \text{ atm}}{(2 \times 10^{-3} \text{ atm})\,(1. \times 10^{-2})^2} = 15$$

$$\Delta G = (-3.22 \times 10^3 \text{ cal}) + (1.987 \text{ cal mol}^{-1} \text{ K}^{-1})\,(700 \text{ K})\,(\ln 15)$$

$$= 547 \text{ cal}$$

$\Delta G = +$; therefore, the system is **not at equilibrium.** The value of RT ln Q must decrease if ΔG is to be zero and if the system is to attain equilibrium. The value of RT ln Q will decrease if the **reaction proceeds spontaneously to the left.**

14.22 14.2 (a) and 14.4 (b), only

14.23 $K_P = K_c\,(RT)^{\Delta n}$ $\quad\quad$ $\Delta n = \Delta$ moles of gases $= 0$

$$\mathbf{K_P} = (4.05)\,[(0.0821 \text{ L atm mol}^{-1} \text{ K}^{-1})\,(773 \text{ K})]^0 = \underline{\mathbf{4.05}}$$

14.24 $K_P = K_c\,(RT)^{\Delta n}$

$$K_P = (5.67 \text{ mol}^2/\text{L}^2)\,[(0.0821 \text{ L atm mol}^{-1} \text{ K}^{-1})\,(1773 \text{ K})]^2$$

$$\mathbf{K_P} = (5.67)\,(2.119 \times 10^4) \text{ atm}^2 = \underline{\mathbf{1.20 \times 10^5 \text{ atm}^2}}$$

14.25 $K_P = K_c\,(RT)^{\Delta n}$

$$(6.5 \times 10^{-2} \text{ atm}^{-1}) = K_c\,[(0.0821 \text{ L atm mol}^{-1} \text{ K}^{-1})\,(373 \text{ K})]^{-1}$$

$$6.5 \times 10^{-2} = K_c\,(3.265 \times 10^{-2}) \quad\quad \mathbf{K_c} = \underline{\mathbf{2.0 \text{ L mol}^{-1}}}$$

14.26 At equilibrium, $K_c = [H_2O(g)]$, $K_p = P_{H_2O(g)}$

Thus, P_{H_2O} = constant that only changes with temperature.

14.27 The concentrations of pure solids and liquids are invariant; they are constants that can be incorporated into K_{eq}.

14.28 (a) $K_c = [CO_2(g)]$ $\quad K_p = P_{CO_2(g)}$

(b) $K_c = \dfrac{[Ni(CO)_4(g)]}{[CO(g)]^4}$ $\quad K_p = \dfrac{P_{Ni(CO)_4(g)}}{p^4_{CO(g)}}$

(c) $K_c = \dfrac{[I_2(g)][CO_2(g)]^5}{[CO(g)]^5}$ $\quad K_p = \dfrac{p_{I_2(g)}\, p^5_{CO_2(g)}}{p^5_{CO(g)}}$

(d) $K_c = \dfrac{[CO_2(g)]}{[Ca(HCO_3)_2(aq)]}$ $\quad K_p = \dfrac{P_{CO_2}}{[Ca(HCO_3)_2]}$

(e) $K_c = [Ag^+(aq)][Cl^-(aq)]$

14.29 $PCl_3(g) + Cl_2(g) \rightleftharpoons PCl_5(g)$

(a) Addition of PCl_3 would drive reaction toward the products to compensate for the excess of PCl_3.

(b) Removal of Cl_2 would cause the reaction to proceed toward the reactants to reestablish equilibrium and make up for the loss of Cl_2.

(c) Removal of PCl_5 would cause the reaction to proceed toward the products to compensate for the loss of PCl_5.

(d) A decrease in the volume of the container would cause the pressure to increase, and the reaction would favor the side which has the least number of moles of gas, namely the products.

(14.29 continued)

(e) Addition of He (an inert gas), without a change in the size of container, would increase the pressure. There would be no effect on the position of equilibrium, however.

14.30 None of the above will effect the equilibrium constant for the reaction. The only change which will effect the equilibrium constant is a change in temperature.

14.31 (a) <u>decreased</u> (b) <u>increased</u> (c) <u>no change</u>

(d) <u>decreased</u> (e) <u>no change</u>

14.32 (a) <u>No change in the value of K</u> (b) <u>No change in the value of K</u>

(c) <u>No change in the value of K</u> (d) <u>The value of K will increase</u>

(e) <u>No change in the value of K</u>

14.33 (a) <u>increased</u> (b) <u>decreased</u> (c) <u>increased</u> (d) <u>no change</u>

14.34 (a) <u>decreased</u> (b) <u>increased</u> (c) <u>no change</u> (d) <u>decreased</u>

14.35

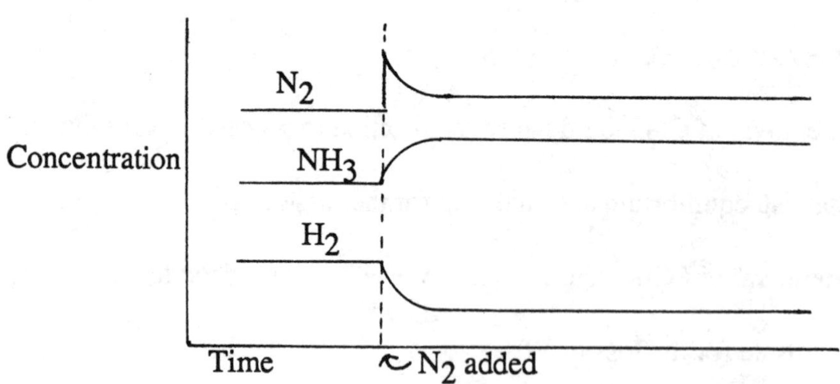

14.36 (a) <u>no change</u> (b) <u>increased</u> (c) <u>decreased</u> (d) <u>increased</u>

14.37 $K_c = \dfrac{[PCl_5]}{[PCl_3]\,[Cl_2]} = \dfrac{1}{K_c \text{ (calculated in Exercise 14.7)}} = \dfrac{1}{5.5} = \mathbf{\underline{0.18}}$

14.38 $K_c = 5.5 \quad \Delta n = +1$

$K_P = K_c(RT)^{\Delta n} = (5.5 \text{ mol /L}) [(0.0821 \text{ L atm mol}^{-1} \text{ K}^{-1}) (298 \text{ K})]^1$

$K_P = (5.5)(2.447 \times 10^{+1} \text{ atm}) = \underline{\mathbf{1.3 \times 10^2 \text{ atm}}}$

14.39 $Q = \dfrac{(0.30 \text{ M}) (0.020 \text{ M})}{(0.040 \text{ M}) (0.50 \text{ M})} = 0.30$

Q does not equal K_c. Therefore, **the system is not at equilibrium. The reaction must proceed to the right to reach equilibrium.**

14.40 $K_c = \dfrac{[PCl_3][Cl_2]}{[PCl_5]} = \dfrac{[PCl_3](1.87 \times 10^{-1})}{1.29 \times 10^{-3}} = 33.3$

$[PCl_3] = \underline{\mathbf{2.30 \times 10^{-1} \text{ mol L}^{-1}}}$

14.41 **(a)** $K_P = \dfrac{p^2_{NO_2}}{p_{N_2O_4}} = \dfrac{(0.844 - 0.563)^2}{0.563} = \underline{\mathbf{1.40 \times 10^{-1} \text{ atm}}}$

(b) $K_P = K_c(RT)^{\Delta n} \quad \Delta n = +1$

$1.40 \times 10^{-1} = K_c \ [(0.0821 \text{ L atm mol}^{-1} \text{ K}^{-1}) (298 \text{ K})]^1$

$K_c = \underline{\mathbf{5.72 \times 10^{-3} \text{ mol L}^{-1} \text{ atm}^{-1}}}$

(c) $\Delta G° = -RT \ln K_P = -(8.3144 \text{ J mol}^{-1} \text{ K}^{-1}) (298 \text{ K}) \ln(0.140)$

$\Delta G° = 4.87 \times 10^3 \text{ J mol}^{-1} = \underline{\mathbf{4.87 \text{ kJ}}}$

14.42 $K_c = \dfrac{[H_2][I_2]}{[HI]^2} = \dfrac{(1.0 \times 10^{-3} \text{ M}) (2.5 \times 10^{-2} \text{ M})}{(2.2 \times 10^{-2} \text{ M})^2} = \underline{\mathbf{5.2 \times 10^{-2}}}$

14.43 $K_P = \dfrac{(P_{NOCl})^2}{(P_{NO})^2 \ P_{Cl_2}} = \dfrac{(0.15 \text{ atm})^2}{(0.65 \text{ atm})^2 (0.18 \text{ atm})} = \underline{\mathbf{0.30 \text{ atm}^{-1}}}$

14.44

	$2N_2O$	+	$3O_2 \rightleftharpoons$	$4NO_2$
Init. Conc.	0.020		0.0560	0
Change	- 2X		-3X	+4X
Equil. Conc.				≈ 0.020

(a) $4X \approx 0.020 \qquad X = 5.0 \times 10^{-3}$

$[N_2O] = 0.020 - 2X = 0.020 - 2(5.0 \times 10^{-3}) =$ **0.010 M**

$[O_2] = 0.0560 - 3X = 0.0560 - 3(5.0 \times 10^{-3}) =$ **0.041 M**

(b) $$K_c = \frac{[NO_2]^4}{[N_2O]^2[O_2]^3} = \frac{(0.020)^4}{(0.010)^2\,(0.041)^3} = \mathbf{23\ L\ mol^{-1}}$$

14.45

	SO_2	+	$NO_2 \rightleftharpoons$	NO	+	SO_3
Init. Conc.	0.0500		0.0500	0		0
Change	-X		-X	+X		+X
Equil. Conc.	0.0500 -X		0.0500 - X	+X		+X

$$K_c = 85.0 = \frac{(X)\,(X)}{(0.0500 - X)^2}$$

$\sqrt{85.0} = X/(0.0500 - X) = 9.22$

$X = 9.22\,(0.0500 - X)$

$X = 4.51 \times 10^{-2}$

$[NO] = [SO_3] =$ **0.0451 M**

$[SO_2] = [NO_2] =$ **0.0049 M**

14.46

	H_2 +	CO_2 $\rightleftharpoons$	CO +	H_2O
Init. Conc.	0.200	0.200	0	0
Change	-X	-X	+X	+X
Equil. Conc.	0.200 -X	0.200 - X	+X	+X

$$K_c = \frac{X^2}{(0.200 - X)^2} = \underline{0.771}$$

$$\sqrt{0.771} = \frac{X}{0.200 - X}$$

$X = 0.0935$

$[H_2] = [CO_2] =$ **<u>0.106 M</u>** $[CO] = [H_2O] =$ **<u>0.0935 M</u>**

14.47

	SO_2 +	NO_2 $\rightleftharpoons$	NO +	SO_3
Init. Conc.	0.0100	0.0200	0.0100	0.0150
Change	-X	-X	+X	+X
Equil. Conc.	0.0100 -X	0.0200 - X	0.0100 +X	0.0150 + X

$$K_c = 8.50 = \frac{(0.0100 + X)\,(0.0150 + X)}{(0.0100 - X)\,(0.0200 - X)}$$

$$8.50 = \frac{1.50 \times 10^{-4} + 2.5 \times 10^{-2}\,X + X^2}{2.00 \times 10^{-4} - 0.0300\,X + X^2}$$

$$84.0\,X^2 - 2.575\,X + 0.01685 = 0$$

From the solution of this quadratic equation (See Appendix A.4): X = 0.00947

$[SO_2] =$ **<u>0.00053 M</u>** $[NO_2] =$ **<u>0.0105 M</u>**

$[NO] =$ **<u>0.0195 M</u>** $[SO_3] =$ **<u>0.0245 M</u>**

14.48 **(a)**

	$2CO_2 \rightleftharpoons$	$2CO$ +	O_2
Init. Conc.	1.0×10^{-3} M	0	0
Change	-2X	+2X	+X
Equil. Conc.	1.0×10^{-3} -2X	2X	X

$$K_c = 6.4 \times 10^{-7} = \frac{(2X)^2X}{(1.0 \times 10^{-3} - 2X)^2}$$

If 2X is small compared to 1.0×10^{-3}, then:

$$6.4 \times 10^{-7} = \frac{(2X)^2X}{(1.0 \times 10^{-3})^2} = \frac{4x^3}{(1.0 \times 10^{-3})^2}$$

$X = 5.4 \times 10^{-5}$ Check! Was 2X small compared to 1.0×10^{-3}?

The value obtained for 2X was about 11% of the1.0×10^{-3}. This is about the limit allowed in most approximations. Using this value, the equilibrium concentrations are:

$[CO_2]$ = **8.9×10^{-4} M** [CO] = **1.1×10^{-4} M** $[O_2]$ = **5.4×10^{-5} M**

To obtain a more precise solution, one would solve the above equation using a series of approximations. The above would be the first approximation. These values would be substituted into the equilibrium expression and the process would be repeated. The values after successive approximations are:

$[CO_2] = 9.0 \times 10^{-4}$ M, $[CO] = 1.0 \times 10^{-4}$ M, $[O_2] = 5.1 \times 10^{-5}$ M

(b) $\frac{1.0 \times 10^{-4}}{1.0 \times 10^{-3}} = 0.10 =$ the fraction of CO_2 decomposed

14.49

	CO	+	$Cl_2 \rightleftharpoons$	$COCl_2$
Init. Conc.	0		0	0.020 M
Change	+X		+X	-X
Equil. Conc.	X		X	0.020 - X

$$K_c = 4.6 \times 10^9 = \frac{0.020 - X}{X^2}$$

Assume that X is very small compared to 0.020. Then:

$$4.6 \times 10^9 = \frac{0.020}{X^2} \qquad X = 2.1 \times 10^{-6}$$

$[CO] = [Cl_2] =$ **2.1×10^{-6} M** $\qquad [COCl_2] =$ **0.020 M**

14.50 $K_P = P_{CO_2} \times P_{H_2O} = 0.25\ atm^2 = X^2$

$$P_{CO_2} = \sqrt{0.25\ atm^2} = \mathbf{0.50\ atm} = P_{CO_2} = P_{H_2O}$$

It is used in baking because it liberates gaseous CO_2 and H_2O that are trapped in bread dough, thus causing it to rise.

14.51

	H_2	+	$I_2 \rightleftharpoons$	$2HI$
Init. Conc.	0.0100 M		0.0100 M	0.0740
Change	+X		+X	+0.050 M - 2X
Equil. Conc.	0.0100 M + X		0.0100 M + X	0.1240 M - 2X

$$K_c = \frac{(0.074)^2}{(0.01 \times 0.01)} = 54.76 \qquad 54.76 = \frac{(0.1240 - 2X)^2}{(0.0100 + X)^2}$$

(14.51 continued)

$$\sqrt{54.76} = \frac{0.1240 - 2X}{0.0100 + X} = 7.40 \qquad x = 5.3 \times 10^{-3}$$

$[HI] = 0.1240 - 2 \times 5.3 \times 10^{-3} =$ **0.113 M**

$[H_2] = [I_2] = 0.0100 + 5.3 \times 10^{-3} =$ **0.0153 M**

14.52

	CO	+	$Cl_2 \rightleftharpoons$	$COCl_2$
Init. Conc.	0.15 M		0.30 M	0
Change	-(0.15 - X)		- (0.15 - X)	+(0.15 - X)
Equil. Conc.	X		0.15 + X	0.15 - X

$$K_c = 4.6 \times 10^9 = \frac{0.15 - X}{(X)(0.15 + X)} \approx \frac{0.15}{X(0.15)}$$

$$X = \frac{0.15}{0.15 \times 4.6 \times 10^9} = 2.2 \times 10^{-10}$$

$[CO] =$ **2.2×10^{-10} M**

$[Cl_2] = 0.15\ M + 2.2 \times 10^{-10}\ M =$ **0.15 M**;

$[COCl_2] = 0.15 - 2.2 \times 10^{-10} =$ **0.15 M**

14.53

	N_2	+	$O_2 \rightleftharpoons$	$2NO$
Init. p	33.6		4.0	0
Change	-X		- X	+ 2X
Equil. p	33.6 - X		4.0 - X	2X

$$K_p = 4.8 \times 10^{-7} = \frac{(2X)^2}{(33.6 - X)(4.0 - X)} \approx \frac{(2X)^2}{(33.6)(4.0)} \qquad X = 4.0 \times 10^{-3}$$

$p_{N_2} = 33.6$ atm $\quad p_{O_2} = 4.0$ atm $\quad p_{NO} =$ **8.0×10^{-3} atm**

14.54 $\dfrac{P_f(N_2)}{P_i(N_2)} = \dfrac{P_f(NO)}{P_i(NO)}$ $\qquad$ $\dfrac{0.80 \text{ atm}}{33.6 \text{ atm}} = \dfrac{P_f(NO)}{8.0 \times 10^{-3} \text{ atm}}$

$P_f(NO)$ = **1.9×10^{-4} atm**

14.55

	$2NO_2 \rightleftharpoons$	N_2O_4
Init. Conc.	1.0 M	O
Change	- 2X	+X
Equil. Conc.	1.0 - 2X	X

$$7.5 = \frac{X}{(1.0 - 2X)^2}$$

$30X^2 - 31X + 7.5 = 0$ $\qquad$ X = 0.3865 (physically sign. soln. of quadratic eq.)

$[NO_2]$ = 1.0 - 2 x 0.3865 = **0.23 M** $\qquad$ $[N_2O_4]$ = **0.39 M**

Double the size of the container!

	$2NO_2 \rightleftharpoons$	N_2O_4
Init. Conc.	0.5 M	0
Change	-2X	X
Equil. Conc.	0.5 - 2X	X

$$7.5 = \frac{X}{(0.5 - 2X)^2} \qquad 30X^2 - 16X + 1.875 = 0 \qquad X = 0.174$$

$[NO_2]$ = 0.5 - 2 x 0.174 = **0.15 M** $\qquad$ $[N_2O_4]$ = **0.17 M**

Yes! The larger container favors the NO_2 while the smaller container favored the N_2O_4. This is what one should expect based upon a knowledge of LeChatelier's Principle.

15 ACID-BASE EQUILIBRIUM IN AQUEOUS SOLUTIONS

15.1 $H_2O + H_2O \rightleftharpoons H_3O^+(aq) + OH^-(aq)$

This is a very important equilibrium because it is present in any aqueous solution regardless of what other reactions may also be taking place.

15.2 In pure water the $[H^+] = 1 \times 10^{-7}$. In the presence of an acid the dissociation of water is suppressed (Le Chatelier's principle) and the $[H^+]$ contributed from the H_2O is less than 10^{-7} M. Only in very dilute acid solutions must the dissociation of water be taken into account.

15.3 (a) $[H^+]$ = 1.0×10^{-3} M $[OH^-]$ = 1.0×10^{-11} M pH = 3.00

(b) $[H^+]$ = 1.25×10^{-1} M $[OH^-]$ = 8.00×10^{-14} M pH = 0.903

(c) $[H^+]$ = 3.2×10^{-12} M $[OH^-]$ = 3.1×10^{-3} M pH = 11.49

(d) $[H^+]$ = 4.2×10^{-13} M $[OH^-]$ = 2.4×10^{-2} M pH = 12.38

(e) $[H^+]$ = 2.1×10^{-4} M $[OH^-]$ = 4.8×10^{-11} M pH = 3.68

(f) $[H^+]$ = 1.3×10^{-5} M $[OH^-]$ = 7.7×10^{-10} M pH = 4.89

(g) $[H^+]$ = 1.2×10^{-12} M $[OH^-]$ = 8.4×10^{-3} M pH = 11.92

(h) $[H^+]$ = 2.1×10^{-13} M $[OH^-]$ = 4.8×10^{-2} M pH = 12.68

15.4 **Acidic** $pH = -\log [H^+ \text{(from acid)} + H^+ \text{(from water)}]$

$$= -\log (1.0 \times 10^{-8} + 1.0 \times 10^{-7}) = \underline{6.96}$$

A more precise answer to this question would require that one consider the effect that the H^+ from the acid would have on the autoionization of water.

	H^+	+	OH^- $\rightleftharpoons$ H_2O
Before acid added	1.0×10^{-7}		1.0×10^{-7}
Acid added	1.0×10^{-8}		
After acid reacts	$X + (1.0 \times 10^{-8})$		X

$[X + (1.0 \times 10^{-8})] [X] = 1.0 \times 10^{-14}$ Solve this quadratic equation:

$X = 9.51 \times 10^{-8}$; $[H^+] = (9.51 \times 10^{-8}) + (1.0 \times 10^{-8}) = 1.05 \times 10^{-7}$: $pH = \underline{6.98}$

15.5 $[H^+] = [OH^-] = \sqrt{2.42 \times 10^{-14}} = \underline{1.56 \times 10^{-7}}$

15.6 $pH = -\log [H^+]$; $pOH = -\log [OH^-]$; $p[OH^-] + p[H^+] = p[H_2O]$

$pOH + pH = K_w = 14$

15.7 (a) acidic (b) basic (c) neutral (d) acidic (e) basic

15.8 (e)<(b)<(c)<(d)<(a)

15.9 $pH = -\log[H^+] = -\log [1.56 \times 10^{-7}] = \underline{6.81}$

15.10 (a) $[H^+] = \underline{0.050\ M}$ $[OH^-] = \underline{2.0 \times 10^{-13}\ M}$

(b) $[H^+] = \underline{1.9 \times 10^{-6}\ M}$ $[OH^-] = \underline{5.3 \times 10^{-9}\ M}$

(c) $[H^+] = \underline{1.0 \times 10^{-4}\ M}$ $[OH^-] = \underline{1.0 \times 10^{-10}\ M}$

(d) $[H^+] = \underline{1.6 \times 10^{-8}\ M}$ $[OH^-] = \underline{6.3 \times 10^{-7}\ M}$

(e) $[H^+] = \underline{1.1 \times 10^{-11}\ M}$ $[OH^-] = \underline{9.1 \times 10^{-4}\ M}$

(f) $[H^+] = \underline{2.5 \times 10^{-13}\ M}$ $[OH^-] = \underline{4.0 \times 10^{-2}\ M}$

15.11 pOH = 14 - pH (a) **12.70** (b) **8.27** (c) **10.00**

(d) **6.20** (e) **3.06** (f) **1.39**

15.12 pH = - log $[H^+]$ pOH = - log$[OH^-]$

(a) pH = **3.00** pOH = **11.00**

(b) pH = **0.90** pOH = **13.10**

(c) pH = **11.49** pOH = **2.51**

(d) pH = **12.38** pOH = **1.62**

(e) pH = **3.68** pOH = **10.32**

(f) pH = **4.89** pOH = **9.11**

(g) pH = **11.92** pOH = **2.08**

(h) pH = **12.68** pOH = **1.32**

15.13 $pK_a = -\log K_a = -\log 3.8 \times 10^{-9} = \underline{8.42}$

15.14 $pK_b = -\log K_b$ $K_b = \text{antilog}(-pK_b) = \text{antilog}(-3.84) = \underline{1.4 \times 10^{-4}}$

15.15 (a) $HC_7H_5O_2 \rightleftharpoons H^+ + C_7H_5O_2^-$ $K_{eq} = \{[H^+][C_7H_5O_2^-]\} / [HC_7H_5O_2]$

(b) $N_2H_4 + H_2O \rightleftharpoons N_2H_5^+ + OH^-$ $K_{eq} = \{[N_2H_5^+][OH^-]\} / [N_2H_4]$

(c) $HCHO_2 \rightleftharpoons H^+ + CHO_2^-$ $K_{eq} = \{[H^+][CHO_2^-]\} / [HCHO_2]$

(d) $HC_8H_{11}N_2O_3 \rightleftharpoons H^+ + C_8H_{11}N_2O_3^-$

$K_{eq} = \{[H^+][C_8H_{11}N_2O_3^-]\} / [HC_8H_{11}N_2O_3]$

(e) $C_5H_5N + H_2O \rightleftharpoons C_5H_5NH^+ + OH^-$

$K_{eq} = \{[C_5H_5NH^+][OH^-]\} / [C_5H_5N]$

15.16 **(a)** $HNO_2 \rightleftharpoons H^+ + NO_2^-$ $K_a = 4.5 \times 10^{-4}$

	Init. conc.(M)	Change	Equil. Conc. (M)
H^+	~0	+X	X
NO_2^-	0	+X	X
HNO_2	0.30	-X	0.30 - X ≈ 0.30

$$\frac{(X)\ (X)}{(0.30 - X)} = 4.5 \times 10^{-4} = \frac{X^2}{0.30}$$

X = **1.2 x 10^-2^ M** = [H^+^]

$X = \underline{\mathbf{1.2 \times 10^{-2}\ M}} = [H^+]$

(b) $HF \rightleftharpoons H^+ + F^-$ $K_a = 6.5 \times 10^{-4}$

	Init. Conc.	Change	Equil. Conc.
H^+	~0	+X	X
F^-	0	+X	X
HF	1.0	-X	1.0 - X ≈ 1.0

$$\frac{X^2}{1.0 - X} \approx \frac{X^2}{1.0} = 6.5 \times 10^{-4}$$

$X = [H^+] = \underline{\mathbf{2.5 \times 10^{-2}\ M}}$

(c) $K_a = 4.9 \times 10^{-10} = \dfrac{X^2}{0.025 - X}$ $X = [H^+] = \underline{\mathbf{3.5 \times 10^{-6}\ M}}$

(d) $K_a = 1.5 \times 10^{-5} = \dfrac{X^2}{0.10 - X}$ $X = [H^+] = \underline{\mathbf{1.2 \times 10^{-3}\ M}}$

(e) $K_a = 1.0 \times 10^{-5} = \dfrac{X^2}{0.050 - X}$ $X = [H^+] = \underline{\mathbf{7.1 \times 10^{-4}\ M}}$

15.17 (a) $NH_3 + H_2O \rightleftharpoons NH_4^+ + OH^-$ $K_b = 1.8 \times 10^{-5}$

	Init. Conc.	Change	Equil. Conc.
NH_4^+	0	+X	X
OH^-	~0	+X	X
NH_3	0.15 M	-X	$0.15 - X \approx 0.15$

$$1.8 \times 10^{-5} = \frac{(X)(X)}{(0.15 - X)} \approx \frac{X^2}{0.15}$$ $X = [OH^-] = \underline{1.6 \times 10^{-3}\ M}$

(b) $N_2H_4 + H_2O \rightleftharpoons N_2H_5^+ + OH^-$ $K_b = 1.7 \times 10^{-6}$

	Init. Conc.	Change	Equil. Conc.
$N_2H_5^+$	0	+X	X
OH^-	~0	+X	X
N_2H_4	0.20	-X	$0.20 - X \approx 0.20$

$$1.7 \times 10^{-6} = \frac{(X)(X)}{(0.20 - X)} \approx \frac{X^2}{0.20}$$ $X = [OH^-] = \underline{5.8 \times 10^{-4}\ M}$

(c) $K_b = 3.7 \times 10^{-4} = \frac{X^2}{0.80 - X}$ $X = [OH^-] = \underline{1.7 \times 10^{-2}\ M}$

(d) $K_b = 1.1 \times 10^{-8} = \frac{X^2}{0.35 - X}$ $X = [OH^-] = \underline{6.2 \times 10^{-5}\ M}$

(e) $K_b = 1.7 \times 10^{-9} = \frac{X^2}{0.010 - X}$ $X = [OH^-] = \underline{4.1 \times 10^{-6}\ M}$

15.18 $[OH^-][H^+] = 1.00 \times 10^{-14}$, $[OH^-] = 1.00 \times 10^{-14} / [H^+]$

(a) $[OH^-] = \underline{8.3 \times 10^{-13}\ M}$ (b) $[OH^-] = \underline{4.0 \times 10^{-13}\ M}$

(c) $[OH^-] = \underline{2.9 \times 10^{-9}\ M}$ (d) $[OH^-] = \underline{8.3 \times 10^{-12}\ M}$

(e) $[OH^-] = \underline{1.4 \times 10^{-11}\ M}$

15.19 $[H^+][OH^-] = 1 \times 10^{-14}$, $pH + (-\log[OH^-]) = 14$, $pH = 14 + \log[OH^-]$

(a) $pH = 14 + \log(1.6 \times 10^{-3}) = 14 - 2.8 = \underline{\mathbf{11.20}}$

(b) $pH = \underline{\mathbf{10.76}}$ **(c)** $pH = \underline{\mathbf{12.23}}$ **(d)** $pH = \underline{\mathbf{9.79}}$ **(e)** $pH = \underline{\mathbf{8.61}}$

15.20 $K_a = \dfrac{[H^+][\text{anion}]}{[\text{undissoc. Acid}]} = \dfrac{(X)(X)}{(0.25 - X)}$

$pH = -\log[H^+]$ $[H^+] = \text{antilog}(-pH) = \text{antilog}(-1.35)$

$[H^+] = 4.47 \times 10^{-2} = X$

$K_a = \dfrac{(4.47 \times 10^{-2})^2}{0.25 - (4.47 \times 10^{-2})} = \dfrac{2.00 \times 10^{-3}}{0.205} = \underline{\mathbf{9.8 \times 10^{-3}}}$

15.21 $K_a = \dfrac{[H^+][\text{anion}]}{[\text{undissoc. Acid}]} = \dfrac{(X)(X)}{(0.10 - X)}$

$pH = 5.37 = -\log[H^+] = -\log(X)$ $X = 4.27 \times 10^{-6}$

$K_a = \dfrac{(4.27 \times 10^{-6})^2}{0.10 - (4.27 \times 10^{-6})} = \dfrac{1.82 \times 10^{-11}}{0.10} = \underline{\mathbf{1.8 \times 10^{-10}}}$

15.22 $K_b = \dfrac{[\text{cation}][OH^-]}{[\text{unreacted based}]} = \dfrac{(X)(X)}{(0.10 - X)}$

$pH = 14 - pOH = 14 - (-\log[OH^-] = 14 + \log(X) = 8.75$

$X = 5.62 \times 10^{-6}$

$K_b = \dfrac{(5.62 \times 10^{-6})^2}{0.10 - (5.62 \times 10^{-6})} = \underline{\mathbf{3.2 \times 10^{-10}}}$

15.23 **(a)** $HCHO_2 \rightleftharpoons H^+ + CHO_2^-$ $K_a = 1.8 \times 10^{-4}$

	Init. Conc.	Change	Equil. Conc.
H^+	~0	+X	X
CHO_2^-	0	+X	X
$HCHO_2$	1.0	-X	1.0 - X

$$K_a = 1.8 \times 10^{-4} = \frac{(X)(X)}{1.0 - X} \approx \frac{X^2}{1.0}$$

$X = [H^+] = 1.3 \times 10^{-2}$ M % ionization = $\frac{1.3 \times 10^{-2}}{1.0} \times 100 =$ **1.3%**

(b) $K_a = 1.4 \times 10^{-5} = \frac{X^2}{0.010 - X}$ $X = [H^+] = [C_3H_5O_2^-]$

$X = 3.7 \times 10^{-4}$ % ionization $= \frac{3.7 \times 10^{-4}}{0.010} \times 100 =$ **3.7%**

(c) $K_a = 4.9 \times 10^{-10} = \frac{X^2}{0.025 - X}$ $X = 3.5 \times 10^{-6}$

% ionization = $\frac{3.5 \times 10^{-6}}{0.025} \times 100 =$ **0.014%**

(d) $K_a = 1.4 \times 10^{-5} = \frac{X^2}{0.35 - X}$ $X = 2.2 \times 10^{-3}$

% ionization $= \frac{2.2 \times 10^{-3}}{0.35} \times 100 =$ **0.63%**

(e) $K_a = 3.1 \times 10^{-8} = \frac{X^2}{0.50 - X}$ $X = 1.245 \times 10^{-4}$

% ionization = $\frac{1.24 \times 10^{-4}}{0.50} \times 100 =$ **0.025%**

(f) strong acid, assume **100% ionization**

15.24 (a) $K_a = 1.8 \times 10^{-5} = \frac{(X)(X)}{1.0 - X}$ $X = 4.24 \times 10^{-3}$

$\% \text{ ionization} = \frac{4.24 \times 10^{-3}}{1.0} \times 100 = \underline{0.42\%}$

(b) $K_a = 1.8 \times 10^{-5} = \frac{(X)(X)}{0.10 - X}$ $X = 1.34 \times 10^{-3}$

$\% \text{ ionization} = \frac{1.34 \times 10^{-3}}{0.10} \times 100 = \underline{1.3\%}$

(c) $K_a = 1.8 \times 10^{-5} = \frac{(X)(X)}{0.010 - X}$ $X = 4.4 \times 10^{-4}$

$\% \text{ ionization} = \frac{4.2 \times 10^{-4}}{0.010} \times 100 = \underline{4.2\%}$

In the equilibrium represented by $HC_2H_3O_2 \rightleftharpoons H^+ + C_2H_3O_2^-$, collisions between ions would be expected to be less frequent in the more dilute solution. Therefore, on a molecular level we would expect the dilute solution to have a higher percent ionization. The above calculation verified this expectation.

15.25 (a) $HC_2H_3O_2 \rightleftharpoons H^+ + C_2H_3O_2^-$

	Init Conc.	Change	Equil. Conc.
H^+	~0	+X	X
$C_2H_3O_2^-$	0.15 M	+X	$0.15 + X \approx 0.15$
$HC_2H_3O_2$	0.25	-X	$0.25 - X \approx 0.25$

$K_a = 1.8 \times 10^{-5} = \frac{(X)(0.15)}{(0.25)}$ $X = [H^+] = \underline{3.0 \times 10^{-5}\text{ M}}$

(continued)

(15.25 continued)

(b) $1.8 \times 10^{-4} = \frac{(X)(0.50)}{(0.50)}$ $X = [H^+] = \mathbf{\underline{1.8 \times 10^{-4}\ M}}$

(c) $4.5 \times 10^{-4} = \frac{(X)(0.40)}{(0.30)}$ $X = [H^+] = \mathbf{\underline{3.4 \times 10^{-4}\ M}}$

(d) $1.8 \times 10^{-5} = \frac{(X)(0.15)}{(0.25)}$ $X = [OH^-] = 3.0 \times 10^{-5}\ M$

$[H^+] = 1.0 \times 10^{-14} / 3.0 \times 10^{-5} = \mathbf{\underline{3.3 \times 10^{-10}\ M}}$

(e) $1.7 \times 10^{-6} = \frac{(X)(0.50)}{(0.30)}$ $X = [OH^-] = 1.02 \times 10^{-6}\ M$

$[H^+] = 1.0 \times 10^{-14} / 1.02 \times 10^{-6} = \mathbf{\underline{9.8 \times 10^{-9}\ M}}$

15.26 $B + H_2O \rightleftharpoons HB^+ + OH^-$

$K_b = \frac{[HB^+][OH^-]}{[B]}$ $[HB^+] = [OH^-] = 2.51 \times 10^{-3}$

$[B] = 0.012 - (2.51 \times 10^{-3})$

$K_b = \frac{(2.51 \times 10^{-3})(2.51 \times 10^{-3})}{0.012 - (2.51 \times 10^{-3})} = \mathbf{\underline{6.6 \times 10^{-4}}}$

15.27 $HC_2H_3O_2 \rightleftharpoons H^+ + C_2H_3O_2^-$

	Init Conc.	H^+ added	Change	Equil. Conc.
H^+	~0	Y	-X	Y - X
$C_2H_3O_2^-$	1.0	0	-X	1.0 - X
$HC_2H_3O_2$	0	0	+X	X

$[H^+]$ from pH value $= 1.82 \times 10^{-5} = Y - X$

$K_a = 1.8 \times 10^{-5} = \frac{[H^+][C_2H_3O_2^-]}{[HC_2H_3O_2]} = \frac{(1.82 \times 10^{-5})(1.0 - X)}{X}$

(continued)

(15.27 continued)

$$1.8 \times 10^{-5} = \frac{(1.82 \times 10^{-5})(1.0 - X)}{X}$$

$(1.8 \times 10^{-5})X = (1.82 \times 10^{-5}) - 1.82 \times 10^{-5}X$ $\quad\quad X = 0.50$

$[H^+] = 1.82 \times 10^{-5}$ M, $\quad [C_2H_3O_2^-] = 0.50$ M, $\quad [HC_2H_3O_2] = 0.50$ M

Amount of HCl added = Y

Amount of H^+ remaining = Y - X = 1.82×10^{-5} M

X = $[HC_2H_3O_2]$ = 0.50 M

Y -(0.50) = 1.82×10^{-5} M $\quad\quad$ Y = 0.50 M

$$\frac{0.50 \text{ mol HCl}}{\text{L}} \times 0.500 \text{ L} \times \frac{36.5 \text{ g}}{\text{mol}} = \mathbf{9.1\ g\ HCl}$$

15.28 $HC_4H_3N_2O_3 \rightleftharpoons H^+ + C_4H_3N_2O_3^-$

$K_a = 1.0 \times 10^{-5}$ $\quad$ M ($NaC_4H_3N_2O_3$) = init. conc. $C_4H_3N_2O_3^-$ =

$$10 \text{ mg} \times \frac{1 \text{ g}}{1000 \text{ mg}} \times \frac{1 \text{ mol}}{150 \text{ g}} \times \frac{1}{0.250 \text{ L}} = 2.67 \times 10^{-4} \text{ M}$$

	Init. Conc.	Change	Equil. Conc.
H^+	0.1	-X	~0.1
$C_4H_3N_2O_3^-$	2.67×10^{-4}	-X	(2.67×10^{-4}) - X
$HC_4H_3N_2O_3$	0	+X	X

$$1.0 \times 10^{-5} = \frac{(0.1)(2.67 \times 10^{-4} - X)}{X}$$

X = 2.7×10^{-4} M

This shows that essentially 100% of the $C_4H_3N_2O_3^-$ is converted to barbituric acid.

15.29 $K_a = 1.4 \times 10^{-5} = \dfrac{(X)(X)}{(0.010 - X)}$ $X = [H^+] = 3.74 \times 10^{-4}$

pH = **3.43**

15.30 $K_a = 1.8 \times 10^{-5} = \dfrac{(X)(X)}{(Y - X)}$ $X = [H^+] = 3.16 \times 10^{-3}$ M (from pH)

$1.8 \times 10^{-5} = \dfrac{(3.16 \times 10^{-3})^2}{Y - (3.16 \times 10^{-3})}$ $Y = [HC_2H_3O_2] =$ **0.55 M**

15.31 $K_b = \dfrac{(X)(X)}{Y - X}$ $K_b = 1.7 \times 10^{-6}$ $X = [OH^-] = 4.365 \times 10^{-4}$ M (from pH)

$1.7 \times 10^{-6} = \dfrac{(4.36 \times 10^{-4})^2}{Y - (4.365 \times 10^{-4})}$ $Y = [N_2H_4] =$ **0.11 M**

15.32 $K_a = \dfrac{(X)(X)}{0.010 - X}$ $X = [H^+] = 2.82 \times 10^{-5}$ M (from pH)

$K_a = \dfrac{(2.82 \times 10^{-5})^2}{0.010 - (2.82 \times 10^{-5})} =$ **7.9×10^{-8}**

15.33 $HC_2H_3O_2 \rightleftharpoons H^+ + C_2H_3O_2^-$

	Init. Conc.	Change	Equil. Conc.
H^+	~0	+X	X
$C_2H_3O_2^-$	0	+X	X
$HC_2H_3O_2$	1.0×10^{-3}	-X	$(1.0 \times 10^{-3}) - X$

$1.8 \times 10^{-5} = \dfrac{(X)(X)}{(1.0 \times 10^{-3}) - X}$

$X^2 + (1.8 \times 10^{-5})X - 1.8 \times 10^{-8} = 0$ (Solve quadratic equation)

$X = 1.25 \times 10^{-4}$ or $[H^+] =$ **1.3×10^{-4}** This is the same answer, to two sign. figures, that one would obtain by assuming $1.0 \times 10^{-3} - X \approx 1.0 \times 10^{-3}$.

15.34 $HCO_2H \rightleftharpoons CHO_2^- + H^+$ $K_a = 1.8 \times 10^{-4}$

	Init. Conc.	Change	Equil. Conc.
H^+	~0	+X	X
CHO_2^-	0	+X	X
$HCHO_2$	0.010	-X	0.010 - X

$$1.8 \times 10^{-4} = \frac{(X)(X)}{0.010 - X}$$

Solving this quadratic equation yields, $X = 1.3 \times 10^{-3}$ (To two sign. figs., the same answer will be obtained if one assumed that $0.010\text{-}X \approx 0.010$.)

$[H^+] = \underline{1.3 \times 10^{-3}\ M}$ $[CHO_2^-] = \underline{1.3 \times 10^{-3}\ M}$

$[HCHO_2] = \underline{0.0087\ M}$ $[OH^-] = \underline{7.7 \times 10^{-12}\ M}$

15.35 $H_2C_6H_6O_6 \rightleftharpoons H^+ + HC_6H_6O_6^-$

$K_{a_1} = \{[H^+]\,[HC_6H_6O_6^-]\} / [H_2C_6H_6O_6]$

$HC_6H_6O_6^- \rightleftharpoons H^+ + C_6H_6O_6^{2-}$

$K_{a_2} = \{[H^+]\,[C_6H_6O_6^{2-}]\} / [HC_6H_6O_6^-]$

15.36 $H_3C_6H_5O_7 \rightleftharpoons H_2C_6H_5O_7^- + H^+$

$K_{a_1} = \{[H_2C_6H_5O_7^-]\,[H^+]\} / [H_3C_6H_5O_7]$

$H_2C_6H_5O_7^- \rightleftharpoons HC_6H_5O_7^{2-} + H^+$

$K_{a_2} = \{[HC_6H_5O_7^{2-}]\,[H^+]\} / [H_2C_6H_5O_7^-]$

$HC_6H_5O_7^{2-} \rightleftharpoons C_6H_5O_7^{3-} + H^+$

$K_{a_3} = \{[C_6H_5O_7^{3-}]\,[H^+]\} / [HC_6H_5O_7^{2-}]$

15.37 $H_2SeO_3 \rightleftharpoons H^+ + HSeO_3^-$ $\qquad K = 3 \times 10^{-3}$

$HSeO_3^- \rightleftharpoons H^+ + SeO_3^{2-}$ $\qquad K = 5 \times 10^{-8}$

First Ionization

	Init. Conc.	Change	Equil. Conc.
H^+	~0.0	+X	X
$HSeO_3^-$	0.0	+X	X
H_2SeO_3	0.50	-X	0.50 - X

$3.0 \times 10^{-3} = \dfrac{(X)(X)}{0.50 - X}$ Solved by successive approximations;

1) Assume 0.50 - X ≈ 0.50 and solve for X; $X = 3.9 \times 10^{-2}$ or 0.04

2) Assume 0.50 - X = 0.50 - 0.04 and solve for X; $X = 3.7 \times 10^{-2}$ or 0.04

3) Assume 0.50 - X = 0.50 - 0.04 No change from second approximation;

therefore, $X = 3.7 \times 10^{-2}$

<u>Second Ionization</u>

	Init. Conc.	Change	Equil. Conc.
H^+	3.7×10^{-2}	+X	$3.7 \times 10^{-2} + X$
SeO_3^{2-}	0	+X	X
$HSeO_3^-$	3.7×10^{-2}	-X	$3.7 \times 10^{-2} - X$

$K = 5.0 \times 10^{-8} = \dfrac{(3.7 \times 10^{-2} - X)X}{(3.7 \times 10^{-2} - X)} \approx \dfrac{(3.7 \times 10^{-2})X}{3.7 \times 10^{-2}}$ $\qquad X = 5.0 \times 10^{-8}$

$[H^+] = 0.037$ M = **0.04 M** $\quad$ pH = **1.4** $\quad$ $[HSeO_3^-]$ = **0.04 M**

$[H_2SeO_3]$ = **0.46 M** $\quad$ $[SeO_3^{2-}]$ = **5.0×10^{-8} M**

15.38 (See Table 15.2) The second ionization will have no noticeable effect on the pH.

We can ignore it. $H_2C_6H_6O_6 \rightleftharpoons H^+ + HC_6H_6O_6^-$

M.W. ($H_2C_6H_6O_6$) = 176

$$M\ (H_2C_6H_6O_6) = 0.500g \times \frac{1\ mol}{176\ g} \times \frac{1}{0.250\ L} = 1.14 \times 10^{-2}$$

$$K_a = 7.9 \times 10^{-5} = \frac{X^2}{1.14 \times 10^{-2}} \qquad X = [H^+] = 9.49 \times 10^{-4}$$

pH = <u>3.02</u>

15.39 Vitamin C = $H_2C_6H_6O_6$

$H_2C_6H_6O_6 \rightleftharpoons H^+ + HC_6H_6O_6^-$ $\qquad K_{a1} = 7.9 \times 10^{-5}$

$HC_6H_6O_6^- \rightleftharpoons H^+ + C_6H_6O_6^{2-}$ $\qquad K_{a2} = 1.6 \times 10^{-12}$

(See exercise 15.37) $\quad K_{a1} = \frac{(X)(X)}{0.050 - X} \approx \frac{X^2}{0.050} = 7.9 \times 10^{-5}$

$X = 1.99 \times 10^{-3} - [H^+] = [HC_6H_6O_6^-]$

$0.050 - X = 0.050 - 0.002 = 0.048 = [H_2C_6H_6O_6]$

$$K_{a2} = \frac{(1.99 \times 10^{-3})\ Y}{1.99 \times 10^{-3}} = 1.6 \times 10^{-12}$$

$Y = [C_6H_6O_6^{2-}] = 1.6 \times 10^{-12}$

$[H^+] = [HC_6H_6O_6^-] =$ **<u>2.0×10^{-3} M</u>** $\qquad [OH^-] =$ **<u>5.0×10^{-12} M</u>**

pH = **<u>2.7</u>** $\qquad [H_2C_6H_6O_6] =$ **<u>0.048 M</u>** $\qquad [C_6H_6O_6^{2-}] =$ **<u>1.6×10^{-12} M</u>**

15.40 (See Exercise 15.37) $H_3PO_4 \rightleftharpoons H^+ + H_2PO_4^-$ $K_{a1} = 7.5 \times 10^{-3}$

$H_2PO_4^- \rightleftharpoons H^+ + HPO_4^{2-}$ $K_{a2} = 6.2 \times 10^{-8}$

$HPO_4^{2-} \rightleftharpoons H^+ + PO_4^{3-}$ $K_{a3} = 2.2 \times 10^{-12}$

$$K_{a1} = \frac{(X)(X)}{1.0 - X} \approx \frac{X^2}{1.0} = 7.5 \times 10^{-3}$$

$X = [H^+] = [H_2PO_4^-] = \underline{\mathbf{0.087\ M}}$

pH = <u>1.1</u> $[H_3PO_4] = 1.0 - 0.087 = \underline{\mathbf{0.91\ M}}$

$$K_{a2} = \frac{(0.087 + Y)\,Y}{0.087 - Y} \approx \frac{(0.087)Y}{0.087} = 6.2 \times 10^{-8}$$

$Y = [HPO_4^{2-}] = \underline{\mathbf{6.2 \times 10^{-8}\ M}}$

$$K_{a3} = \frac{(0.087 + Z)Z}{6.2 \times 10^{-8} - Z} \approx \frac{(0.087)Z}{6.2 \times 10^{-8}} = 2.2 \times 10^{-12}$$

$Z = [PO_4^{3-}] = \underline{\mathbf{1.6 \times 10^{-18}\ M}}$

15.41 $H_2C_6H_6O_6 \rightleftharpoons H^+ + HC_6H_6O_6^-$ $K = 7.9 \times 10^{-5}$

$HC_6H_6O_6^- \rightleftharpoons H^+ + C_6H_6O_6^{2-}$ $K = 1.6 \times 10^{-12}$

$$M(H_2C_6H_6O_6) = 0.500\ g \times \frac{1\ mol}{176\ g} \times \frac{1}{0.200\ L} = 1.42 \times 10^{-2}\ M$$

<u>First Ionization</u>

	Init. Conc.	Change	Equil. Conc.
H^+	0.1 (from pH)	+X	$0.1 + X \approx 0.1$
$HC_6H_6O_6^-$	0	+X	+X
$H_2C_6H_6O_6$	1.42×10^{-2}	-X	$(1.42 \times 10^{-2}) - X \approx 1.42 \times 10^{-2}$

The second ionization will have no noticeable effect on the concentrations.

(15.41 continued)

$$K_{a1} = \frac{(0.1)\,X}{1.42 \times 10^{-2}} = 7.9 \times 10^{-5} \qquad X = 1.1 \times 10^{-5}$$

$$\text{fraction dissociated} = \frac{1.1 \times 10^{-5}}{1.42 \times 10^{-2}} = \underline{7.9 \times 10^{-4}}$$

15.42 First Ionization of H_2CO_3

	Init. Conc.	Change	Equil. Conc.
H^+	1.0×10^{-3} (from pH)	+X	$1.0 \times 10^{-3} + X \approx 1.0 \times 10^{-3}$
HCO_3^-	0	+X	X
H_2CO_3	0.10	-X	$0.10 - X \approx 0.10$

$$K_{a1} = \frac{(1.0 \times 10^{-3})\,(X)}{0.10} = 4.3 \times 10^{-7}$$

$X = [HCO_3^-] = \underline{4.3 \times 10^{-5}\ M} = \underline{4.3 \times 10^{-5}\ mol/L}$

Second Ionization

	Init. Conc.	Change	Equil. Conc.
H^+	1.0×10^{-3}	+Y	$1.0 \times 10^{-3} + Y \approx 1.0 \times 10^{-3}$
CO_3^{2-}	0	+Y	Y
HCO_3^-	4.3×10^{-5}	-Y	$4.3 \times 10^{-5} - Y \approx 4.3 \times 10^{-5}$

$$K_{a2} = \frac{(1.0 \times 10^{-3})\,Y}{4.3 \times 10^{-5}} = 5.6 \times 10^{-11} \qquad Y = [CO_3^{2-}] = \underline{2.4 \times 10^{-12}\ M}$$

15.43 $K_{a1} \times K_{a2} = 1.1 \times 10^{-21} = \dfrac{[H^+]^2[S^{2-}]}{[H_2S]}$

$$1.1 \times 10^{-21} = \frac{[H^+]^2(8.4 \times 10^{-15})}{0.10} \qquad [H^+] = \underline{1.1 \times 10^{-4}\ M}$$

15.44 $K_{a1} \times K_{a2} = 1.1 \times 10^{-21} = \frac{[H^+]^2[S^{2-}]}{[H_2S]}$ $[H^+] = 2.51 \times 10^{-5}$ (from pH)

$$1.1 \times 10^{-21} = \frac{(2.51 \times 10^{-5})^2[S^{2-}]}{0.10}$$

$[S^{2-}] = \mathbf{1.7 \times 10^{-13}\ M}$

15.45 First Ionization

	Init. Conc.	Change	Equil. Conc.
H^+	?	?	3.7×10^{-8} (from pH)
HCO_3^-	0	+X	X
H_2CO_3	2.6×10^{-2}	-X	2.6×10^{-2} - X

$$K_{a1} = 4.3 \times 10^{-7} = \frac{(3.7 \times 10^{-8})X}{(2.6 \times 10^{-2}) - X}$$

$X = [HCO_3^-] = \mathbf{2.4 \times 10^{-2}\ M}$

Second Ionization

	Init. Conc.	Change	Equil. Conc.
H^+	--	--	3.7×10^{-8}
CO_3^{2-}	0	+X	X
HCO_3^-	2.4×10^{-2}	-X	2.4×10^{-2} - X

$$K_{a2} = 5.6 \times 10^{-11} = \frac{(3.7 \times 10^{-8})X}{(2.4 \times 10^{-2} - X)} = \frac{(3.7 \times 10^{-8})X}{2.4 \times 10^{-2}}$$

$X = \mathbf{3.6 \times 10^{-5}}$

$[HCO_3^-] = 2.4 \times 10^{-2} - 3.6 \times 10^{-5} = \mathbf{2.4 \times 10^{-2}\ M}$

15.46 A buffer is any solution that contains both a weak acid and a weak base and has the property that the addition of small quantities of a strong acid are neutralized by the weak base while small quantities of a strong base are neutralized by the weak acid.

(a) $NaCHO_2$ provides weak conjugate base CHO_2^-; $HCHO_2$ is the weak acid.

(b) C_5H_5N provides the weak base; C_5H_5NHCl provides weak acid $C_5H_5NH^+$.

(c) $NH_4C_2H_3O_2$ provides weak base $C_2H_3O_2^-$ and the weak acid NH_4^+.

(d) $NaHCO_3$ provides weak base HCO_3^-; HCO_3^- is <u>both</u> a weak acid and a weak base.

15.47 No. HCl is a strong acid and is completely dissociated. Cl^- is a very weak conjugate base and cannot neutralize another "acid".

15.48 For additions of strong acid, $HPO_4^{2-} + H_3O^+ \longrightarrow H_2PO_4^- + H_2O$.

For additions of strong base, $H_2PO_4^- + OH^- \longrightarrow HPO_4^{2-} + H_2O$

15.49 $K_a = 1.38 \times 10^{-4} = \dfrac{[H^+][C_3H_5O_3^-]}{[HC_3H_5O_3]}$ $\quad H^+ = 5.62 \times 10^{-5}$ M

$$\frac{[C_3H_5O_3^-]}{[HC_3H_5O_3]} = \frac{[NaC_3H_5O_3]}{[HC_3H_5O_3]} = \frac{1.38 \times 10^{-4}}{5.62 \times 10^{-5}} = 2.45$$

$$\text{Reciprocal value} = \frac{[HC_3H_5O_3]}{[NaC_3H_5O_3]} = \underline{\mathbf{0.41}}$$

15.50 **(a)** $NH_3 + H_2O \rightleftharpoons NH_4 + OH^-$

$K_b = 1.8 \times 10^{-5} = \frac{[NH_4^+][OH^-]}{[NH_3]} = \frac{(0.10)[OH^-]}{(0.10)}$ $[OH^-] = 1.8 \times 10^{-5}$

$[H^+] = 1.0 \times 10^{-14} / 1.8 \times 10^{-5} = 5.556 \times 10^{-10}$ **pH = 9.26**

(b) $HC_2H_3O_2 \rightleftharpoons H^+ + C_2H_3O_2^-$ $K_a = 1.8 \times 10^{-5} = \frac{[H^+](0.40)}{(0.20)}$

$[H^+] = 9.0 \times 10^{-6}$ M **pH = 5.05**

(c) $N_2H_4 + H_2O \rightleftharpoons N_2H_5^+ + OH^-$ $K_b = 1.7 \times 10^{-6} = \frac{(0.10)[OH^-]}{(0.15)}$

$[OH^-] = 2.55 \times 10^{-6}$ **pH = 8.41**

(d) $HCl \longrightarrow H^+ + Cl^-$ (100% ionization) $[H^+] = 0.20$ **pH = 0.70**

15.51 $HC_2H_3O_2 \rightleftharpoons H^+ + C_2H_3O_2^-$

$K_a = 1.8 \times 10^{-5} = \frac{(7.08 \times 10^{-6})[C_2H_3O_2^-]}{1.00}$ $[C_2H_3O_2^-] = 2.54$ M

$\frac{2.54 \text{ mol } C_2H_3O_2^-}{L} \times 1.00 \text{ L} \times \frac{1 \text{ mol } NaC_2H_3O_2}{\text{mol } C_2H_3O_2^-} \times \frac{82.1 \text{ g}}{\text{mol}} = \mathbf{210\ g}$

15.52 pH = 10.00, $[H^+] = 1.0 \times 10^{-10}$ $[OH^-] = 1.0 \times 10^{-4}$

$NH_3 + H_2O \rightleftharpoons NH_4^+ + OH^-$

$K_b = 1.8 \times 10^{-5} = \frac{[NH_4^+](1.0 \times 10^{-4})}{[NH_3]}$

$\frac{[NH_4^+]}{[NH_3]} = 0.18$ $\frac{[NH_3]}{[NH_4^+]} = \frac{1}{0.18} = \mathbf{5.6}$

15.53 $HC_2H_3O_2 \rightleftharpoons H^+ + C_2H_3O_2^-$

	Init. Conc.	Change	Equil. Conc.
H^+	Y	-X	$Y - X = 1.0 \times 10^{-3}$
$C_2H_3O_2^-$	0.010	-X	0.010 - X
$HC_2H_3O_2^-$	0.010	+X	0.010 + X

$$K_a = 1.8 \times 10^{-5} = \frac{(1.0 \times 10^{-3})(0.010 - X)}{(0.010 + X)}$$

$X = 9.6 \times 10^{-3}$ $\quad$ $Y = 9.6 \times 10^{-3} + 1.0 \times 10^{-3} = 1.06 \times 10^{-2}$ M HCl

1.1×10^{-2} moles of HCl must be added

15.54 (a) Initial pH $\quad 1.8 \times 10^{-5} = \frac{[H^+][1.00]}{[1.00]}$ $\quad [H^+] = 1.8 \times 10^{-5}$

pH 4.74

pH after the addition of 0.10 mol NaOH per 0.500 L or 0.20 M; pH = ?

(Note: There will not be dilution during the addition of NaOH. The 0.20 M has been calculated using the volume of the buffer.)

	Init. Conc.	Effect of NaOH	Change	Equil. Conc.
$C_2H_3O_2^-$	1.00	+0.20	+X	$1.20 + X \approx 1.20$
H^+	~0		+X	X
$HC_2H_3O_2$	1.00	-0.20	-X	$0.80 - X \approx 0.80$

$$K_a = 1.8 \times 10^{-5} = \frac{(X)(1.20)}{(0.80)}$$ $\quad X = [H^+] = 1.20 \times 10^{-5}$

pH = 4.92 $\quad$ **ΔpH** = 4.92 - 4.74 = **0.18**

(15.54 continued)

(b) Initial pH = 4.74

pH after the addition of 0.20 M NaOH; equals ?

	Init. Conc.	Effect of NaOH	Change	Equil. Conc.
$C_2H_3O_2^-$	0.50	+0.20	+X	$0.70 + X \approx 0.70$
H^+	~0		+X	X
$HC_2H_3O_2$	0.50	-0.20	-X	$0.30 - X \approx 0.30$

$K_a = 1.8 \times 10^{-5} = \frac{(X)(0.70)}{(0.30)}$ $X = [H^+] = 7.71 \times 10^{-6}$

pH = 5.11 **ΔpH** = 5.11 - 4.74 = **0.37**

(c) Initial pH = 5.11 (Same as final pH in Exercise 15.54 b)

pH after the addition of the NaOH = ?

$K_a = 1.8 \times 10^{-5} = \frac{[H^+](0.90)}{(0.10)}$ $-\log [H^+] = 5.70$

ΔpH = 0.59

(d) Initial pH = 5.35

pH after the addition of 0.20 M NaOH = ?

	Init. Conc.	Effect of NaOH	Change	Equil. Conc.
$C_2H_3O_2^-$	0.80	+0.20	-X	1.0 - X
H^+	~0		-?	?
$HC_2H_3O_2$	0.20	-0.20	+X	0 + X

Since all of the $HC_2H_3O_2$ is consumed by the NaOH, the equilibrium must

(continued)

(15.54 continued)

shift in the direction that tends to restore $HC_2H_3O_2$. This is hydrolysis of the $C_2H_3O_2^-$.

$$C_2H_3O_2^- + H_2O \longrightarrow HC_2H_3O_2 + OH^-$$

$$K_{hy} = K_b(C_2H_3O_2^-) = K_w/K_a = \frac{[HC_2H_3O_2][OH^-]}{[C_2H_3O_2^-]}$$

	Init. Conc.	Change by Hydrolysis	Equil. Conc.
$HC_2H_3O_2$	0	+X	X
OH^-	~0	+X	X
$C_2H_3O_2^-$	1.0	-X	1.0 - X ≈ 1.0

$1.0 \times 10^{-14}/1.8 \times 10^{-5} = \dfrac{(X)(X)}{1.0}$ $\qquad X = [OH^-] = 2.36 \times 10^{-5}$

pH = 9.37 $\qquad$ **ΔpH = 9.37 - 5.35 = <u>4.02</u>**

(e) Initial pH = 5.70 (Same as final pH in part c)

After addition of NaOH, there will be: 1.00 M $C_2H_3O_2^-$, 0.00 M $HC_2H_3O_2$, and 0.10 M excess NaOH. The M of OH^- contributed by hydrolysis can be neglected when excess base is present. We will demonstrate below that it's contribution is too small to change the pH.

	Init. Conc.	Change	Equil. Conc.
$C_2H_3O_2^-$	1.00	-X	1.00 - X ≈ 1.0
OH^-	0.10	+X	X
$HC_2H_3O_2$	0	+X	X

(15.54 continued)

$$K_{hy} = K_w / K_a = 5.56 \times 10^{-10} = \frac{(X)(0.10 + X)}{1.0}$$

$X = 5.56 \times 10^{-9}$ $\qquad$ $[OH^-] = 0.10 + 5.56 \times 10^{-9} = 0.10$

pOH = 1.00 $\qquad$ pH = 13.00 $\qquad$ **ΔpH = 7.30**

15.55 Initial pH = ?

	Init. Conc.	Change	Equil. Conc.
$HCHO_2$	0.45 M	-X	$0.45 - X \approx 0.45$ M
H^+	~0	+X	X
CHO_2^-	0.55 M	+X	$0.55 + X \approx 0.55$ M

$$K_a = 1.8 \times 10^{-4} = \frac{(X)(0.55)}{0.45} \qquad X = [H^+] = 1.47 \times 10^{-4}$$

Initial pH = 3.83

Final pH = ?

	Init. Conc.	Effect of HCl	Change	Equil. Conc.
$HCHO_2$	0.45 M	+ 0.10	-X	$0.55 - X \approx 0.55$
H^+	~0		+X	X
CHO_2^-	0.55 M	-0.10	+X	$0.45 + X \approx 0.45$

$$K_a = 1.8 \times 10^{-4} = \frac{(X)(0.45)}{0.55} \qquad X = [H^+] = 2.20 \times 10^{-4}$$

Final pH = 3.66

ΔpH = -0.17

15.56 Initial pH = 3.83 Final pH = ?

	Init. Conc.	Effect of NaOH	Change	Equil. Conc.
$HCHO_2$	0.45 M	-0.20	-X	$0.25 - X \approx 0.25$
H^+	~0		+X	X
CHO_2^-	0.55 M	+0.20	+X	$0.75 + X \approx 0.75$

$K_a = 1.8 \times 10^{-4} = \frac{(X)(0.75)}{0.25}$ $X = [H^+] = 6.00 \times 10^{-5}$

Final pH = 4.22 $\Delta pH = \underline{0.39}$

15.57 The pH does not change. In Exercise 15.50 (a) the concentration of NH_3 was 0.10 M and that of NH_4^+ was 0.10 M and the pH was 9.26. If that solution is diluted tenfold, the concentration of the NH_3 andNH_4^+ would each be 0.010 M. The calculated pH of the resulting solution is 9.26 or unchanged by the dilution of the buffered solution.

15.58 Is HCO_3^- an acid or a base? It is both an acid and a base, but as which is it the stronger?

$K_a (HCO_3^-) = K_{a2} (H_2CO_3) = 5.6 \times 10^{-11}$

$K_b (HCO_3^-) = K_{hy} (HCO_3^-) = K_w / K_{a1} (H_2CO_3) =$

$1.0 \times 10^{-14} / 4.3 \times 10^{-7} = 2.33 \times 10^{-8}$

Since it is a stronger base than it is an acid, let's ignore its acid properties and calculate its pH as a base.

(continued)

(15.58 continued)

$K_b = 2.33 \times 10^{-8} = \frac{[OH^-][H_2CO_3]}{0.50} = \frac{X^2}{0.50}$ $X = [OH^-] = 1.0 \times 10^{-4}$

pH = 10.0

(The above assumption is not very accurate. The actual pH can be calculated by using the formula $[H^+] = \sqrt{K_{a1} \times K_{a2}}$. Then, $[H^+]$ would be calculated to be 4.91×10^{-9} and pH would be 8.31. The derivation of the equation $[H^+] = \sqrt{K_{a1} \times K_{a2}}$ requires the simultaneous consideration of both equilibria and is derived in the solution to Exercise 15.80. pH = 10 will be used in this solution. If you can derive the equation $[H^+] = \sqrt{K_{a1} \times K_{a2}}$, please use pH = 8.3.) Final pH = ?

	Init. Conc.	Effect of HCl	Change	Equil. Conc.
HCO_3^-	0.50	-0.05	+X	$0.45 + X \approx 0.45$ M
H^+	--	--	Y	Y
H_2CO_3	0	+0.05	-X	$0.05 - X \approx 0.05$ M

$K_a = K_{a1} = \frac{(Y)(0.45)}{(0.05)} = 4.3 \times 10^{-7}$

$Y = [H^+] = 4.78 \times 10^{-8}$ pH = 7.32

Δ**pH** = 7.32 - 10.0 = **-2.7** (or 7.32 - 8.31 = - 0.99)

15.59 $K_a = 1.8 \times 10^{-5} = \frac{[H^+][C_2H_3O_2^-]}{[HC_2H_3O_2]}$ $[H^+] = 5.62 \times 10^{-5}$

(continued)

(15.59 continued)

$$\frac{[C_2H_3O_2^-]}{[HC_2H_3O_2]} = 0.320 = \frac{\text{moles } C_2H_3O_2^- / V_T}{\text{moles } HC_2H_3O_2 / V_T} = \frac{\text{moles } C_2H_3O_2^-}{\text{moles } HC_2H_3O_2}$$

Moles $C_2H_3O_2^-$ + moles $HC_2H_3O_2$ = initial number of moles of $NaC_2H_3O_2$ = (0.10 mole /L)(0.100 L) or 0.010 moles. Let X = moles $C_2H_3O_2^-$. Then, 0.010 - X will equal moles of $HC_2H_3O_2$.

$$\frac{X}{0.010 - X} = 0.320$$

$X = 2.43 \times 10^{-3}$

$0.010 - X = 7.57 \times 10^{-3}$ mole $HC_2H_3O_2$

From; $HCl + C_2H_3O_2^- \longrightarrow HC_2H_3O_2 + Cl^-$, 7.57×10^{-3} moles $HC_2H_3O_2$ required 7.57×10^{-3} moles HCl.

$$7.57 \times 10^{-3} \text{ mole HCl} \times \frac{1 \text{ L}}{6.0 \text{ mole HCl}} \times \frac{1{,}000 \text{ mL}}{\text{L}} = 1.26 \text{ mL} = \underline{1.3 \text{ mL}}$$

15.60 (d) < (c) < (a) < (b)

15.61 (c) < (d) < (b) < (a)

15.62 PH_2^- is a stronger base than HS^-.

15.63 CN^- is a stronger base than NO_2^-.

15.64 Ammonia

15.65 (e) < (c) < (d) < (a) < (b)

15.66 $K_a \times K_b = K_w = 1.0 \times 10^{-14}$

15.67 Hydrolysis: When a salt dissolves in water, it dissociates fully to produce cations and anions that may subsequently react chemically with the solvent (H_2O) in a process called hydrolysis; e.g., the cation of the salt undergoes hydrolysis in the following equation $M^+ + H_2O \rightleftharpoons MOH + H^+$ while an anion is being hydrolyzed in the reaction, $X^- + H_2O \rightleftharpoons HX + OH^-$.

(a) neutral (b) acidic (c) basic (d) acidic

15.68 $NaC_4H_7O_2$ most basic

$C_6H_5NH_3NO_3$ most acidic

15.69 The second hydrolysis reaction occurs to a negligible extent compared to the first,

e.g.: $K_{h_1} = K_w / K_{a_2} = (1 \times 10^{-14}) / (1 \times 10^{-7}) = 1 \times 10^{-7}$

$K_{h_2} = K_w / K_{a_1} = (1 \times 10^{-14}) / (1.5 \times 10^{-2}) = 7 \times 10^{-13}$

15.70 (a) $C_2H_3O_2^- + H_2O \rightleftharpoons HC_2H_3O_2 + OH^-$

$K_b = K_w / K_a = 1.0 \times 10^{-14} / 1.8 \times 10^{-5} = 5.56 \times 10^{-10}$

$$Kb = \frac{[HC_2H_3O_2][OH^-]}{[C_2H_3O_2^-]} = \frac{(X)(X)}{(1.0 \times 10^{-3}) - X}$$

$X = 7.45 \times 10^{-7} = [OH^-]$ pOH = 6.13 pH = **7.87**

(b) $NH_4^+ \longrightarrow NH_3 + H^+$

$$K_a = K_w / K_b = 5.56 \times 10^{-10} = \frac{(X)(X)}{0.125 - X}$$

$X = [H^+] = 8.34 \times 10^{-6}$ pH = **5.08**

(15.70 continued)

(c) $CO_3^{2-} + H_2O \rightleftharpoons HCO_3^- + OH^-$

$K_b = K_w/K_{a2} = 1.786 \times 10^{-4} = \frac{(X)(X)}{0.10 - X}$

$X = [OH^-] = 4.23 \times 10^{-3}$ pOH = 2.37 pH = **11.63**

(d) $CN^- + H_2O \rightleftharpoons HCN + OH^-$

$K_b = K_w/K_a = 2.04 \times 10^{-5} = \frac{(X)(X)}{0.10 - X}$

$X = [OH^-] = 1.43 \times 10^{-3}$ pH = **11.15**

(e) $NH_3OH^+ \rightleftharpoons NH_2OH + H^+$

$K_a = K_w/K_b = 9.09 \times 10^{-7} = \frac{(X)(X)}{0.20 - X}$

$X = [H^+] = 4.26 \times 10^{-4}$ pH = **3.37**

15.71 $C_5H_5NH^+ \rightleftharpoons C_5H_5N + H^+$

$K_a = 1.0 \times 10^{-14}/1.7 \times 10^{-9} = \frac{(X)(X)}{0.10 - X} = \frac{X^2}{0.10}$

$X = [C_5H_5N] = 7.67 \times 10^{-4}$

% of $C_5H_5NH^+$ reacted $= \frac{7.67 \times 10^{-4}}{0.10} \times 100 =$ **0.77%**

15.72 $Base^- + H_2O \rightleftharpoons H\text{-}Base + OH^-$

$K_b = K_w/K_a = \frac{(2.24 \times 10^{-5})(2.24 \times 10^{-5})}{0.10 - (2.24 \times 10^{-5})} = 5.02 \times 10^{-9}$

$K_w/K_a = 1.0 \times 10^{-14}/K_a = 5.02 \times 10^{-9}$ $K_a =$ **2.0×10^{-6}**

15.73 $OCl^- + H_2O \rightleftharpoons HOCl + OH^-$

$K_b = K_w / K_a = 1.0 \times 10^{-14} / 3.1 \times 10^{-8}$

$$K_b = \frac{[HOCl][OH^-]}{[OCl^-]} = \frac{(X)(X)}{0.67 - X} = 3.23 \times 10^{-7}$$

$X^2 = 0.67 \times 3.23 \times 10^{-7}$ $X = 4.65 \times 10^{-4} = [OH^-]$

pH = **10.67**

15.74 $C_8H_{11}N_2O_3^- + H_2O \rightleftharpoons HC_8H_{11}N_2O_3 + OH^-$

$K_b = K_w / K_a = 1.0 \times 10^{-14} / 3.7 \times 10^{-8} = 2.7 \times 10^{-7}$

$$\frac{10 \text{ mg}}{250 \text{ mL}} \times \frac{1{,}000 \text{ mL}}{\text{L}} \times \frac{1 \text{ g}}{1{,}000 \text{ mg}} \times \frac{1 \text{ mol}}{206.2 \text{ g}} = 1.9 \times 10^{-4} \text{ M}$$

$$K_b = 2.7 \times 10^{-7} = \frac{(X)(X)}{1.9 \times 10^{-4} - X} \approx \frac{X^2}{1.9 \times 10^{-4}}$$

$X = [OH^-] = 7.2 \times 10^{-6}$

pH = **8.86**

15.75 $C_4H_3N_2O_3^- + H_2O \rightleftharpoons HC_4H_3N_2O_3 + OH^-$

$K_b = K_w / K_a = 1.0 \times 10^{-14} / 1.0 \times 10^{-5} = 1.0 \times 10^{-9}$

$$K_b = 1.0 \times 10^{-9} = \frac{(X)(X)}{0.0010 - X} \approx \frac{X^2}{0.0010}$$

$X = [HC_4H_3N_2O_3] = $ **1.0×10^{-6} M**

15.76 $C_6H_6O_6^{2-} + H_2O \rightleftharpoons HC_6H_6O_6^- + OH^-$

$K_b = K_w / K_{a2} = 1.0 \times 10^{-14} / 1.6 \times 10^{-12} = 6.25 \times 10^{-3}$

$$K_b = 6.25 \times 10^{-3} = \frac{(X)(X)}{0.20 - X} \approx \frac{X^2}{0.20}$$

$X = [OH^-] = 3.54 \times 10^{-2}$ Oops! $0.20 - X$ is not ≈ 0.20! Must solve the quadratic equation: $\frac{X^2}{0.20 - X} = 6.25 \times 10^{-3} \approx \frac{X^2}{0.20 - 3.54 \times 10^{-2}}$

$X = [OH^-] = 3.24 \times 10^{-2}$ or 3.21×10^{-2} pH = **12.51** (by either method)

15.77 $PO_4^{3-} + H_2O \rightleftharpoons HPO_4^{2-} + OH^-$

$K_b = K_w / K_{a3} = 1.0 \times 10^{-14} / 2.2 \times 10^{-12} = 4.55 \times 10^{-3}$

$$K_b = 4.55 \times 10^{-3} = \frac{(X)(X)}{0.50 - X} \approx \frac{X^2}{0.50}$$

$X = [OH^-] = 4.77 \times 10^{-2}$. Once again, we see that we cannot drop the variable in the denominator. $0.50 - X$ is not $= 0.50$.

$$4.55 \times 10^{-3} = \frac{(X)(X)}{0.50 - X}$$

(Solve the quadratic equation or solve $4.55 \times 10^{-3} = \frac{X^2}{0.50 - 4.77 \times 10^{-2}}$

Both methods give the same pH value.)

$X = [OH^-] = 4.54 \times 10^{-2}$ pH = **12.66**

Note: The HPO_4^{2-} can be hydrolyzed to form $H_2PO_4^-$, H_3PO_4 and additional OH^-. However, the contribution from these will not change the pH in the first two decimal places.

15.78 $CN^- + H_2O \rightleftharpoons HCN + OH^-$

$K_b = K_w/K_a = 1.0 \times 10^{-14}/4.9 \times 10^{-10} = 2.04 \times 10^{-5}$

$$K_b = 2.04 \times 10^{-5} = \frac{(X)(X)}{0.0010 - X} \approx \frac{X^2}{0.0010}$$

$X = [OH^-] = 1.43 \times 10^{-4}$

Again, we see that the variable in the denominator is not negligible. Therefore, we must solve. (See Exercise 15.77)

$$2.04 \times 10^{-5} = \frac{X^2}{0.0010 - X} \quad \text{or} \quad \frac{X^2}{0.0010 - 1.43 \times 10^{-4}}$$

$X = [OH^-] = 1.32 \times 10^{-4}$ **pH = <u>10.12</u>**

15.79 $C_7H_5O_2^- + H_2O \rightleftharpoons HC_7H_5O_2 + OH^-$

$K_b = K_w/K_a = 1.0 \times 10^{-14}/6.5 \times 10^{-5} = 1.54 \times 10^{-10}$

$$K_b = 1.54 \times 10^{-10} = \frac{(X)(X)}{0.020 - X} \approx \frac{X^2}{0.020}$$

$X = [OH^-] = 1.75 \times 10^{-6}$ **pH = <u>8.24</u>**

15.80 0.10 M NH_4^+ and 0.10 M NO_2^-

$K_a(NH_4^+) = K_w/K_b = 1.0 \times 10^{-14}/1.8 \times 10^{-5} = 5.56 \times 10^{-10}$

$K_b(NO_2^-) = K_w/K_a = 1.0 \times 10^{-14}/4.5 \times 10^{-4} = 2.22 \times 10^{-11}$

The values are too close to be able to neglect one or the other. You will need to consider both equations simultaneously. Consider what you already know.

(1) $NH_4^+ \rightleftharpoons NH_3 + H^+$ $K_a(NH_4^+) = K_w/K_b$

(15.80 continued)

(2) $NO_2^- + H_2O \rightleftharpoons HNO_2 + OH^-$ $\quad K_b(NO_2^-) = K_w/K_a$

(3) Initially, $[NH_4^+]^- = [NO_2^-]$ and this will probably not change significantly, since one is a very weak acid while the other is a very weak base.

(4)$[H^+][OH^-] = 1.0 \times 10^{-14}$ or $[OH^-] = 1.0 \times 10^{-14}/[H^+]$

Divide $K_a(NH_4^+)$ by $K_b(NO_2^-)$

$$\frac{K_a(NH_4^+)}{K_b(NO_2^-)} = \frac{[NH_3][H^+]/[NH_4^+]}{[HNO_2][OH^-]/[[NO_2^-]}$$

Since the denominators are equal:

$$\frac{K_a(NH_4^+)}{K_b(NO_2^-)} = \frac{[NH_3][H^+]}{[HNO_2][OH^-]} = \frac{[NH_3][H^+]}{[HNO_2]\,K_w/[H^+]}$$

$$\frac{K_a(NH_4^+)}{K_b(NO_2^-)} = \frac{[NH_3][H^+]^2}{[HNO_2]\,K_w}$$

If $[NH_4^+] \approx [NO_2^-]$, then $[NH_3] \approx [HNO_2]$ and the equation becomes:

$$\frac{K_a(NH_4^+)}{K_b(NO_2^-)} = \frac{[H^+]^2}{K_w}$$

$$[H^+] = \sqrt{K_a(NH_4^+)\,K_w/K_b(NO_2^-)}$$

$$= \sqrt{K_a(NH_4^+)\,K_a(HNO_2)}$$

$$H^+ = \sqrt{5.56 \times 10^{-10} \times 4.5 \times 10^{-4}} = 5.00 \times 10^{-7}$$

pH = <u>6.30</u>

15.81 Yes - due to hydrolysis

15.82 The endpoint occurs when the indicator changes color, which may or may not occur at the time that the equivalence point is reached.

15.83 (a) Since the titration involves a strong acid and a strong base, the **pH at the equivalence point will be 7.00.**

(b) $\dfrac{0.0200 \text{ mol H}^+ \text{ (from HNO}_3)}{1{,}000 \text{ mL}} \times 15.0 \text{ mL} \times \dfrac{1 \text{ mol OH}^- \text{ (required)}}{1 \text{ mol H}^+ \text{ (available)}}$

$\times \dfrac{1{,}000 \text{ mL KOH (soln.)}}{0.0100 \text{ mol OH}^-}$ = **30.0 mL KOH required to titrate to equivalence point**

(c) mol H^+ available = $\dfrac{0.0200 \text{ mol H}^+}{1{,}000 \text{ mL}} \times 15.0 \text{ mL} = 3.00 \times 10^{-4} \text{ mol H}^+$

mol OH^- available = $\dfrac{0.0100 \text{ mol OH}^-}{1{,}000 \text{ mL}} \times 10.0 \text{ mL} = 1.00 \times 10^{-4} \text{ mol OH}^-$

Excess $H^+ = 3.00 \times 10^{-4} - 1.00 \times 10^{-4} = 2.00 \times 10^{-4}$ mol

$\dfrac{2.00 \times 10^{-4} \text{ mol}}{15.0 \text{ mL} + 10.0 \text{ mL}} \times \dfrac{1{,}000 \text{ mL}}{\text{L}} = 8.00 \times 10^{-3} \text{ M}$

pH = - log 8.00×10^{-3} = **2.10**

(d) mol H^+ available = $\dfrac{0.0200 \text{ mol H}^+}{1{,}000 \text{ mL}} \times 15.0 \text{ mL} = 3.00 \times 10^{-4} \text{ mol H}^+$

mol OH^- available = $\dfrac{0.0100 \text{ mol OH}^-}{1{,}000 \text{ mL}} \times 35.0 \text{ mL} = 3.50 \times 10^{-4} \text{ mol OH}^-$

Excess $OH^- = 3.50 \times 10^{-4} - 3.00 \times 10^{-4} = 5.00 \times 10^{-5}$ mol OH^- excess

$\dfrac{5.0 \times 10^{-5} \text{ mol OH}^-}{15.0 \text{ mL} + 35.0 \text{ mL}} \times \dfrac{1{,}000 \text{ mL}}{\text{L}} = 1.00 \times 10^{-3} \text{ M OH}^-$

pOH = 3.00 **pH = 11.00**

15.84 Titration Reaction: $NaOH + HC_4H_3N_2O_3 \longrightarrow NaC_4H_3N_2O_3 + H_2O$

$$\frac{0.010 \text{ mol acid}}{\text{L}} \times 0.0250 \text{ L} \times \frac{1 \text{ mol base}}{1 \text{ mol acid}} \times \frac{\text{L (base)}}{0.020 \text{ mol base}}$$

= 0.0125 L (base) or 12.5 mL NaOH solution needed

$$\frac{0.010 \text{ mol acid}}{\text{L}} \times 0.0250 \text{ L} \times \frac{1 \text{ mol salt}}{1 \text{ mol acid}} = 2.5 \times 10^{-4} \text{ mol salt}$$

$$\text{Concentration of the salt} = \frac{2.5 \times 10^{-4} \text{ mol}}{0.025 \text{ L} + 0.0125 \text{ L}} = 6.7 \times 10^{-3} \text{ M}$$

$$C_4H_3N_2O_3^- + H_2O \rightleftharpoons HC_4H_3N_2O_3 + OH^-$$

	Init. Conc.	Change	Equil. Conc.
$HC_4H_3N_2O_3$	0	+X	X
OH^-	~0	+X	X
$C_4H_3N_2O_3^-$	6.7×10^{-3}	-X	$6.7 \times 10^{-3} - X \approx 6.7 \times 10^{-3}$

$$K_b = K_w / K_a = 1.0 \times 10^{-14} / 1.0 \times 10^{-5} = X^2 / 6.7 \times 10^{-3}$$

$X = [OH^-] = 2.6 \times 10^{-6}$ pOH = 5.59 pH = <u>8.41</u>

15.85 $HF + NaOH \rightleftharpoons NaF + H_2O$

(a) $\frac{0.200 \text{ mol HF}}{1{,}000 \text{ mL}} \times 50.0 \text{ mL} = 0.0100 \text{ mol HF}$

$$\frac{0.100 \text{ mol NaOH}}{1{,}000 \text{ mL}} \times 5.0 \text{ m} = 0.00050 \text{ mol NaOH}$$

After the initial acid-base reaction, there will be 0.0100 - 0.0005 or 0.0095 mol HF and 0.0005 mol NaF or F^-. This is a buffered solution.

$HF \rightleftharpoons H^+ + F^-$ (continued)

(15.85 continued)

	Init. Conc.	Change	Equil. Conc.
H^+	~0	+X	X
F^-	0.00050 mol /0.055 L	+X	0.00050 /0.055 + X
HF	0.0095 mol /0.055 L	-X	0.0095 /0.055

$$K_a = 6.5 \times 10^{-4} = \frac{(X)[(0.00050 /0.055) + X]}{(0.0095 /0.055)}$$

$X = [H^+] = 6.99 \times 10^{-3}$ M **pH 2.16**

(b) 0.0100 mol HF + 0.0050 mol NaOH yields 0.0050 mol excess HF and 0.0050 mol NaF.

$HF \rightleftharpoons H^+ + F^-$

	Init. Conc.	Change	Equil. Conc.
H^+	~0	+X	X
F^-	0.0050 mol /0.100 L	+X	≈ 0.0050 /0.100
HF	0.0050 mol /0.100 L	-X	≈ 0.0050 /0.100

$$K_a = 6.5 \times 10^{-4} = \frac{(X)\,(0.050)}{(0.050)}$$

$X = [H^+] = 6.5 \times 10^{-4}$ **pH 3.19** (Note: pH = pK_a at half neutralization)

(c) $0.0100 \text{ mol HF} \times \frac{1 \text{ mol NaOH}}{1 \text{ mol HF}} \times \frac{1 \text{ L NaOH}}{0.100 \text{ mol NaOH}} \times \frac{1{,}000 \text{ mL}}{\text{L}}$

= 100 mL NaOH solution required.

$0.0100 \text{ mol HF} \times \frac{1 \text{ mol } F^- \text{ (or NaF)}}{1 \text{ mol HF}} = 0.0100 \text{ mol } F^-$

(continued)

(15.85 continued)

$$\frac{0.0100 \text{ mol F}^-}{50.0 \text{ mL} + 100 \text{ mL}} \times \frac{1{,}000 \text{ mL}}{\text{L}} = 0.0667 \text{ M F}^-$$

$F^- + H_2O \rightleftharpoons HF + OH^-$

	Init. Conc.	Change	Equil. Conc.
F^-	0.0667	-X	0.0667 - X ≈ 0.0667
OH^-	~0	+X	X
HF	0	+X	X

$$K_b = K_w / K_a = \frac{1.0 \times 10^{-14}}{6.5 \times 10^{-4}} \approx \frac{(X)(X)}{0.0667}$$

$X = [OH^-] = 1.01 \times 10^{-6}$ pOH = 5.99 **pH = 8.01**

[Note: If the concentration of OH^- produced by the dissociation of water is considered, the pH will be slightly less. That is, if the initial concentration of OH^- is taken as 1×10^{-7} rather than ≈ 0, a slightly different and more precise answer will be obtained.]

15.86 Initial pH $HC_4H_7O_2 \rightleftharpoons H^+ + C_4H_7O_2^-$

$$K_a = 1.5 \times 10^{-5} = \frac{(X)(X)}{0.10 - X}$$ $X = [H^+] = 1.22 \times 10^{-3}$

pH = 2.91

pH after adding 0.0010 mol NaOH;

0.0100 mol butyric acid plus 0.0010 mol NaOH

$$1.5 \times 10^{-5} = \frac{(X)\{(0.0010 / V) + X\}}{\{(0.0090 / V) - X)\}}$$ $X = [H^+] = 1.35 \times 10^{-4}$

pH = 3.87

(continued)

(15.86 continued)

pH after adding 0.0050 mol NaOH;

$$1.5 \times 10^{-5} = \frac{(X)\{(0.0050/V) + X\}}{\{(0.0050/V) - X\}} \qquad X = [H^+] = 1.5 \times 10^{-5}$$

pH = <u>4.82</u>

pH after adding 0.0090 mol NaOH;

$$1.5 \times 10^{-5} = \frac{(X)\{(0.0090/V) + X\}}{\{(0.0010/V) - X\}} \qquad X = [H^+] = 1.67 \times 10^{-6}$$

pH = <u>5.78</u>

pH after adding 0.010 mol NaOH; 0.010 mol NaOH and 0.010 mol

$HC_4H_7O_2$ will form 0.010 mol $C_4H_7O_2^-$ and 0.010 mol Na^+ plus water. The

$C_4H_7O_2^-$ will undergo hydrolysis.

$$C_4H_7O_2^- + H_2O \rightleftharpoons HC_4H_7O_2 + OH^-$$

$$K_b = K_w/K_a = 1.0 \times 10^{-14}/1.5 \times 10^{-5} = \frac{(X)(X)}{(0.010\ \text{mol}/0.10\ \text{L}) - X}$$

$X = [OH^-] = 8.16 \times 10^{-6}$ **pH = <u>8.91</u>**

pH after adding 0.011 mol NaOH;

0.010 mol $HC_4H_7O_2$ plus 0.011 mol NaOH will yield 0.010 mol $C_4H_7O_2^-$ and

0.001 mol of excess NaOH. The excess of the strong base will determine the

pH. 0.001 mol NaOH = 0.001 mol OH^-.

0.001 mol OH^- /0.100 L = 0.01 M OH^- **pH = <u>12.0</u>**

Plot a curve of pH vs. moles of NaOH added!

pH at equivalence point = <u>8.91</u>

Indicator: thymol blue or phenolphthalein

15.87 ?mol H^+ (initial) = 50.0 mL acid $\times \frac{0.10 \text{ mol } H^+}{10^3 \text{ mL acid}}$ = **5.0 x 10^{-3} mol H^+**

If mol H^+ > mol OH^-, the **mol H^+ (XS) = mol H^+ - mol OH^-**

If mol OH^- > mol H^+, the **mol OH^- (XS) = mol OH^- - mol H^+**

$[H^+]$ = mol H^+ /final total volume in liters

$[OH^-]$ = mol OH^- /final total volume in liters

point	mL base added:	mol base	M H^+	pH
1	0.00	0.00	0.10	1.00
2	10.00	0.0010	0.067	1.18
3	20.00	0.0020	0.043	1.37
4	30.00	0.0030	0.025	1.60
5	40.00	0.0040	0.011	1.95
6	45.00	0.0045	0.0053	2.28
7	49.00	0.0049	0.0010	3.00
8	50.00	0.0050	$1.0\text{x}10^{-7}$	7.00
9	51.00	0.0051	$1.0\text{x}10^{-11}$	11.00
10	55.00	0.0055	$2.1\text{x}10^{-12}$	11.68
11	60.00	0.0060	$1.1\text{x}10^{-12}$	11.96
12	70.00	0.0070	$6.0\text{x}10^{-13}$	12.22
13	80.00	0.0080	$4.3\text{x}10^{-13}$	12.36
14	90.00	0.0090	$3.5\text{x}10^{-3}$	12.46
15	100.00	0.0100	$3.0\text{x}10^{-13}$	12.52

These results will yield a plot very much like Figure 15.3 with an equivalence point of pH = 7.0.

15.88

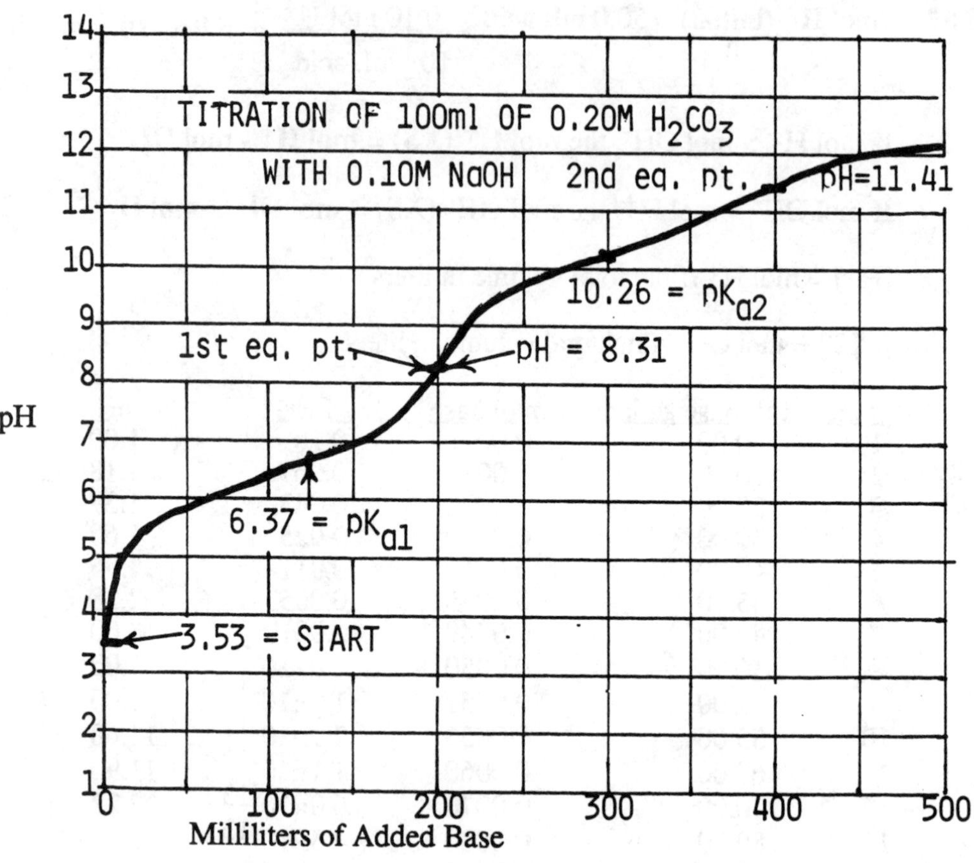

15.89 Acid and basic forms of an indicator differ in color ($HIn \rightleftharpoons H^+ + In^-$). Therefore, depending on the pH range of your indicator, it will change to HIn in acid solution and In^- in basic solution. This color change ideally should correspond to the endpoint of the titration. If too much indicator is added, it may interfere with the endpoint because it will react with the base in the titration.

15.90 Thymol Blue or Phenolphthalein

Congo Red pH range is too low. It would change color before the equivalence point is reached.

15.91 No. pH range for the color change is too low.

15.92 (a) HCN $K_a = 4.9 \times 10^{-10}$ If the concentration of the salt is about 0.10 M NaCN at the equivalence point, the pH at the equivalence point is:

$K_w / K_a = 1.0 \times 10^{-14} / 4.9 \times 10^{-10} = X^2 / 0.1$

$X = [OH^-] = 1.43 \times 10^{-3}$ **pH = <u>11.2</u>**

In Table 15.5, **alizarin yellow** is the only suitable indicator shown.

(b) $C_6H_5NH_2$ $K_b = 3.8 \times 10^{-10}$ Assume that at the equivalence point the concentration of $C_6H_5NH_3Cl$ is approximately 0.10 M.

$$C_6H_5NH_3^+ \rightleftharpoons C_6H_5NH_2 + H^+$$

$$K_a = K_w / K_b = 1.0 \times 10^{-14} / 3.8 \times 10^{-10} = \frac{(X)(X)}{0.10 - X}$$

$X = [H^+] = 1.62 \times 10^{-3}$ **pH = <u>2.79</u>**

The only suitable indicator listed in Table 15.5 is **thymol blue.**

15.93 Using the Henderson-Hasselbalch equation:

$$pH = pK_a + \log \frac{[anion]}{[acid]}$$

$$7.0 = -\log 1 \times 10^{-5} + \log \frac{[anion]}{[acid]}$$

$$2.0 = \log \frac{[anion]}{[acid]} \qquad [Anion]/100 = [Acid]$$

The solution will be green.

16 SOLUBILITY AND COMPLEX ION EQUILIBRIA

16.1 The concentration of the solid is left out of the solubility equilibrium expression of a salt because it is not a variable and can be (and is) included within the constant K_{sp}.

16.2 (a) $Ag_2S\ (s) \rightleftharpoons 2Ag^+(aq) + S^{2-}(aq)$

$K_{sp} = [Ag^+]^2\ [S^{2-}]$ (b) $K_{sp} = [Ca^{2+}]\ [F^-]^2$

(c) $K_{sp} = [Fe^{3+}]\ [OH^-]^3$ (d) $K_{sp} = [Mg^{2+}]\ [C_2O_4^{2-}]$

(e) $K_{sp} = [Bi^{3+}]^2\ [S^{2-}]^3$ (f) $K_{sp} = [Ba^{2+}]\ [CO_3^{2-}]$

16.3 (a) $K_{sp} = [Pb^{2+}]\ [F^-]^2$ (b) $K_{sp} = [Cu^+]^2\ [S^{2-}]$

(c) $K_{sp} = [Fe^{2+}]^3\ [PO_4^{3-}]^2$ (d) $K_{sp} = [Li^+]^2\ [CO_3^{2-}]$

(e) $K_{sp} = [Ca^{2+}]\ [IO_3^-]^2$ (f) $K_{sp} = [Ag^+]^2\ [Cr_2O_7^{2-}]$

16.4 $CuCl(s) \longrightarrow Cu^+(aq) + Cl^-(aq)$

$K_{sp} = [Cu^+][Cl^-] = (1.0 \times 10^{-3})(1.0 \times 10^{-3}) = \underline{\mathbf{1.0 \times 10^{-6}}}$

16.5 $PbCO_3(s) \longrightarrow Pb^{2+}(aq) + CO_3^{2-}(aq)$

$K_{sp} = [Pb^{2+}][CO_3^{2-}] = (1.8 \times 10^{-7})(1.8 \times 10^{-7}) = \underline{\mathbf{3.2 \times 10^{-14}}}$

16.6 $BaC_2O_4(s) \longrightarrow Ba^{2+}(aq) + C_2O_4^{2-}(aq)$

$$\frac{0.0781\ g}{L} \times \frac{1\ mol}{225.4\ g} = 3.466 \times 10^{-4}\ mol/L$$

$K_{sp} = [Ba^{2+}][C_2O_4^{2-}] = (3.466 \times 10^{-4})(3.466 \times 10^{-4}) = \underline{\mathbf{1.20 \times 10^{-7}}}$

16.7 $CaCrO_4(s) \longrightarrow Ca^{2+}(aq) + CrO_4^{2-}(aq)$

$K_{sp} = [Ca^{2+}][CrO_4^{2-}] = (1.0 \times 10^{-2})(1.0 \times 10^{-2}) = \underline{\mathbf{1.0 \times 10^{-4}}}$

16.8 $PbI_2(s) \longrightarrow Pb^{2+}(aq) + 2I^-(aq)$

$K_{sp} = [Pb^{2+}][I^-]^2 = (1.5 \times 10^{-3})(2 \times 1.5 \times 10^{-3})^2 = \underline{\mathbf{1.4 \times 10^{-8}}}$

16.9 $$\frac{0.0981\ g}{0.200\ L} \times \frac{1\ mol}{245.2\ g} = 2.000 \times 10^{-3}\ mol/L$$

$PbF_2(s) \longrightarrow Pb^{2+}(aq) + 2F^-(aq)$

$K_{sp} = [Pb^{2+}][F^-]^2 = (2.000 \times 10^{-3})(2 \times 2.000 \times 10^{-3})^2 = \underline{\mathbf{3.20 \times 10^{-8}}}$

16.10 $MgF_2(s) \longrightarrow Mg^{2+}(aq) + 2F^-(aq)$

$$\frac{7.6 \times 10^{-2}\ g}{L} \times \frac{1\ mol}{62.3\ g} = 1.22 \times 10^{-3}\ mol/L$$

$K_{sp} = [Mg^{2+}][F^-]^2 = (1.22 \times 10^{-3})(2 \times 1.22 \times 10^{-3})^2 = \underline{\mathbf{7.3 \times 10^{-9}}}$

16.11 $$\frac{2.5 \times 10^{-12}\ g}{L} \times \frac{1\ mol}{514\ g} = 4.86 \times 10^{-15}\ mol/L$$

$Bi_2S_3(s) \longrightarrow 2Bi^{3+}(aq) + 3S^{2-}(aq)$

$K_{sp} = [Bi^{3+}]^2[S^{2-}]^3 = (2 \times 4.86 \times 10^{-15})^2(3 \times 4.86 \times 10^{-15})^3 = \underline{\mathbf{2.9 \times 10^{-70}}}$

16.12 pH = 8.83 $[OH^-] = -\log(14 - 8.83) = 6.76 \times 10^{-6}$

$Ni(OH)_2(s) \longrightarrow Ni^{2+}(aq) + 2OH^-(aq)$

$K_{sp} = [Ni^{2+}][OH^-]^2 = (1/2 \times 6.76 \times 10^{-6})(6.76 \times 10^{-6})^2 = \underline{\mathbf{1.5 \times 10^{-16}}}$

16.13 $\dfrac{0.47\ g\ MgC_2O_4}{0.500\ L} \times \dfrac{1\ mol}{112\ g} = 8.39 \times 10^{-3}\ M$

$MgC_2O_4(s) \longrightarrow Mg^{2+}(aq) + C_2O_4^{2-}(aq)$

	Init. Conc.	Added	Equil. Conc.
Mg^{2+}	0	8.39×10^{-3}	8.39×10^{-3}
$C_2O_4^{2-}$	2.0×10^{-3}	8.39×10^{-3}	10.39×10^{-3}

$K_{sp} = (8.39 \times 10^{-3})(10.39 \times 10^{-3}) = \underline{\mathbf{8.7 \times 10^{-5}}}$

16.14 **(a)** $PbS(s) \longrightarrow Pb^{2+}(aq) + S^{2-}(aq)$

	Init. Conc.	Change	Equil. Conc.
Pb^{2+}	0	+X	X
S^{2-}	0	+X	X

$K_{sp} = 7 \times 10^{-27} = (X)(X)$ X = molar solubility = $\underline{\mathbf{8 \times 10^{-14}\ M}}$

(b) $Fe(OH)_2(s) \longrightarrow Fe^{2+}(aq) + 2OH^-(aq)$

	Init. Conc.	Change	Equil. Conc.
Fe^{2+}	0	+X	X
OH^-	1×10^{-7}	+ 2X	2X

$K_{sp} = 2 \times 10^{-15} = (X)(2X)^2$ X = molar solubility = $\underline{\mathbf{8 \times 10^{-6}\ M}}$

(16.14 continued)

(c) $BaSO_4(s) \longrightarrow Ba^{2+}(aq) + SO_4^{2-}(aq)$

	Init. Conc.	Change	Equil. Conc.
Ba^{2+}	0	+X	X
SO_4^{2-}	0	+X	X

$K_{sp} = 1.5 \times 10^{-9} = (X)(X)$ X = molar solubility = **$\underline{3.9 \times 10^{-5}\ M}$**

(d) $Hg_2Cl_2(s) \longrightarrow Hg_2^{2+}(aq) + 2Cl^-(aq)$

	Init. Conc.	Change	Equil. Conc.
Hg_2^{2+}	0	+X	X
Cl^-	0	+ 2X	2X

$K_{sp} = 2 \times 10^{-18} = (X)(2X)^2$ X = molar solubility = **$\underline{8 \times 10^{-7}\ M}$**

(e) $CaF_2(s) \longrightarrow Ca^{2+}(aq) + 2F^-(aq)$

	Init. Conc.	Change	Equil. Conc.
Ca^{2+}	0	+X	X
F^-	0	+2X	2X

$K_{sp} = 1.7 \times 10^{-10} = (X)(2X)^2$

X = molar solubility = **$\underline{3.5 \times 10^{-4}\ M}$**

(f) $MgC_2O_4(s) \longrightarrow Mg^{2+}(aq) + C_2O_4^{2-}(aq)$

$K_{sp} = 8.6 \times 10^{-5} = (X)(X)$ X = molar solubility = **$\underline{9.3 \times 10^{-3}\ M}$**

16.15 $Mg(OH)_2(s) \longrightarrow Mg^{2+}(aq) + 2OH^-(aq)$

	Init. Conc.	Change	Equil. Conc.
Mg^{2+}	0	+X	X
OH^-	1×10^{-7}	+2X	$1 \times 10^{-7} + 2X \approx 2X$

$K_{sp} = 1.2 \times 10^{-11} = (X)(2X)^2$ $\quad X = 1.44 \times 10^{-4}$

$[OH^-] = 2.88 \times 10^{-4}$ $\quad$ **pH = <u>10.46</u>**

16.16 $CaSO_4(s) \longrightarrow Ca^{2+}(aq) + SO_4^{2-}(aq)$

$K_{sp} = 2 \times 10^{-4} = (X)(X)$ $\quad$ X = molar solubility = 1.4×10^{-2} M

$$\frac{1.4 \times 10^{-2} \text{ mol } CaSO_4}{L} \times 0.600 \text{ L} \times \frac{136 \text{ g}}{\text{mol}} = \underline{\mathbf{1 \text{ g } CaSO_4}}$$

16.17 $HgS(s) \longrightarrow Hg^{2+}(aq) + S^{2-}(aq)$

$K_{sp} = [Hg^{2+}][S^{2-}] = [Hg^{2+}]^2 = 1.6 \times 10^{-54}$ $\quad [Hg^{2+}] = 1.26 \times 10^{-27}$ M

$$\frac{1 \text{ L}}{1.26 \times 10^{-27} \text{ mol}} \times \frac{1 \text{ mol}}{6.022 \times 10^{23} \text{ ions}} = \underline{\mathbf{1.3 \times 10^3 \text{ L /ion}}}$$

16.18 Volume of plaster = $\pi r^2 h = 3.14 \times (0.5 \text{ cm})^2(1.50 \text{ cm}) = 1.18 \text{ cm}^3$

Mass of plaster = $1.18 \text{ cm}^3 \times 0.97 \text{ g /mL} \times 1 \text{ mL /cm}^3 = 1.14$ g

$CaSO_4(s) \longrightarrow Ca^{2+}(aq) + SO_4^{2-}(aq)$ $\quad K_{sp} = 2. \times 10^{-4} = (X)(X)$

X = molar solubility = 1.4×10^{-2} mol /L

$(1.4 \times 10^{-2} \text{ mol /L}) \times 136 \text{ g /mol} = 1.90 \text{ g /L}$

Liters required to dissolve 1.14 g: 1.14 g x 1L /1.90 g = 0.6 L or 600 mL

Days required: 0.6 L x 1d /2.0 L = **<u>0.3 day</u>**

16.19 In a solution, a precipitate will form only if the mixture is supersaturated. That is, when the value of the ion product exceeds the value of its K_{sp}.

16.20 (a) The ion concentrations are: 5.0×10^{-2} M Ag^+, 5.0×10^{-2} M NO_3^-, 1.0×10^{-3} M Na^+ and 1.0×10^{-3} M $C_2H_3O_2^-$. Possible salts include $AgNO_3$ (soluble -- no K_{sp} value), $NaC_2H_3O_2$ (? K_{sp}, soluble), $NaNO_3$ (soluble), $AgC_2H_3O_3$ (possible precipitate -- $K_{sp} = 2.3 \times 10^{-3}$). For $AgC_2H_3O_3$, ion product = $(5.0 \times 10^{-2})(1.0 \times 10^{-3}) = 5.0 \times 10^{-5}$ which is less than its K_{sp}. Therefore, **no precipitate will form.**

(b) 1.0×10^{-2} M Ba^{2+}, 2.0×10^{-2} M NO_3^-,2.0×10^{-2} M Na^+, and 2.0×10^{-2} M F^-. The possible salts include: $Ba(NO_3)_2$ (soluble -- no K_{sp} value), BaF_2 (possible precipitate -- $K_{sp} = 1.7 \times 10^{-6}$), NaF (soluble -- no K_{sp} value), $NaNO_3$ (soluble -- no K_{sp} value given). The only possible precipitate, BaF_2, has an ion product value = $(1.0 \times 10^{-2})(2.0 \times 10^{-2})^2 = 4.0 \times 10^{-6}$, which is greater than its K_{sp} value. **BaF_2 will precipitate.**

(c) The ion concentrations are: 9.33×10^{-3} M Ca^{2+}, 1.87×10^{-2} M Cl^-, 1.67×10^{-1} M Na^+, and 8.33×10^{-2} M SO_4^{2-}. The possible salts include: $CaCl_2$ (soluble), $CaSO_4$ (possible precipitate -- $K_{sp} = 2 \times 10^{-4}$), Na_2SO_4 (soluble), NaCl (soluble). For $CaSO_4$, the ion product value = $(9.33 \times 10^{-3})(8.33 \times 10^{-2})$ = 7.8×10^{-4}, which is greater than its K_{sp} value. **$CaSO_4$ will precipitate.**

16.21 K_{sp} of $Fe(OH)_2 = 2 \times 10^{-15} = [Fe^{2+}][OH^-]^2 = (0.010)(X)^2$

$X^2 = 2 \times 10^{-15}/0.010 = 2 \times 10^{-13}$ $X = [OH^-] = 4.5 \times 10^{-7}$

pOH = 6.35 **pH = <u>7.65</u>** This is the maximum pH at which the value of the ion product will equal or exceed the solubility product constant.

16.22 Possible precipitation: $Ag^+ + Cl^- \longrightarrow AgCl(s)$ $K_{sp} = 1.7 \times 10^{-10}$

Ion	Init.Conc.	Conc. after Mix	Change	Equil. Conc.
Ag^+	0.20 M	0.10 M	- ~0.050	0.050 + Y
NO_3^-	0.20 M	0.10 M	none	0.10
H^+	0.10 M	0.050 M	none	0.050
Cl^-	0.10 M	0.050 M	- ~0.050	Y

$K_{sp} = 1.7 \times 10^{-10} = (0.050 + Y)(Y) \approx (0.050)\,Y$

$Y = 3.4 \times 10^{-9}$ $[Ag^+] = 0.050 + 3.4 \times 10^{-9} =$ <u>**0.050 M**</u>

$[NO_3^-]$ = <u>**0.10 M**</u> $[H^+]$ = <u>**0.050 M**</u> $[Cl^-]$ = <u>**3.4×10^{-9} M**</u>

16.23 **(a)** The only possible precipitate is $CaCO_3$ ($K_{sp} = 9 \times 10^{-9}$).

Ion prod. = (0.025)(0.0050) = 1.25×10^{-4} Since Ion Product > K_{sp},

<u>**$CaCO_3$ will precipitate.**</u>

(b) The only possible precipitate is $PbCl_2$ ($K_{sp} = 1.6 \times 10^{-5}$)

Ion Product = $(0.010)(0.060)^2 = 3.6 \times 10^{-5}$

Ion Product > K_{sp} <u>**$PbCl_2$ will precipitate**</u>

(c) The only possible precipitate is FeC_2O_4 ($K_{sp} = 2.1 \times 10^{-7}$)

Ion Product = $(1.5 \times 10^{-3})(2.2 \times 10^{-3}) = 3.3 \times 10^{-6}$

Ion Product > K_{sp} <u>**FeC_2O_4 will precipitate.**</u>

16.24 K_{sp} (HgS) = 1.6×10^{-54} = $(0.0010)[S^{2-}]$ $\qquad$ $[S^{2-}] = 1.6 \times 10^{-51}$ M

For $H_2S \rightleftharpoons 2H^+ + S^{2-}$ $\qquad$ $K = 1.1 \times 10^{-21}$ and $[H_2S] = 0.10$ M

$$1.1 \times 10^{-21} = \frac{[H^+]^2(1.6 \times 10^{-51})}{0.10} \qquad [H^+] = \underline{\mathbf{2.6 \times 10^{14}\ M}}$$

An impossible value! It should be no suprise that HgS is insoluble in 12 M HCl.

16.25 $K_{sp} = 1.2 \times 10^{-23} = [Zn^{2+}]\,[S^{2-}]$

$$\frac{[H^+]^2[S^{2-}]}{[H_2S]} = 1.1 \times 10^{-21} \text{ and } [H_2S] = 0.10$$

In 12 M HCl, $\dfrac{(12)^2[S^{2-}]}{(0.10)} = 1.1 \times 10^{-21}$ $\qquad$ $[S^{2-}] = 7.64 \times 10^{-25}$ M

$[Zn^{2+}](7.64 \times 10^{-25}) = 1.2 \times 10^{-23}$ $\qquad$ $[Zn^{2+}] = 16$ M

This calculation shows that ZnS will be soluble in 12 M HCl until the concentration of the zinc ions exceeds 16 M. That is a limit that is not likely to be exceeded. **ZnS is very soluble in 12 M HCl.**

16.26 K_{sp} (PbS) = 7×10^{-27}, K_{sp} (NiS) = 2×10^{-21}

Since NiS is the more soluble of the two salts, maximum separation will occur when the $[S^{2-}]$ is only slightly less than that required to precipitate any of the nickel ions. $\qquad$ $2 \times 10^{-21} = (0.010)[S^{2-}]$

$[S^{2-}] = 2.0 \times 10^{-19}$ M $\qquad$ If this value is exceeded, some Ni^{2+} will precipitate.

$$\frac{[H^+]^2[S^{2-}]}{[H_2S]} = 1.1 \times 10^{-21} = \frac{[H^+]^2(2.0 \times 10^{-19})}{(0.10)}$$

$[H^+] = 2.34 \times 10^{-2}$ $\quad$ **pH = <u>1.63</u>** At a pH slightly below 1.63, no Ni^{2+} will precipitate and nearly all of the Pb^{2+} will be precipitated in a sat. H_2S solution.

16.27 K_{sp} (ZnS) = 1.2×10^{-23} K_{sp} (FeS) = 3.7×10^{-19}

To selectively precipitate ZnS, one would adjust the pH so that there is a maximum allowed concentration of S^{2-} that can exist without FeS forming. That is: $3.7 \times 10^{-19} = [Fe^{2+}][S^{2-}] = (0.10)[S^{2-}]$ or $[S^{2-}] = 3.7 \times 10^{-18}$ M. The pH of a saturated H_2S solution with this $[S^{2-}]$ is $= \frac{[H^+]^2[S^{2-}]}{[H_2S]} = 1.1 \times 10^{-21}$

$[H^+] = [(1.1 \times 10^{-21})(0.10) / 3.7 \times 10^{-18}]^{1/2} = [2.97 \times 10^{-5}]^{1/2} = 5.5 \times 10^{-3}$

Needs to have a $[H^+]$ of slightly greater than 5.5×10^{-3} M

$[Zn^{2+}][S^{2-}] = 1.2 \times 10^{-23}$ $[Zn^{2+}] = 1.2 \times 10^{-23} / 3.7 \times 10^{-18} =$ **$\underline{3.2 \times 10^{-6}\ M}$**

16.28 K_{sp} ($BaCrO_4$) = 2.4×10^{-10} K_{sp} = ($PbCrO_4$) = 1.8×10^{-14}

Since the ion concentrations are equal, the **$PbCrO_4$ will precipitate first,** as revealed by its smaller K_{sp} value.

Calculation of $[CrO_4^{2-}]$ when Ba^{2+} begins to precipitate = 2.4×10^{-10} =

$[Ba^{2+}]\ [CrO_4^{2-}] = (0.010)[CrO_4^{2-}]$ $[CrO_4^{2-}] = 2.4 \times 10^{-8}$ M

The concentration of Pb^{2+} when the $[CrO_4^{2-}]$ reaches 2.4×10^{-8} M will be:

$1.8 \times 10^{-14} = [Pb^{2+}]\ [CrO_4^{2-}] = [Pb^{2+}]\ (2.4 \times 10^{-8})$

$[Pb^{2+}] = \underline{7.5 \times 10^{-7}\ M}$

In summary, the $PbCrO_4$ will begin to precipitate first. It will continue to precipitate until the CrO_4^{2-} concentration reaches 2.4×10^{-8} M. At that point

(16.28 continued)

and at high concentrations of CrO_4^{2-}, both $PbCrO_4$ and $BaCrO_4$ will precipitate. When the concentration of CrO_4^{2-} reaches that 2.4×10^{-8} M value, the concentration of Pb^{2+} will have been reduced to 7.5×10^{-7} M.

16.29 $K_{a1} \times K_{a2} = 4.0 \times 10^{-6} = \frac{[H^+]^2[C_2O_4^{2-}]}{[H_2C_2O_4]}$

For maximum separation: ion product MgC_2O_4 equals K_{sp} (MgC_2O_4)

$8.6 \times 10^{-5} = [Mg^{2+}]\,[C_2O_4^{2-}] = (0.10\text{ M})\,[C_2O_4^{2-}]$

$[C_2O_4^{2-}] = 8.6 \times 10^{-4}$ M

$4.0 \times 10^{-6} = \frac{[H^+]^2[C_2O_4^{2-}]}{[H_2C_2O_4]} = \frac{[H^+]^2(8.6 \times 10^{-4})}{(0.10)}$

$[H^+] = 2.16 \times 10^{-2}$, pH = 1.66 **pH of less than 1.66**

16.30 The common ion effect is the reduction of solubility caused by the presence of a common ion.

16.31 K_{sp} ($CaCO_3$) $= 9 \times 10^{-9} = [Ca^{2+}][CO_3^{2-}] = (X)(X + 0.50)$

X = **$\underline{2 \times 10^{-8}\text{ mol/L}}$**

= molar solubility of $CaCO_3$ in 0.50 M Na_2CO_3

16.32 K_{sp} (AgCl) $= 1.7 \times 10^{-10} = [Ag^+][Cl^-] = (X)(X + 0.060)$

X = **$\underline{2.8 \times 10^{-9}\text{ mol/L}}$ = molar solubility of AgCl in 0.020 M $AlCl_3$**

16.33 $K_{sp} = 1.6 \times 10^{-5} = [Pb^{2+}]\,[Cl^-]^2 = (X)(X + 0.060)^2$

$X = 4.4 \times 10^{-3}$ if $X + 0.060$ is assumed to be ≈ 0.060. Not a good assumption.

Assume $X + 0.060 \approx 2(4.4 \times 10^{-3}) + 0.060$ or 0.069.

Then $1.6 \times 10^{-5} = (X)\,(0.069)^2$ or $X = 3.4 \times 10^{-3}$

3.4×10^{-3} mol /L is the calculated molar solubility of $PbCl_2$ in

0.020 M $AlCl_3$

16.34 $K_{sp} = 1.9 \times 10^{-12} = [Ag^+]^2[CrO_4^{2-}] = (2X + 0.10)^2(X) \approx (0.10)^2(X)$

$X =$ **$\underline{1.9 \times 10^{-10}\ \text{mol}\ Ag_2CrO_4\ /L}$**

16.35 $K_{sp} = 1.9 \times 10^{-12} = [Ag^+]^2[CrO_4^{2-}] = (2X)^2(X + 0.10) \approx (4X^2)(0.10)$

$X =$ **$\underline{2.2 \times 10^{-6}\ \text{mol}\ Ag_2CrO_4\ /L}$**

16.36 $K_{sp} = 1.7 \times 10^{-10} = [Ca^{2+}][F^-]^2 = (X)(2X + 0.010)^2 \approx (X)(0.010)^2$

$X =$ **$\underline{1.7 \times 10^{-6}\ \text{mol}\ CaF_2\ /L}$**

16.37 X = moles of NaF added per liter

$K_{sp}\,(BaF_2) = [Ba^{2+}][F^-]^2 = (6.8 \times 10^{-4})(2 \times 6.8 \times 10^{-4} + X)^2 = 1.7 \times 10^{-6}$

(from the solution of the quadratic equation) $X = 4.9 \times 10^{-2}$ mol NaF /L

$$\frac{4.9 \times 10^{-2}\ \text{mol}}{\text{L}} \times \frac{42\ \text{g}}{\text{mol}} = \mathbf{\underline{2.1\ g\ NaF}}$$

16.38 Added HCl

$Mg(OH)_2 + 2HCl \longrightarrow Mg^{2+} + 2Cl^- + 2H_2O$

0.00250 mol HCl will form 0.00125 mol Mg^{2+}

$[Mg^{2+}] = 1.25 \times 10^{-3}$ mol /1.025 L = 1.22×10^{-3} M

$Mg(OH)_2(s) \rightleftharpoons Mg^{2+} + 2OH^-$

$K_{sp} = 1.2 \times 10^{-11} = (1.22 \times 10^{-3} + X)(2X)^2 \approx (1.22 \times 10^{-3})\ 4X^2$

$X = 4.96 \times 10^{-5}$

$[Mg^{2+}] = 1.22 \times 10^{-3} + 4.96 \times 10^{-5} =$ **1.3×10^{-3} M**

$[OH^-] = 2(4.96 \times 10^{-5}) = 9.9 \times 10^{-5}$ **pH = 10.0**

16.39 M NaOH = (2.20 g /40.0 g /mol) /0.250 L = 0.220 M

	Init. Conc.	Change	Equil. Conc.	Assume
Na^+	0.220 M	-	- - -	- -
OH^-	0.220 M	-2X	0.220 - 2X	≈ 0.020
Fe^{2+}	0.10 M	-X	0.10 - X	≈0 or Y
Cl^-	0.20 M	-	- - -	- -

$K_{sp} = 2 \times 10^{-15} = [Fe^{2+}][OH^-]^2 = (Y)(0.020)^2$

$Y = 5.0 \times 10^{-12}$ **$[Fe^{2+}] = 5 \times 10^{-12}$ M**

The amount $Fe(OH)_2$ formed will be: [0.10 mol /L - (5×10^{-12} mol /L)] x

0.250 L x 89.9 g /mol = **2.2 g $Fe(OH)_2$ precipitated**

16.40 1.75 g NaOH / 0.250 L /40.0 g /mol = 0.175 M

	Init. Conc.	Change	Equil. Conc.	Assume	Equil. Conc.
OH^-	0.175 M	-2X	0.175 - 2X	X ≈ 0.0875	Y
Ni^{2+}	0.10 M	-X	0.10 - X		0.0125 + 1/2 Y

$K_{sp} = [Ni^{2+}][OH^-]^2 = 1.6 \times 10^{-14} = (0.0125 + 1/2\ Y)(Y)^2 = 0.0125\ Y^2$

$Y = 1.1 \times 10^{-6} = [OH^-]$ pOH = 5.95

pH = <u>8.05</u>

Mole of $Ni(OH)_2$ precipitated [0.175 mol /L (OH^-) ÷ 2] (0.250 L) =

2.19×10^{-2} moles $Ni(OH)_2$

2.19×10^{-2} moles x 92.7 g /mole = **<u>2.0 g $Ni(OH)_2(s)$</u>**

16.41 K_{sp} $Mn(OH)_2 = 4.5 \times 10^{-14}$ K_{sp} $Fe(OH)_2 = 2 \times 10^{-15}$

	Init. Conc.	Added	Change	Equil. Conc.	Assume	Equil. Conc.
Fe^{2+}	0.100		-Y	0.100 - Y	Y ≈ 0.10	Fe^{2+}
Mn^{2+}	0	X		X	X ≈ 0.100	0.10
OH^-	1×10^{-7}	2X	-2Y	2X - 2Y		OH^-

K_{sp} $Mn(OH)_2 = 4.5 \times 10^{-14} = (0.10)\ [OH^-]^2$, $[OH^-] = 6.7 \times 10^{-7}$

$K_{sp}\ Fe(OH)_2 = 2 \times 10^{-15} = [Fe^{2+}]\ (6.7 \times 10^{-7})^2$

$[Fe^{2+}]$ = <u>4.5×10^{-3} M</u> **pH** = 14 + log 6.7 x 10^{-7} = **<u>7.83</u>**

$[Mn^{2+}]$ = <u>0.10 M</u>

16.42 A complex ion is an ion that contains several atoms including a metal ion. A ligand is the substance that is combined with the metal ion in the formation of a complex ion. Ligands are usually Lewis bases (electron-pair donors).

16.43 (a) $Ag^+ + 2Cl^- \rightleftharpoons AgCl_2^-$ $\qquad K_{form} = \dfrac{[AgCl_2^-]}{[Ag^+][Cl^-]^2}$

(b) $K_{form} = \dfrac{[Ag(S_2O_3)_2^{3-}]}{[Ag^+][S_2O_3^{2-}]^2}$ $\qquad$ (c) $K_{form} = \dfrac{[Zn(NH_3)_4^{2+}]}{[Zn^{2+}][NH_3]^4}$

16.44 (a) $Fe(CN)_6^{4-} \rightleftharpoons Fe^{2+} + 6CN^-$ $\qquad K_{inst} = \dfrac{[Fe^{2+}][CN^-]^6}{[Fe(CN)_6^{4-}]}$

(b) $K_{inst} = \dfrac{[Cu^{2+}][Cl^-]^4}{[CuCl_4^{2-}]}$ $\qquad$ (c) $K_{inst} = \dfrac{[Ni^{2+}][NH_3]^6}{[Ni(NH_3)_6^{2+}]}$

16.45 $AgI_2^-(aq) \rightleftharpoons Ag^+(aq) + 2I^-(aq)$

A more dilute solution would favor the right side of this equilibrium. The presence of the ions, Ag^+ and I^-, would in turn favor the formation of solid AgI via $Ag^+(aq) + I^-(aq) \longrightarrow AgI(s)$.

16.46 K_{sp} (AgI) = 8.5×10^{-17} $\qquad K_{form}$ $Ag(CN)_2^- = 5.3 \times 10^{18}$

$AgI(s) \rightleftharpoons Ag^+(aq) + I^-(aq)$

$Ag^+(aq) + 2CN^-(aq) \rightleftharpoons Ag(CN)_2^-(aq)$

$[I^-] = [Ag^+] + [Ag(CN)_2^-]$ $\qquad [CN^-] + ([Ag(CN)_2^-] \times 2) = 0.010$ M

Let X = moles of AgI that will dissolve per L.

Let Y = moles of $Ag(CN)_2^-$ that will form per L.

(continued)

(16.46 continued)

	Init. Conc.	Change	Equil. Conc.	Assume	Equil. Conc.
Ag^+	X	-Y	X - Y	X ≈ Y	$[Ag^+]$
I^-	X	0	X	Y ≈ 0.0050	0.0050
CN^-	0.010	- 2Y	0.010 - 2Y	2Y ≈ 0.010	$[CN^-]$
$Ag(CN)_2^-$	0	+Y	Y		0.0050

K_{sp} (AgI) = 8.5×10^{-17} = $[Ag^+]$ (0.0050) $[Ag^+] = 1.7 \times 10^{-14}$ M

$$K_{form} = \frac{0.0050}{(1.7 \times 10^{-14})\,[CN^-]^2} = 5.3 \times 10^{18} \qquad [CN^-] = 2.4 \times 10^{-4}\ M$$

From the table above: $[CN^-] = 0.010 - 2Y = 2.4 \times 10^{-4}$ $Y = 4.9 \times 10^{-3}$ M

$X - Y = [Ag^+] = 1.7 \times 10^{-14} = X - 4.9 \times 10^{-3}$ $X = 4.9 \times 10^{-3}$ M

Molar solubility of AgI in 0.010 M KCN = total moles of Ag^+ =

$Y + (X - Y) =$ **<u>4.9×10^{-3} mol /L</u>**

16.47 K_{sp} $Zn(OH)_2 = 4.5 \times 10^{-17}$ $Zn(NH_3)_4^{2+} \rightleftharpoons Zn^{2+} + 4NH_3$ K_{inst} = ?

	Init. Conc.	Change	Equil. Conc.	Assume	Equil. Conc.
Zn^{2+}	5.7×10^{-3}	-X	5.7×10^{-3} - X	X ≈ 5.7×10^{-3}	$[Zn^{2+}]$
OH^-	$2 \times 5.7 \times 10^{-3}$	0	0.0114		0.0114
NH_3	1.0	-4X	1.0 - 4X	≈ 1.0	1.0
$Zn(NH_3)_4^{2+}$	0	+X	X		5.7×10^{-3}

Using K_{sp}: $4.5 \times 10^{-17} = [Zn^{2+}] (0.0114)^2$ $[Zn^{2+}] = 3.5 \times 10^{-13}$

$$K_{inst} = \frac{(3.5 \times 10^{-13})(1.0)^4}{5.7 \times 10^{-3}} = \underline{\mathbf{6.1 \times 10^{-11}}}$$

16.48 When NH_4Cl dissolves, it forms NH_4^+ and Cl^-. The NH_4^+ is an acid and produces H^+ upon hydrolysis: $NH_4^+ + H_2O \longrightarrow NH_3 + H^+(aq)$. The H^+ will react with the OH^- released as $Mg(OH)_2$ dissolves. According to LeChatelier's Principle, as a stress is created the equilibrium between solid $Mg(OH)_2$ and its ion will shift toward the side that has lost the OH^-.

16.49 $AgC_2H_3O_2(s) \rightleftharpoons Ag^+ + C_2H_3O_2^- \quad K_{sp} = 2.3 \times 10^{-3}$

$HC_2H_3O_2 \rightleftharpoons H^+ + C_2H_3O_2^- \quad K_a = 1.8 \times 10^{-5}$

$$1.8 \times 10^{-5} = \frac{[H^+][C_2H_3O_2^-]}{[HC_2H_3O_2]} = \frac{[C_2H_3O_2^-]^2}{1.0}$$

$[C_2H_3O_2^-] = 4.24 \times 10^{-3}$ Ion Product for the possible precipitate $AgC_2H_3O_2$ is: $1.0 \times 4.24 \times 10^{-3} = 4.24 \times 10^{-3}$. The Ion Product exceeds the value of K_{sp}; therefore, **a precipitate will form.**

16.50 K_{sp} (FeS) $= 3.7 \times 10^{-19} = [Fe^{2+}][S^{2-}] = (0.20)[S^{2-}]$

$[S^{2-}] = 1.85 \times 10^{-18}$

$$1.1 \times 10^{-21} = \frac{[H^+]^2[S^{2-}]}{[H_2S]} = \frac{[H^+]^2(1.85 \times 10^{-18})}{(0.10)}$$

$[H^+] = 7.7 \times 10^{-3}$

Moles of H^+ that must be added $= 7.7 \times 10^{-3}$ plus that to form H_2S from 0.20 moles of FeS $= 7.7 \times 10^{-3} + 2 \times 0.20 =$ **0.41**

16.51 $K_{sp}\ Mg(OH)_2 = 1.2 \times 10^{-11} = [Mg^{2+}][OH^-]^2$

$K_b\ (NH_3) = 1.8 \times 10^{-5} = \frac{[NH_4^+][OH^-]}{[NH_3]}$

$[Mg^{2+}] = 0.10$ Therefore, $[OH^-]^2 = 1.2 \times 10^{-11} / 0.10$

$[OH^-] = 1.1 \times 10^{-5}$ $NH_4^+ + OH^- \longrightarrow NH_3 + H_2O$

From the dissolving of $Mg(OH)_2$ the amount of OH^- should equal twice the concentration of dissolved $Mg(OH)_2$. However, some OH^- will be consumed in the above reaction. Final concentration of $OH^- = 0.20 - X = 1.1 \times 10^{-5}$. The value of X will be the amount of NH_3 formed. $[NH_3] = 0.20$ M

$K_b = 1.8 \times 10^{-5} = \frac{[NH_4^+][OH^-]}{[NH_3]} = \frac{[NH_4^+]\ 1.1 \times 10^{-5}}{0.20}$

$[NH_4^+] = 0.33$ M Moles of NH_4Cl that must be added to the 1 L are

$= 0.20 + 0.33 =$ **0.53 moles of NH_4Cl added.**

16.52 $K_{sp} = [Ag^+][C_2H_3O_2^-] = 2.3 \times 10^{-3} = (0.200)\ [C_2H_3O_2^-]$

$[C_2H_3O_2^-] = 1.15 \times 10^{-2}$ $HC_2H_3O_2 \rightleftharpoons H^+ + C_2H_3O_2^-$

$[H^+] = 0.10 - X$ $[HC_2H_3O_2] = X$

$1.8 \times 10^{-5} = \frac{(0.10 - X)(1.15 \times 10^{-2})}{X}$

$X = 9.98 \times 10^{-2}$ or 0.10 M

Amount of $NaC_2H_3O_2$ required would be > [0.10 mol /L + 0.0115 mol /L] x 0.200 L x 82 g /mol > **1.8 g of $NaC_2H_3O_2$**

16.53 $[Ag^+] = 0.20$ M

$K_{sp} = [Ag^+][C_2H_3O_2^-] = 2.3 \times 10^{-3} = (0.20)[C_2H_3O_2^-]$

$[C_2H_3O_2^-] = 1.15 \times 10^{-2}$ M

	$HC_2H_3O_2$	$\rightleftharpoons H^+$	+ $C_2H_3O_2^-$	
Init.	0.10	~0	~0	Y = amount that reacts with F^-
	-X	+X -Y	+X	$X = 1.15 \times 10^{-2}$
Final	$0.10 - 1.15 \times 10^{-2}$	?	1.15×10^{-2}	

$$K_a = \frac{[H^+][C_2H_3O_2^-]}{[HC_2H_3O_2]} = 1.8 \times 10^{-5} = \frac{[H^+][1.15 \times 10^{-2}]}{0.10 - 1.15 \times 10^{-2}}$$

$[H^+] = 1.39 \times 10^{-4}$

F^-	+ H^+	$\longrightarrow$ HF
?	?	0
-Y	-Y	+Y
?	1.39×10^{-4}	1.14×10^{-2}

$Y = (1.15 \times 10^{-2}) - (1.39 \times 10^{-4})$

$= 1.14 \times 10^{-2}$

$HF \rightleftharpoons H^+ + F^-$

$K_a = 6.5 \times 10^{-4} = [H^+][F^-]/[HF] = 1.39 \times 10^{-4}\,[F^-]/1.14 \times 10^{-2}$

$[F^-] = 5.33 \times 10^{-2}$ M

Moles F^- added $= 5.33 \times 10^{-2} + 1.14 \times 10^{-2} = 6.47 \times 10^{-2}$

6.47×10^{-2} mol $L^{-1} \times 0.200$ L $\times$ 58.1 g/mol = **<u>0.75g KF</u> or more must be added to precipitate any $AgC_2H_3O_2$.**

16.54 $NH_3 + H_2O \rightleftharpoons NH_4^+ + OH^-$

$K_b = 1.8 \times 10^{-5} = [OH^-]^2 / 0.10$

$[OH^-]$ from $NH_3 = 1.34 \times 10^{-3}$ M

	$Mg(OH)_2(s) \longrightarrow$	$Mg^{2+}(aq)$	+	$2OH^-(aq)$
Initial		0		1.34×10^{-3}
Change		+X		+2X
Equil.		X		$2X + 1.34 \times 10^{-3}$

$K_{sp} = [Mg^{2+}][OH^-]^2 = 1.2 \times 10^{-11} = (X)(2X + 1.34 \times 10^{-3})^2$

$\approx (X)(1.34 \times 10^{-3})^2$

X = molar solubility of $Mg(OH)_2$ = 6.7 x 10^{-6} mol /L

17 ELECTROCHEMISTRY

17.1 (a) Electrolytic cells convert electrical energy into chemical energy and galvanic cells convert chemical energy into electrical energy.

(b) In metallic conduction, electrons move through a metal. In electrolytic conduction, ions move through a solution.

(c) oxidation - loss of electrons (occurs at anode)

reduction - gain of electrons (occurs at cathode)

17.2 Oxidation-reduction maintains electrical neutrality.

17.3 Reduction takes place at the cathode and oxidation takes place at the anode.

17.4 One volt is equal to one joule per coulomb; it is a measure of the energy that is capable of being extracted from the flowing electric charge. One ampere is equivalent to one coulomb per second, and is a measure of the current.

17.5

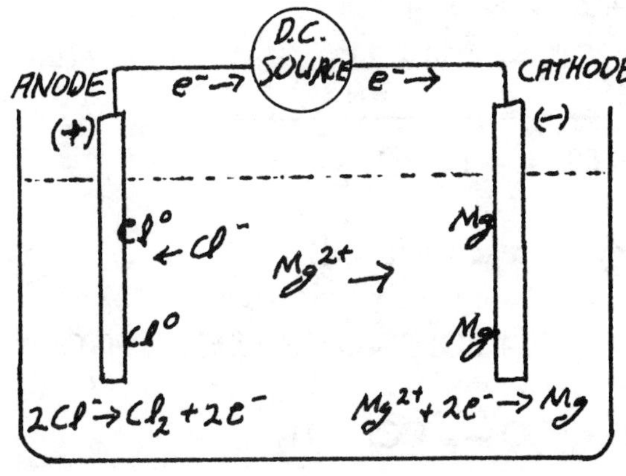

17.6 $2H_2O \longrightarrow O_2 + 4H^+ + 4e^-$ (oxidation)

$2H_2O + 2e^- \longrightarrow H_2 + 2OH^-$ (reduction)

17.7 The products would be O_2 at the anode and H_2 at the cathode due to the oxidation and reduction of water.

17.8 Na_2SO_4 and H_2SO_4 are needed to maintain electrical neutrality by carrying the charge through the solution. H^+ and OH^- ions are produced during the oxidation and reduction of water. Ions of opposite charge are required in the vicinity of these ions to "neutralize" their charge.

17.9 anode: $2I^- \longrightarrow I_2 + 2e^-$

cathode: $Ni^{2+} + 2e \longrightarrow Ni$

cell: $Ni^{2+} + 2I^- + \text{electrical energy} \longrightarrow Ni + I_2$

17.10 anode: $2H_2O \longrightarrow O_2 + 4H^+ + 4e^-$

cathode: $Ni^{2+} + 2e \longrightarrow Ni$

cell: $2Ni^{2+} + 2H_2O + \text{electrical energy} \longrightarrow 2Ni + O_2 + 4H^+$

17.11 (a) cathode: $2H_2O + 2e^- \longrightarrow H_2 + 2OH^-$

anode: $2Cl^- \longrightarrow Cl_2 + 2e^-$

net: $2H_2O + 2Cl^- \longrightarrow H_2 + Cl_2 + 2OH^-$

(b) In a stirred solution, Cl_2 reacts with OH^-

$$Cl_2 + 2OH^- \longrightarrow Cl^- + OCl^- + H_2O$$

Net reaction is: $Cl^- + H_2O \longrightarrow OCl^- + H_2$

17.12 Advantage: prevents the formation of hypochlorite and avoids the formation of dangerous mixtures of H_2 and Cl_2.

Disadvantage: NaOH contaminated with NaCl

17.13 Advantage: NaOH not contaminated by Cl^- is produced.

Disadvantage: possibility for mercury pollution.

17.14 It keeps Na and Cl_2 apart so they cannot react with each other to reform NaCl.

17.15 Cryolite reduces the melting temperature of Al_2O_3 from 2000°C to 1000°C.

17.16 H_2O is more easily reduced than Al^{3+}.

17.17 $Mg^{2+}(aq) + CaO(s) + H_2O \longrightarrow Mg(OH)_2(s) + Ca^{2+}(aq)$

$Mg(OH)_2(s) + 2HCl \longrightarrow MgCl_2(s) + 2H_2O$

$$MgCl_2(\ell) \xrightarrow[\text{energy}]{\text{electrical}} Mg(\ell) + Cl_2(g)$$

17.18 For the electrolytic purification of copper see discussion on copper in Section 17.3. The process is economically feasible because the impurities, silver, gold and platinum, can be sold for enough money to pay for the electricity required for the electrolysis.

17.19 Electroplating is the process by which a metal is caused to be deposited ("plated out") on an electrode in an electrolysis cell. To have nickel plated onto an object in a $NiSO_4$ solution, the object must be part of the cathode.

17.20 A faraday is the amount of electricity that must be supplied to a cell in order to supply one mole of electrons. One faraday equals 96,500 amperes x seconds.

17.21 (a) 2 (b) 1 (c) 5 (d) 2 (e) 8

17.22 $1\text{ C} \times \frac{1\text{ F}}{96{,}500\text{ C}} \times \frac{6.022 \times 10^{23}\text{ e}^-}{1\text{ F}} = \underline{6.24 \times 10^{18}\text{ e}^-}$

17.23 (a) 1 (b) 4 (c) 10 (d) 2 (e) 8

17.24 (a) $8950\text{ C} \times \frac{1\text{ F}}{96{,}500\text{ C}} = \underline{0.0927\text{ F}}$

(b) $1.5\text{ A} \times 30\text{ s} \times \frac{1\text{ C/s}}{1\text{ A}} \times \frac{1\text{ F}}{96{,}500\text{ C}} = \underline{4.7 \times 10^{-4}\text{ F}}$

(c) $14.7\text{ A} \times 10\text{ min} \times \frac{60\text{ s}}{\text{min}} \times \frac{1\text{ C/s}}{1\text{ A}} \times \frac{1\text{ F}}{96{,}500\text{ C}} = \underline{9.1 \times 10^{-2}\text{ F}}$

17.25 (a) $10{,}500\text{ C} \times \frac{1\text{ s}}{25.0\text{ C}} \times \frac{1\text{ min}}{60.0\text{ s}} = \underline{7.00\text{ min}}$

(b) $0.65\text{ F} \times \frac{96{,}500\text{ C}}{1\text{ F}} \times \frac{1\text{ s}}{15\text{ C}} \times \frac{1\text{ min}}{60\text{ s}} = \underline{70\text{ min}}$

(c) $0.20\text{ mol }(Cu^{2+}/Cu) \times \frac{2\text{ F}}{1\text{ mol }(Cu^{2+}/Cu)} \times \frac{96{,}500\text{ C}}{1\text{F}} \times \frac{1\text{ s}}{12\text{ C}} \times \frac{1\text{ min}}{60\text{ s}} =$

$\underline{54\text{ min}}$

17.26 (a) $\frac{84{,}200\text{ C}}{6.30\text{ A}} \times \frac{1\text{ A}}{1\text{ C} \times \text{s}^{-1}} \times \frac{1\text{ min}}{60.0\text{ s}} = \underline{223\text{ min}}$

(b) $\frac{1.25\text{ F}}{8.40\text{ A}} \times \frac{96{,}500\text{ C}}{1\text{ F}} \times \frac{\text{A} \times \text{s}}{\text{C}} \times \frac{1\text{ min}}{60.0\text{ s}} = \underline{239\text{ min}}$

(c) $\frac{0.500\text{ mol Al}}{18.3\text{ A}} \times \frac{3 \times 96{,}500\text{ C}}{1\text{ mol }Al^{3+}} \times \frac{1\text{ A}}{1\text{ C} \times \text{s}^{-1}} \times \frac{1\text{ min}}{60.0\text{ sec}} = \underline{132\text{ min}}$

17.27 (a) $10.0 \text{ mL } O_2 \text{ (STP)} \times \frac{1 \text{ mol } O_2}{22{,}400 \text{ mL } O_2 \text{ (STP)}} \times \frac{4 \text{ F}}{1 \text{ mol } O_2 \text{ (STP)}} =$

$\underline{1.79 \times 10^{-3} \text{ F}}$

(b) $10.0 \text{ g Al} \times \frac{1 \text{ mol Al}}{26.98 \text{ g Al}} \times \frac{3 \text{ F}}{1 \text{ mol Al}} =$ **$\underline{1.11 \text{ F}}$**

(c) $5.00 \text{ g Na} \times \frac{1 \text{ mol Na}}{22.99 \text{ g Na}} \times \frac{1 \text{ F}}{1 \text{ mol Na}} =$ **$\underline{0.217 \text{ F}}$**

(d) $5.00 \text{ g Mg} \times \frac{1 \text{ mol Mg}}{24.31 \text{ g Mg}} \times \frac{2 \text{ F}}{1 \text{ mol Mg}} =$ **$\underline{0.411 \text{ F}}$**

17.28 $25 \text{ A} \times 8.0 \text{ hr} \times \frac{3600 \text{ s}}{1 \text{ hr}} \times \frac{1 \text{ C s}^{-1}}{1 \text{ A}} \times \frac{23.0 \text{ g Na}}{96{,}500 \text{ C}} =$

$\underline{170 \text{ g Na}}$ and **$\underline{260 \text{ g } Cl_2}$** (only 2 significant figures)

17.29 $0.50 \text{ A} \times 1.0 \text{ hr} \times \frac{1 \text{ C s}^{-1}}{1 \text{ A}} \times \frac{3600 \text{ s}}{1 \text{ hr}} \times \frac{8.00 \text{ g } O_2}{96{,}500 \text{ C}} =$

$\underline{0.15 \text{ g } O_2}$ and **$\underline{0.019 \text{ g } H_2}$**

$0.15 \text{ g } O_2 \times \frac{22.4 \text{ L } O_2 \text{ (STP)}}{32.00 \text{ g } O_2} =$ **$\underline{0.11 \text{ L } O_2\text{(STP)}}$** and **$\underline{0.21 \text{ L } H_2 \text{ (STP)}}$**

17.30 $115 \text{ A} \times 8.00 \text{ hr} \times \frac{1 \text{ C} \times \text{s}^{-1}}{1 \text{ A}} \times \frac{3600 \text{ s}}{1 \text{ hr}} \times \frac{(63.54/2) \text{ g Cu}}{96{,}500 \text{ C}} =$

$\underline{1{,}090 \text{ g Cu}}$ (3 significant figures)

17.31 (a) $8.00 \text{ hr} \times 8.46 \text{ A} \times \frac{1 \text{ C s}^{-1}}{1 \text{ A}} \times \frac{3600 \text{ s}}{1 \text{ hr}} \times \frac{107.9 \text{ g Ag}}{96{,}500 \text{ C}} =$ **$\underline{272 \text{ g Ag}}$**

(b) $\frac{272 \text{ g Ag}}{0.00254 \text{ cm Ag}} \times \frac{1 \text{ cm}^3 \text{ Ag}}{10.5 \text{ g Ag}} =$ **$\underline{1.02 \times 10^4 \text{ cm}^2}$**

17.32 $\frac{21.4\ g\ Ag}{10.0\ A} \times \frac{1\ A}{1\ C \times s^{-1}} \times \frac{96{,}500\ C}{107.9\ g\ Ag} =$ **1910 s** (3 significant figures)

17.33 $\frac{35.3\ g\ Cr}{6.00\ A} \times \frac{1\ A}{1\ C\ s^{-1}} \times \frac{3\ F}{1\ mol\ Cr^{3+}} \times \frac{96{,}500\ C}{1\ F} \times \frac{1\ mol\ Cr}{52.00\ g\ Cr} \times \frac{1\ hr}{3600\ s} =$

9.10 hr

17.34 $\frac{5.00\ g\ Cu}{5.00\ A} \times \frac{1\ A}{1\ C\ s^{-1}} \times \frac{96{,}500\ C}{(63.54\ /2)\ g\ Cu} \times \frac{1\ min}{60\ s} =$ **50.6 min**

17.35 $\frac{0.225\ g\ Ni}{10.0\ min} \times \frac{96{,}500\ C}{(58.71\ /2)\ g\ Ni} \times \frac{1\ min}{60\ s} \times \frac{1\ A}{1\ C\ s^{-1}} =$ **1.23 A**

17.36 $\frac{1.33\ g\ Cl_2}{45.0\ min} \times \frac{96{,}500\ C}{35.45\ g\ Cl_2} \times \frac{1\ min}{60\ s} \times \frac{1\ A}{1\ C \times s^{-1}} =$ **1.34 A**

17.37 $\frac{50.0\ mL\ O_2(STP)}{3.00\ hr} \times \frac{4\ F}{22{,}400\ mL\ O_2\ (STP)} \times \frac{96{,}500\ C}{1\ F} \times \frac{1\ hr}{3600\ s} \times \frac{1\ A}{1\ C \times s^{-1}}$

= **0.0798 A**

17.38 A coulometer is an apparatus that allows us to experimentally determine the weight of a substance that has been deposited on an electrode during electrolysis. Coulometers can be very accurate and can be hooked up in series, which allows for the passage of the same number of faradays through two or more such cells. See Figure 17.13.

17.39 $0.500\ L \times \frac{0.270\ mol\ Cr_2(SO_4)_3}{1\ L} \times \frac{6 \times 96{,}500\ C}{1\ mol\ Cr_2(SO_4)_3} \times \frac{1\ s}{3.00\ C} \times \frac{1\ min}{60\ s} =$

434 min

17.40 **(a)** $1.25 \text{ g Cu} \times \frac{1 \text{ F}}{(63.54/2) \text{ g Cu}} = \mathbf{0.0393\ F}$

(b) $\frac{3.42 \text{ g X}}{0.0393 \text{ F}} \times \frac{2 \text{ F}}{1 \text{ mol X}} = \underline{\mathbf{174\ g\ X/mol\ X}}$

17.41 $0.125 \text{ mol Cu} \times \frac{2 \text{ F}}{1 \text{ mol Cu}} \times \frac{1 \text{ mol Cr}}{3 \text{ F}} = \underline{\mathbf{0.0833\ mol\ Cr}}$

17.42 $\frac{0.250 \text{ A} \times 35.0 \text{ min}}{0.400 \text{ L}} \times \frac{1 \text{ C} \times \text{s}^{-1}}{1 \text{ A}} \times \frac{60 \text{ s}}{1 \text{ min}} \times \frac{1 \text{ mol OH}^-}{96{,}500 \text{ C}} =$

$\frac{0.0136 \text{ mol (OH}^-)}{\text{L}}$ **pH =** $\underline{\mathbf{12.134}}$

17.43 $\frac{15.5 \text{ mL HCl}}{25.0 \text{ min}} \times \frac{1 \text{ min}}{60 \text{ s}} \times \frac{0.250 \text{ mol HCl}}{10^3 \text{ mL HCl}} \times \frac{1 \text{ mol OH}^-}{1 \text{ mol HCl}} \times \frac{2 \text{ F}}{2 \text{ mol OH}^-} \times$

$\frac{96{,}500 \text{ C}}{1 \text{ F}} \times \frac{1 \text{ A}}{1 \text{ C s}^{-1}} = \underline{\mathbf{0.249\ A}}$

17.44

	Init	STP
P	767 -27 torr	760 torr
V	288 mL	? mL
T	300 K	273 K

$288 \text{ mL} \times \frac{740 \text{ torr} \times 273 \text{ K}}{760 \text{ torr} \times 300 \text{ K}} = \underline{\mathbf{255\ mL\ (STP)}}$

$\frac{1.22 \text{ C} \times \text{s}^{-1} \times 30.0 \text{ min}}{255 \text{ mL H}_2 \text{ (STP)}} \times \frac{60 \text{ s}}{1 \text{ min}} \times \frac{11{,}200 \text{ mL H}_2}{6.022 \times 10^{23} \text{ e}^-} =$

$\underline{\mathbf{1.60 \times 10^{-19}\ C/e^-}}$

17.45 $1 \text{ m}^2 \text{ Cr (plate)} \times \frac{7.19 \text{ g Cr}}{1 \text{ cm}^3 \text{ Cr}} \times \frac{6 \times 96{,}500 \text{ A s}}{52.00 \text{ g Cr (plate)}} \times \frac{0.050 \text{ mm}}{25 \text{ min}} \times$

$\frac{1 \text{ cm}}{10 \text{ mm}} \times \frac{(100 \text{ cm})^2}{1 \text{ m}^2} \times \frac{1 \text{ min}}{60 \text{ s}} = \underline{\mathbf{3 \times 10^3\ A}}$ (1 significant figure)

17.46 The electron flow takes place on the surface of the zinc. Electrons are removed from the zinc and are picked up by the Cu^{2+} ions that are in the vicinity. The energy change appears as heat.

17.47 The salt-bridge is needed in order to maintain electrical neutrality.

17.48 In galvanic cells the anode is negative and the cathode is positive. In electrolytic cells the anode is positive and the cathode is negative.

17.49

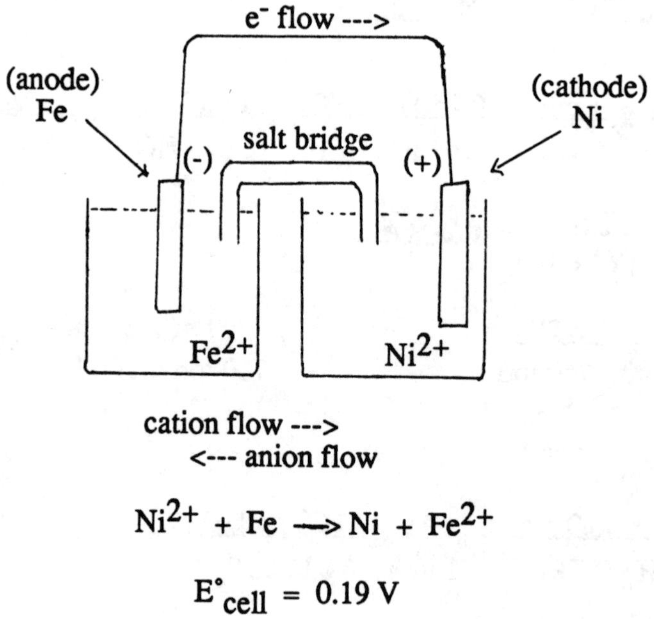

$$Ni^{2+} + Fe \longrightarrow Ni + Fe^{2+}$$

$$E^{\circ}_{cell} = 0.19 \text{ V}$$

17.50 In a galvanic cell, the negative electrode is the anode; the positive electrode is the cathode. These can be determined with a voltmeter. Another method would be to do a chemical analysis of the products formed at each electrode. Oxidation occurs at the anode, reduction at the cathode.

17.51 See Figure 17.15(a) for a sketch of a hydrogen electrode. When the hydrogen gas is at 1.00 atm and hydrogen ion concentration is 1.00 M, the hydrogen electrode will have a potential of exactly 0.000V.

17.52 (a) (anode) $Zn(s) \longrightarrow Zn^{2+} + 2e^-$

(cathode) $Ga^{3+} + 3e^- \longrightarrow Ga(s)$

(b) $3Zn(s) + 2Ga^{3+} \longrightarrow 3Zn^{2+} + 2Ga(s)$

(c) $E^\circ_{cell} = E^\circ_{Ga} - E^\circ_{Zn} = E^\circ_{Ga} - (-0.76\ V) = 0.23\ V$

$E^\circ_{Ga} = \underline{-0.53\ V}$

(d) $E^\circ_{cell} = 0.34\ V - (-0.53\ V) = \underline{0.87\ V}$

17.53 (a) Ca^{2+} (b) F_2 (c) H_2O (d) $S_2O_8^{2-}$ (e) Br_2

17.54 (a) ClO_3^- (b) $Cr_2O_7^{2-}$ (c) MnO_4^- (d) PbO_2

17.55 (a) Fe (b) Mg (c) I^- (d) SO_4^{2-} (e) Mn

17.56 (a) Na (b) Cl_2 (c) Cu (d) Sn (e) H_2

17.57 (a) $2Al(s) + 3Ni^{2+} \longrightarrow 3Ni(s) + 2Al^{3+}$

(b) $3PbO_2(s) + 2Cr^{3+} + 3SO_4^{2-} + H_2O \longrightarrow 3PbSO_4(s) + 2H^+ + Cr_2O_7^{2-}$

(c) $2Ag^+ + Pb(s) \longrightarrow 2Ag(s) + Pb^{2+}$

(d) $Cl_2(g) + Mn^{2+} + 2H_2O \longrightarrow 2Cl^- + 4H^+ + MnO_2(s)$

(e) $2H^+ + Mn(s) \longrightarrow Mn^{2+} + H_2(g)$

17.58 Spontaneous reactions are (a), (d), (e). The other reactions are spontaneous in the reverse direction.

17.59 (a) E° = -2.76 - (-2.38) = **-0.38 V** non-spontaneous as written

(b) E° = -0.13 - (1.36) = **-1.49 V** non-spontaneous as written

(c) E° = 2.00 - (1.36) = **+0.64 V** spontaneous

(d) E° = 1.33 - (1.49) = **-0.16 V** non-spontaneous as written

(e) E° = 1.23 - (1.36) = **-0.13 V** non-spontaneous as written

17.60 (a) $Pb + SO_4^{2-} + Hg_2Cl_2 \longrightarrow 2Hg + 2Cl^- + PbSO_4(s)$

E° = 0.27 - (-0.36) = **0.63 V**

(b) $2Ag + 2Cl^- + Cu^{2+} \longrightarrow 2AgCl(s) + Cu$ E° = **0.12 V**

(c) $Mn + Cl_2 \longrightarrow Mn^{2+} + 2Cl^-$ E° = **2.39 V**

(d) $2Al + 3Br_2 \longrightarrow 2Al^{3+} + 6Br^-$ E° = **2.76 V**

17.61 (a) E° = -0.25 V - (-1.67 V) = **1.42 V**

(b) E° = 1.69 V - (1.33 V) = **0.36 V**

(c) E° = 0.80 V - (-0.13 V) = **0.93 V**

(d) E° = 1.36 V - (1.28 V) = **0.08 V**

(e) E° = 0.00 V - (-1.03 V) = **1.03 V**

17.62 **(a)** $E^\circ = 0.77\ V - (-0.14\ V) =$ **0.91 V**

(b) $E^\circ = 0.00\ V - (0.34\ V) =$ **-0.34 V**

(c) $E^\circ = -2.38\ V - (-1.67\ V) =$ **-0.71 V**

(d) $E^\circ = -0.76\ V - (-1.03\ V) =$ **0.27 V**

(e) $E^\circ = 1.69\ V - (0.27\ V) =$ **1.42 V**

17.63 **(a)** $K_c = [Ni^{2+}]/[Sn^{2+}]$ At equilibrium

$\log K_c = n E^\circ/0.0592$ (at 25° C) $n = 2$ $E^\circ = -0.14\ V - (-0.25\ V) = 0.11\ V$

$K_c =$ **5×10^3**

(b) $n = 2$ $E^\circ = 1.36\ V - (1.09\ V) = 0.27\ V$ $K_c =$ **1×10^9**

(c) $n = 1$ $E^\circ = 0.80\ V - (0.77\ V) = 0.03\ V$ $K_c =$ **3**

17.64 **(a)** $E^\circ = 0.77\ V - (-0.14\ V) = 0.91\ V$ $\log K_c = nE^\circ/0.0592$ (at 25° C) $n = 2$

$\log K_c = 2 \times 0.91/0.0592 = 30.74$ $K_c =$ **6×10^{30}**

(b) $K_c =$ **3×10^{-12}**

(c) $K_c =$ **1×10^{-72}**

(d) $K_c =$ **1×10^9**

(e) $K_c =$ **9×10^{47}**

17.65 $\log K_c = n\,E°/0.0592$ (assume 25° C)

(a) $n = 2$ $E° = -2.76\text{ V} - (-2.38\text{ V}) = -0.38\text{ V}$ $\log K_c = -12.84$

$K_c = \underline{\mathbf{1 \times 10^{-13}}}$

(b) $E° = -1.49$ V $n = 2$ $K_c = \underline{\mathbf{5 \times 10^{-51}}}$

(c) $E° = 0.64$ V $n = 2$ $K_c = \underline{\mathbf{4 \times 10^{21}}}$

(d) $E° = -0.16$ V $n = 30$ $K_c = \underline{\mathbf{8 \times 10^{-82}}}$

(e) $E° = -0.13$ V $n = 4$ $K_c = \underline{\mathbf{2 \times 10^{-9}}}$

17.66 $\Delta G° = -nFE°$

(a) $\Delta G° = -2\text{ mol} \times \dfrac{96{,}500\text{ C}}{1\text{ mol e}^-} \times 0.91\text{ V} \times \dfrac{10^{-3}\text{ kJ}}{1\text{ V} \times \text{C}} = \underline{\mathbf{-180\text{ kJ}}}$ (2 sign. fig.)

(b) $\Delta G° = -2 \times 96{,}500 \times (-0.34) \times 10^{-3} = \underline{\mathbf{66\text{ kJ}}}$

(c) $\Delta G° = -6 \times 96{,}500 \times (-0.71) \times 10^{-3} = \underline{\mathbf{410\text{ kJ}}}$

(d) $\Delta G° = -2 \times 96{,}500 \times 0.27 \times 10^{-3} = \underline{\mathbf{-52\text{ kJ}}}$

(e) $\Delta G° = -2 \times 96{,}500 \times 1.42 \times 10^{-3} = \underline{\mathbf{-274\text{ kJ}}}$

17.67 $\Delta G° = -nFE°$ (a) $E° = -2.76\text{ V} - (-2.38\text{ V}) = -0.38\text{ V}$ $n = 2$

$$\Delta G° = -2\text{ mol e}^- \times \frac{96{,}500\text{ C}}{1\text{ mol e}^-} \times (-0.38\text{ V}) \times \frac{1\text{ J}}{1\text{ V} \times \text{C}} \times \frac{10^{-3}\text{ kcal}}{4.184\text{ J}} = \underline{\mathbf{18\text{ kcal}}}$$

(17.67 continued)

(b) $E^\circ = -1.49\ V$ $n = 2$ $\Delta G^\circ = -2 \times 96{,}500 \times (-1.49) \times \frac{10^{-3}}{4.184} = \underline{\mathbf{68.7\ kcal}}$

(c) $E^\circ = 0.64\ V$ $n = 2$ $\Delta G^\circ = -2 \times 96{,}500 \times 0.64 \times \frac{10^{-3}}{4.184} = \underline{\mathbf{-30\ kcal}}$

(d) $E^\circ = -0.16\ V$ $n = 30$ $\Delta G^\circ = -30 \times 96{,}500 \times (-0.16) \times \frac{10^{-3}}{4.184} = \underline{\mathbf{110\ kcal}}$

(e) $E^\circ = -0.13\ V$ $n = 4$ $\Delta G^\circ = -4 \times 96{,}500 \times (-0.13) \times \frac{10^{-3}}{4.184} = \underline{\mathbf{12\ kcal}}$

17.68 Nernst Equation: $\mathbf{E = E^\circ - \frac{0.0592}{n} \times \log}$ **(mass action expression)**

(a) $E^\circ = 0.34\ V - (-0.76\ V) = \mathbf{1.10\ V}$

$E = 1.10\ V - (0.0592/2) \log [Zn^{2+}]/[Cu^{2+}] = \underline{\mathbf{1.07\ V}}$

(b) $E^\circ = -0.14\ V - (-0.25\ V) = \mathbf{0.11 V}$

$E = 0.11\ V - (0.0592/2) \log [Ni^{2+}]/[Sn^{2+}] = \underline{\mathbf{0.16\ V}}$

(c) $E^\circ = 2.87\ V - (-3.05\ V) = \mathbf{5.92\ V}$

$E = 5.92\ V - (0.0592/2) \log [Li^+]^2 [F^-]^2 / p_{F_2} = \underline{\mathbf{5.94\ V}}$

(d) $E^\circ = -0.0\ V - (-0.76\ V) = \mathbf{0.76\ V}$

$E = 0.76\ V - (0.0592/2) \log [Zn^{2+}]\ p_{H_2}/[H^+]^2 = \underline{\mathbf{0.64\ V}}$

(e) $E^\circ = -0.00\ V - (-0.44\ V) = \mathbf{0.44\ V}$

$E = 0.44\ V - (0.0592/2) \log P_{H_2}[Fe^{2+}]/[H^+]^2 = \underline{\mathbf{0.46\ V}}$

17.69 **(a)** $E^\circ = -0.25\ V - (-1.67\ V) = \mathbf{1.42\ V}$

$E = 1.42\ V - (0.0592/6)\log[(0.020)^2/(0.80)^3] = \mathbf{1.45\ V}$

$\Delta G = -nFE = -6 \times 96{,}500 \times 1.45 \times 10^{-3} = \mathbf{-840\ kJ}$

(b) $E^\circ = -0.14\ V - (-0.25\ V) = \mathbf{0.11 V}$

$E = E^\circ - (0.0592/2)\log[(0.010)/(1.10)] = \mathbf{0.17\ V}$

$\Delta G = -2 \times 96{,}500 \times 0.17 \times 10^{-3} = \mathbf{-33\ kJ}$

(c) $E^\circ = +0.80\ V - (-0.76\ V) = 1.56\ V$

$E = 1.56\ V - (0.0592/2)\log[(0.010)/(0.050)^2] = \mathbf{1.54\ V}$

$\Delta G = -2 \times 96{,}500 \times 1.54 \times 10^{-3} = \underline{\mathbf{-297\ kJ}}$

17.70 **(a)** $E = [-0.13\ V - (-0.14\ V)] - (0.0592/2)\log[(1.50)/(0.050)] = \underline{\mathbf{-0.03\ V}}$

(b) $E = [-0.74\ V - (-0.76\ V)] - (0.0592/6)\log[(0.020)^3/(0.010)^2] = \underline{\mathbf{0.03\ V}}$

(c) $E = (1.69\ V - 0.34\ V) - (0.0592/2)\log[(0.0010)/(0.010)(0.10)^4] =$

$\underline{\mathbf{1.26\ V}}$

17.71 $E = 0.34\ V - (0.0592/2)\ \log[1/(2 \times 10^{-4})] = \underline{\mathbf{0.23\ V}}$

17.72 $E = 1.33\ V - (1.49\ V) = -0.16\ V$

$\Delta G = \Delta G^\circ + 2.303\ RT$

$$\log(\{[MnO_4^-]^6\ [Cr^{3+}]^{10}\}/[Mn^{2+}]^6\ [Cr_2O_7^{2-}]^5\ [H^+]^{22})$$

$$\Delta G^\circ = -nFE^\circ = -30\ \text{mol}\ e^- \times \frac{96{,}500\ C}{1\ \text{mol}\ e^-} \times (-0.16\ V) \times \frac{10^{-3}\ kJ}{1\ V \times C} = 463.2\ kJ$$

(17.72 continued)

$\Delta G = 463.2\ kJ\ +\ 2.303 \times 8.314\ J \times K^{-1} \times 298\ K \times \frac{1\ kJ}{10^3\ J} \times$

$\log \frac{(0.0010)^6(0.0010)^{10}}{(0.10)^6(0.010)^5(1.0 \times 10^{-6})^{22}} = 463.2\ kJ + 5.71\ kJ \times \log 10^{100} =$

$\underline{1.0 \times 10^3\ kJ}$ Since the reaction as written involves free energy increase, the spontaneous reaction would be the reverse reaction.

17.73 $\frac{[H^+]^2[S^{2-}]}{[H_2S]} = 1.1 \times 10^{-21} = \frac{(0.0010)^2[S^{2-}]}{(0.10)}$ $[S^{2-}] = 1.1 \times 10^{-16}$

$[Ag^+]^2[S^{2-}] = 2 \times 10^{-49} = [Ag^+]^2\ (1.1 \times 10^{-16})$ $[Ag^+] = 4.26 \times 10^{-17}$

$E = E^\circ - (0.0592\ /n)\ \log\ (1\ /[Ag^+]) = 0.80\ V - 0.0592\ \log\ (2.35 \times 10^{16}) =$

$\underline{-0.17\ V}$

17.74 $\frac{[H^+][C_2H_3O_2^-]}{[HC_2H_3O_2]} = 1.8 \times 10^{-5} = \frac{[H^+]^2}{0.10}$ $[H^+]^2 = 1.8 \times 10^{-6}$

$2H^+ + Fe \longrightarrow H_2 + Fe^{2+}$ $E = E^\circ - (0.0592\ /n)\ \log\ [Fe^{2+}]\ /[H^+]^2$

$E = [(0.00\ V - (-0.44\ V)] - (0.0296)\ \log\ (0.10)\ /(1.8 \times 10^{-6}) =$ **$\underline{0.30\ V}$**

17.75 Anode: Cl^- (?M) + Ag —> AgCl + 1 e^-

Cathode: AgCl + 1 e^- —> Ag + Cl^- (1 M)

Cl^- (? M) —> Cl^- (1 M) A Concentration Cell

$E = 0.0435\ V$ $E^\circ = 0$ $E = E^\circ - (0.0592\ /1)\ \log\ \{(1)\ /[Cl^-]_A\}$

$0.0435\ V\ /(0.0592\ V) = -\log\ (1/[Cl^-]_A)$ $[Cl^-]_A =$ **$\underline{5.43\ M}$**

17.76 $Mg(s) + 2Ag^+ \rightarrow Mg^{2+} + 2Ag(s)$ $\quad E = 0.80\ V - (-2.38\ V) = 3.18\ V$

(a) $E = 3.18\ V - 0.0296 \log [(0.100)/(0.100)^2] = \underline{\mathbf{3.15\ V}}$

(b) $?\ mol\ Ag^+ = 1.00\ g\ Ag \times \frac{1\ mol\ Ag^+}{107.9\ g\ Ag^+} = 9.268 \times 10^{-3}\ mol\ Ag^+$

$?\ mol\ Mg^{2+} = 9.268 \times 10^{-3}\ mol\ Ag \times \frac{1\ mol\ Mg^{2+}}{2\ mol\ Ag^+} = 4.634 \times 10^{-3}\ mol\ Mg^{2+}$

$M_f = M_i + \Delta M \quad 0.100\ M\ (Ag^+) - \frac{9.268 \times 10^{-3}\ mol\ Ag^+}{0.200\ L\ Ag^+\ soln} = 0.054\ M\ Ag^+$

$0.100\ M\ (Mg^{2+}) + \frac{4.634 \times 10^{-3}\ mol\ Mg^{2+}}{0.250\ L\ Mg^{2+}\ soln} = 0.119\ M\ (Mg^{2+})$

$E = 3.18\ V - 0.0296 \log \frac{(0.119)}{(0.054)^2} = \underline{\mathbf{3.13\ V}}$

(c) $?\ mol\ Mg^{2+} = 0.080\ g\ Mg \times \frac{1\ mol\ Mg^{2+}}{24.31\ g\ Mg} = 3.29 \times 10^{-3}\ mol\ Mg^{2+}$

$3.29 \times 10^{-3}\ mol\ Mg^{2+} \times \frac{2\ mol\ Ag^+}{1\ mol\ Mg^{2+}} = 6.58 \times 10^{-3}\ mol\ Ag^+$

$0.100\ M\ Ag^+ - \frac{6.58 \times 10^{-3}\ mol\ Ag^+}{0.200\ L\ Ag^+\ soln} = 0.067\ M\ Ag^+(final)$

$0.100\ M\ (Mg^{2+}) + \frac{3.29 \times 10^{-3}\ mol\ Mg^{2+}}{0.250\ L\ Mg^{2+}\ soln} = 0.113\ M\ Mg^{2+}\ (final)$

$E = 3.18\ V - 0.0296 \log \frac{(0.113)}{(0.067)^2} = \underline{\mathbf{3.14\ V}}$

17.77 $25.0\ g\ Pb \times \frac{2 \times 96{,}500\ C}{207.2\ g\ Pb} \times \frac{1.5\ V}{25\ W} \times \frac{1\ W}{1\ V \times C \times s^{-1}} \times \frac{1\ hr}{3600\ s} = \underline{\mathbf{0.39\ hr}}$

17.78 $\Delta G° = \Delta H° - T\Delta S° = -242\ kJ - 383\ K \times (188.7 - 130.6 - 205.0/2) \times 10^{-3}\ kJ/K =$

$-225\ kJ$ $\quad 1.0 \times 10^3\ W \times \frac{1\ J}{1\ W \times s} \times \frac{100\ J}{70\ J} \times \frac{2.016\ g\ H_2}{225 \times 10^3\ J}$

$=$ **$\underline{0.013\ g\ H_2/s}$ (reacting)** $\quad$ **$\underline{0.10\ g\ O_2/s}$**

17.79 $5.00\ min \times 110\ V \times 1.00\ A \times \frac{1\ W}{1 V \times A} \times \frac{1\ kJ}{10^3\ W \times s} \times \frac{60\ s}{1\ min} =$ **$\underline{33.0\ kJ}$**

17.80 $C_{12}H_{26}(\ell) + 37/2\ O_2(g) \longrightarrow 12CO_2(g) + 13H_2O(g)$

$\Delta H° = [12 \times \Delta H°_f(CO_2) + 13 \times \Delta H°_f(H_2O(g))] - [\Delta H°_f(C_{12}H_{26}(\ell))] =$

$[12 \times (-394) + 13 \times (-242) - (291)]\ kJ = -8165\ kJ$

$1.0\ kW\ hr \times \frac{1\ kJ}{1\ kW\ s} \times \frac{3600\ s}{1\ hr} \times \frac{1\ mol\ (C_{12}H_{26})}{8165\ kJ} \times \frac{170\ g\ (C_{12}H_{26})}{1\ mol\ C_{12}H_{26}} \times$

$\frac{10^{-3}\ L}{0.74\ g} \times \frac{100\%}{30\%} =$ **$\underline{0.34\ L}$ $(C_{12}H_{26})$**

17.81 A <u>concentration cell</u> is one in which the cathode and anode compartments contain the same electrode materials, but different concentrations of the ions.

17.82 (a) $E = E° - 0.0592/n\ \log$ (mass action expression)

$E = 0 - (0.592/2)\ \log(0.0010/0.10) =$ **$\underline{0.059\ V}$**

17.83 $E = E° - (0.0592/n)\ \log$ (mass act. exp.)

$E = 0 - (0.0592/3)\ \log(0.0020/0.10) =$ **$\underline{0.034\ V}$**

17.84 $E = E^\circ - (0.0592/n)\log(\text{mass act. exp.})$ $\quad 1/2\ H_2 + Ag^+ \longrightarrow H^+ + Ag$

$E = (0.80\text{ V} - 0\text{ V}) - (0.0592/1)\log\{[H^+]/[Ag^+]\}$

$K_{sp} = 5 \times 10^{-13} = [Ag^+][Br^-]$ $\qquad [Ag^+] = 5 \times 10^{-13}/0.010 = 5 \times 10^{-11}$

$E = 0.80\text{ V} - 0.0592 \times \log(1/5 \times 10^{-11}) =$ **0.19 V**

17.85 $E = E^\circ - (0.0592/n)\log[Pb^{2+}]$; $0.51\text{V} = (0.13 - 0.00\text{ V}) - (0.0592/2)\log[Pb^{2+}]$

$[Pb^{2+}] = 1 \times 10^{-13}$ $\quad K_{sp} = [Pb^{2+}][CrO_4^{2-}] = (1 \times 10^{-13})(0.10) =$ **1×10^{-14}**

17.86 $[H^+][HS^-]/[H_2S] = 1.1 \times 10^{-7}$ and $[H^+][S^{2-}]/[HS^-] = 1.0 \times 10^{-14}$

Since, $[H^+] \sim [HS^-]$, the $[S^{2-}] = 1.0 \times 10^{-14}$

$E = E^\circ - (0.0592/n)\log\{[Zn^{2+}]/[Cu^{2+}]\}$

$0.67\text{ V} = 1.10\text{ V} - (0.0592/2)\log(1.0/[Cu^{2+}])$

$[Cu^{2+}] = 3.0 \times 10^{-15}$

$K_{sp} = [Cu^{2+}][S^{2-}] = (3.0 \times 10^{-15})(1.0 \times 10^{-14}) =$ **3.0×10^{-29}**

but $K_{sp} = 8.5 \times 10^{-36}$ (Table 16.1)

Why is the K_{sp} which we calculated more than a million times larger? The clue is the problem statement that, "The solution--formed was not buffered." As S^{2-} is consumed by the precipitation of CuS, more H_2S ionizes to supply additonal S^{2-}. For each mole of S^{2-} produced, two moles of H^+ are also supplied.

(continued)

(17.86 continued)

Since the solution is not buffered, the concentration of H^+ increases to about 0.20 M.

$$\frac{[H^+]^2[S^{2-}]}{[H_2S]} = 1.1 \times 10^{-21} = \frac{(0.20)^2[S^{2-}]}{(0.10)} \qquad [S^{2-}] = 2.8 \times 10^{-21}$$

Using this value, the $K_{sp} = 8.4 \times 10^{-36}$ (This value is in agreement with the 8.5×10^{-36} found in Table 16.1).

17.87 (anode) $Zn(s) \longrightarrow Zn^{2+} + 2e^-$

(cathode) $2MnO_2(s) + 2NH_4^+ + 2e^- \longrightarrow Mn_2O_3(s) + 2NH_3 + H_2O$

17.88 The products formed at the electrodes diffuse away and the cell is rejuvenated.

17.89 (anode) $Zn(s) + 2OH^- \longrightarrow Zn(OH)_2(s) + 2e^-$

(cathode) $2MnO_2(s) + 2H_2O + 2e^- \longrightarrow 2MnO(OH)(s) + 2OH^-$

net: $Zn(s) + 2MnO_2(s) + 2H_2O \longrightarrow Zn(OH)_2(s) + 2MnO(OH)(s)$

Electrolyte is aqueous KOH.

17.90 (anode) $Zn(s) + 2OH^- \longrightarrow Zn(OH)_2(s) + 2e^-$

(cathode) $Ag_2O(s) + H_2O + 2e^- \longrightarrow 2Ag(s) + 2OH^-$

net: $Zn(s) + Ag_2O(s) + H_2O \longrightarrow Zn(OH)_2(s) + 2Ag(s)$

17.91 During discharge:

(anode) $Pb(s) + SO_4^{2-} \longrightarrow PbSO_4(s) + 2e^-$

(cathode) $PbO_2(s) + 4H^+ + SO_4^{2-} + 2e^- \longrightarrow PbSO_4(s) + 2H_2O$

When being charged, the reactions are reversed.

17.92 (anode) $Cd(s) + 2\,OH^- \longrightarrow Cd(OH)_2(s) + 2e^-$

(cathode) $NiO_2(s) + 2H_2O + 2e^- \longrightarrow Ni(OH)_2(s) + 2\,OH^-$

17.93 Fuel cells produce electrical energy from gaseous fuels undergoing reaction in a carefully designed environment. The reactants in a fuel cell may be continually supplied so that energy can be withdrawn as long as the outside fuel supply is maintained.

17.94 Fuel cells operate under more nearly reversible conditions. Therefore, their thermodynamic efficiency is higher; i.e., more of the available energy can be used to do work.

18 METALS AND THEIR COMPOUNDS; THE REPRESENTATIVE METALS

18.1 They are usually found in the combined state. Sources are the oceans and land-based deposits of carbonates, sulfates, oxides, and sulfides.

18.2 An ore is a mixture of substances that contains a particularly desirable constituent in a high enough concentration that its extraction from the mixture is economically worthwhile.

18.3 The three steps are: concentration, reduction, and refining.

18.4 Gold has a much larger density than sand and mud particles and is not as easily washed away.

18.5 An amalgam is a solution of a metal in mercury. Gold ore is mixed with mercury, which dissolves the metallic gold. The mercury is then separated from the stone and distilled, leaving the pure gold behind.

18.6 In flotation, the ore is finely ground and added to a mixture of oil and water. A stream of air is then blown through the mixture and the oil covered mineral is carried to the surface where it can be removed. In roasting, a sulfide ore is heated in air, converting the metal sulfide to an oxide that is more conveniently reduced.

18.7 $Al_2O_3 + 2OH^- \longrightarrow 2AlO_2^- + H_2O$, $AlO_2^- + H_2O + H^+ \longrightarrow Al(OH)_3$

$2Al(OH)_3 \longrightarrow Al_2O_3 + 3H_2O$

18.8 In compounds, metals exist in positive oxidation states and must be reduced to obtain the metal in a pure metallic form.

18.9 It must have a small ΔH°_f.

18.10 It has a large, negative ΔH°_f.

18.11 $ZnO(s) \longrightarrow Zn(s) + 1/2\ O_2(g)$ $\quad\quad \Delta H^\circ = +83.2\ \text{kcal mol}^{-1}$

$\Delta S^\circ = (10.0 + 1/2 \times 49.0 - 10.4)\ \text{cal (mol K)}^{-1} = 24.1\ \text{cal mol}^{-1}\ \text{K}^{-1}$

$\Delta G^\circ_T = \Delta H^\circ - T\Delta S^\circ = 83.2\ \text{kcal /mol} - T(24.1 \times 10^{-3}\ \text{kcal mol}^{-1}\text{K}^{-1}) = 0$

$T = 3450\ \text{K}$ <u>(3180°C)</u>

18.12 $\Delta G^\circ = -2.303\ RT\ \log K_p$, $\quad \Delta G^\circ = \Delta H^\circ - T\Delta S^\circ$

When $K_p = 1$, then $\Delta G^\circ = 0$ and $\Delta H^\circ = T\Delta S^\circ$ $\quad\quad \Delta H^\circ = 155\ \text{kJ mol}^{-1}$

$\Delta S^\circ = S^\circ(Cu(s)) + 1/2\ S^\circ(O_2(g)) - S^\circ(CuO(s)) = 33.3\ \text{J (mol K)}^{-1} +$

$1/2 \times 205.0\ \text{J (mol K)}^{-1} - 43.5\ \text{J (mol K)}^{-1} = 92.3\ \text{J (mol K)}^{-1}$

$T = 1.55 \times 10^5\ \text{J mol}^{-1}/92.3\ \text{J mol}^{-1}\ \text{K}^{-1} = 1680\ \text{K} =$ **1410°C** (3 sign. figs.)

18.13 $\Delta G^\circ = -RT \ln K_p$ and $\Delta G^\circ = \Delta H^\circ - T\Delta S^\circ$; $\quad \Delta G^\circ = 180.3 \frac{\text{kcal}}{\text{mol}} - T\left(61.65 \frac{\text{cal}}{\text{mol K}}\right)$

$\Delta G^\circ_{373} = 157.3\ \text{kcal /mol}$, $\Delta G^\circ_{773} = 132.6\ \text{kcal /mol}$, $\Delta G^\circ_{2273} = 40.2\ \text{kcal /mol}$

$\ln K_p = -\Delta G^\circ / RT$ $\quad\quad K_p = e^{-\Delta G^\circ / RT}$ $\quad\quad$ $\mathbf{K_{p\,(373)} = 6.71 \times 10^{-93}}$

$\mathbf{K_p\,(773) = 3.21 \times 10^{-38}}$ $\quad$ $\mathbf{K_p(2273) = 1.36 \times 10^{-4}}$

18.14 (a) $3Fe_2O_3 + CO \longrightarrow 2Fe_3O_4 + CO_2$

$Fe_3O_4 + CO \longrightarrow 3FeO + CO_2$

$FeO + CO \longrightarrow Fe + CO_2$

(b) $CaCO_3 \xrightarrow{heat} CaO + CO_2$

$CaO + SiO_2 \longrightarrow CaSiO_3$

18.15 It is plentiful and inexpensive.

18.16 $2PbO + C \longrightarrow 2Pb + CO_2$ and $PbO + H_2 \longrightarrow Pb + H_2O$

18.17 The chemical reducing agent itself would be even more difficult to prepare.

18.18 They tend to have relatively low melting points.

18.19 $2NaCl(\ell) \xrightarrow{electrolysis} 2\,Na(\ell) + Cl_2(g)$

$2Al_2O_3(\ell) \xrightarrow[cryolite]{electrolysis} 4Al(\ell) + 3O_2(g)$

18.20 To remove impurities and to lower the carbon content. The Bessemer converter, open hearth furnace and the basic oxygen process are described in Section 18. The basic oxygen process is the principal steel-making method today.

18.21 The Mond process is used in the refining of nickel. In this process impure nickel is treated with carbon monoxide at moderately low temperatures. The $Ni(CO)_4$ gas that is produced is then heated to 200°C and decomposes to give pure nickel plus CO.

18.22 The lower the electonegativity, the more metallic the element. Metallic character decreases left to right and increases from top to bottom. Lithium is more metallic than Be, which is more metallic than B. Carbon is less metallic than Si, which is less metallic than Ge. (In Group IVA, C is a nonmetal and Pb is a metal.)

18.23 (a) Li (b) Al (c) Cs (d) Sn (e) Ga

18.24 Ga_2O_3

18.25 Al_2O_3

18.26 Amphoteric - able to function as either an acid or base.

$2Al + 6H^+ \longrightarrow 2Al^{3+} + 3H_2$

$2Al + 2OH^- + 2H_2O \longrightarrow 2AlO_2^- + 3H_2$

$Be + 2H^+ \longrightarrow Be^{2+} + H_2$

$Be + 2OH^- \longrightarrow BeO_2^{2-} + H_2$

18.27 Many are amphoteric and form covalent compounds.

18.28 ϕ = charge /ion radius. The larger the value of ϕ on the cation, the greater the covalent character in a metal-nonmetal bond.

18.29 (a) $GeCl_4$ (b) Bi_2O_5 (c) PbS (d) Li_2S (e) MgS

18.30 (a) SnO (b) $AlCl_3$ (c) BeF_2 (d) PbS (e) SnS

18.31 Charge transfer from anion to cation which absorbs photons in the visible portion of the spectrum.

18.32 (a) Ag_2S (b) CuBr (c) SnS_2 (d) Al_2S_3

18.33 Red

18.34 Because their oxides are basic and alkali means basic. Oxidation states are zero and 1+.

18.35 They are relatively rare and compounds of Na and K usually serve just as well.

18.36 They are less expensive to produce.

18.37 $Na^+(g) \longrightarrow Na^+(aq)$ $\Delta H° = ?$ **(1)** $Na(s) \longrightarrow Na^+(aq)$ $\Delta H°_1 = -239.7$

(2) $Na(g) \longrightarrow Na(s)$ $\Delta H°_2 = -108.7$ **(3)** $Na^+(g) \longrightarrow Na(g)$ $\Delta H°_3 = -493.7$

$\Delta H° = \Delta H°_1 + \Delta H°_2 + \Delta H°_3 =$ **$\underline{-842.1\ kJ\ mol^{-1}}$**

18.38 $Na(s) \longrightarrow Na^{2+}(aq) + 2\,e^-$ (overall process) $\Delta H° =$ (negative)

$Na(s) \longrightarrow Na(g)$ $\Delta H°_{atomization} = 108.7\ kJ\ mol^{-1}$

$Na(g) \longrightarrow Na^+(g) + 1\,e^-$ $I.E._{(1)} = 495.8\ kJ\ mol^{-1}$

$Na^+(g) \longrightarrow Na^{2+}(g) + 1\,e^-$ $I.E._{(2)} = 4{,}565\ kJ\ mol^{-1}$

$Na^{2+}(g) \longrightarrow Na^{2+}(aq)$ $\Delta H°_{hydration} = ?$

(ΔH_{hyd} would have to be larger than **$\underline{-5169\ kJ\ mol^{-1}}$**)

18.39

K(s)	—>	$K^+(aq)$	+ 1e$^-$	$\Delta H° = ?$
K(s)	—>	K(g)		$\Delta H° = 90.0$ kJ /mol
K(g)	—>	$K^+(g)$	+ 1e$^-$	$\Delta H° = 418$ kJ /mol
$K^+(g)$	—>	$K^+(aq)$		$\Delta H° = -759$ kJ /mol
				$\Delta H° = -251$ kJ /mol

(continued)

(18.39 continued)

$\Delta G° = -nFE° = \Delta H° - T\Delta S°$

$\Delta S° = \frac{-nFE° - \Delta H°}{-T}$ = [1 x 96,500 C x 2.92 V x J /(V x C)] /298 K

+ (-251 x 10^3 J) /298 K = **103 J K^{-1}**

18.40 Na and K. Francium is least abundant because it is radioactive with a short half-life.

18.41 In the ocean; in salt deposits.

18.42 $MCl(\ell) + Na(g) \longrightarrow NaCl(\ell) + M(g)$ [M = K, Rb, Cs]

18.43 Cooling nuclear reactors; sodium vapor lamps.

18.44 (a) yellow (b) red (c) violet

18.45 View the flame through blue "cobalt glass".

18.46 $2Rb + 2H_2O \longrightarrow 2RbOH + H_2(g)$

18.47 Because of the very large hydration energy of the tiny Li^+ ion.

18.48 It dissolves, giving a blue solution. These solutions contain solvated electrons.

18.49 (a) $2Li + Br_2 \longrightarrow 2LiBr$

$2Na + Br_2 \longrightarrow 2NaBr$

(b) $2Li + S \longrightarrow Li_2S$

$2Na + S \longrightarrow Na_2S$

(c) $6Li + N_2 \longrightarrow 2Li_3N$

$Na + N_2 \longrightarrow$ no reaction

18.50 $4Li + O_2 \longrightarrow 2Li_2O$ $2Na + O_2 \longrightarrow Na_2O_2$

$M + O_2 \longrightarrow MO_2$ [M = K, Rb, Cs]

18.51 KO_2

$4KO_2 + 2CO_2 \longrightarrow 2K_2CO_3 + 3O_2$

$2KO_2 + 2H_2O \longrightarrow 2KOH + O_2 + H_2O_2$

18.52 Because of hydrolysis; $O_2^{2-} + H_2O \longrightarrow HO_2^- + OH^-$

18.53 A metal that reacts with traces of O_2 and removes them from an otherwise inert atmosphere.

18.54 Caustic soda, lye. Uses include: making soap; neutralizing acids; in drain cleaners; making detergents, pulp, and paper; removing sulfur from petroleum.

18.55 $Na_2CO_3 \cdot NaHCO_3 \cdot 2H_2O$

Solvay process:

$CaCO_3 \xrightarrow{heat} CaO + CO_2$

$CO_2 + H_2O \longrightarrow H_2CO_3$

$H_2CO_3 + NH_3 \longrightarrow NH_4^+ + HCO_3$

$HCO_3^- + Na^+ \longrightarrow NaHCO_3$

$2NaHCO_3 \xrightarrow{heat} Na_2CO_3 + H_2O + CO_2$

$2NH_4Cl + CaO \longrightarrow CaCl_2 + 2NH_3 + H_2O$

Net reaction: $2NaCl + CaCO_3 \longrightarrow Na_2CO_3 + CaCl_2$

18.56 Buffer: The HCO_3^- can neutralize both acids and bases.

$HCO_3^- + H_3O^+ \longrightarrow H_2CO_3 + H_2O$

$HCO_3^- + OH^- \longrightarrow CO_3^{2-} + H_2O$

Common name: baking soda Fire extinguisher:

$2NaHCO_3(s) \xrightarrow{heat} Na_2CO_3(s) + H_2O(g) + CO_2(g)$

18.57 K_2CO_3

$KOH + CO_2 \longrightarrow KHCO_3$

$2KHCO_3 \xrightarrow{heat} K_2CO_3 + H_2O + CO_2$

18.58 Li_2CO_3

18.59 Their oxides are basic and their ores are found in the earth. They are all larger.

18.60 Calcium and magnesium in mineral deposits ($CaCO_3$, $CaSO_4{\cdot}2H_2O$, $CaCO_3{\cdot}MgCO_3$, $MgCl_2{\cdot}KCl{\cdot}H_2O$) and in the sea.

Radium is found in pitchblend - an uranium ore.

18.61 From dolomite: $CaCO_3{\cdot}MgCO_3 \xrightarrow{heat} CaO{\cdot}MgO + 2CO_2$

$CaO + H_2O \longrightarrow Ca^{2+} + 2OH^-$

$MgO + H_2O \longrightarrow Mg(OH)_2(s)$

$Mg(OH)_2 + 2HCl \longrightarrow MgCl_2 + 2H_2O$

$MgCl_2(\ell) \xrightarrow{electrolysis} Mg(\ell) + Cl_2(g)$

(continued)

(18.61 continued)

From sea water:

$CaO + H_2O + Mg^{2+} \longrightarrow Ca^{2+} + Mg(OH)_2(s)$

$Mg(OH)_2 + 2HCl \longrightarrow MgCl_2 + 2H_2O$

$MgCl_2(\ell) \xrightarrow{\text{electrolysis}} Mg(\ell) + Cl_2(g)$

18.62 Their hydration energies are larger than those of the alkali metals, which offsets their larger ionization energies.

18.63 Calcining: heating a substance strongly.

Lime is CaO.

$CaO + H_2O \longrightarrow Ca(OH)_2$

It is an inexpensive strong base.

18.64 $2Mg + O_2 \longrightarrow 2MgO$ + light

18.65 (a) brick red (b) crimson (c) yellowish-green

18.66 Their oxides provide a water-insoluble protective film that prevents further oxidation. Ca, Sr, and Ba react with water.

18.67 $2Mg + O_2 \longrightarrow 2MgO$

$Mg + S \longrightarrow MgS$

$3Mg + N_2 \longrightarrow Mg_3N_2$

18.68 $Be + 2H^+ \longrightarrow Be^{2+} + H_2$

$Be + 2H_2O + 2OH^- \longrightarrow Be(OH)_4{}^{2-} + H_2(g)$

18.69 See Figure 18.13. Formation of the additional two Be–Cl coordinate covalent bonds suggests that the Be in $BeCl_2$ seeks additional electrons to complete its octet.

18.70 Because Be is so very small and highly charged, electron density is drawn toward Be^{2+}, making bonds covalent.

Organomagnesium compounds contain portions of organic molecules covalently bonded to Mg.

18.71 (a) $Ca + 2H_2O \longrightarrow Ca(OH)_2 + H_2$

(b) $K + 2H_2O \longrightarrow 2KOH + H_2$

18.72 Solubility of the hydroxides increases and the sulfates decrease from top to bottom in Group IIA.

18.73 To make lime, as a mild abrasive, an antacid, chalk.

18.74 $Mg(OH)_2$ suspended in H_2O.

18.75 $CaSO_4 \cdot 2H_2O$

$CaSO_4 \cdot 2H_2O \xrightarrow{\text{heat}} CaSO_4 \cdot 1/2H_2O + 3/2H_2O$

$CaSO_4 \cdot 1/2H_2O + 3/2H_2O \longrightarrow CaSO_4 \cdot 2H_2O$

18.76 It is opaque to X rays.

18.77 $MgSO_4 \cdot 7H_2O$ Used to treat fabrics, as a fertilizer, and medicinally.

18.78 IIIA: 1+, 3+

IVA: 2+, 4+

VA: 3+, 5+

18.79 Ga, In, Tl, Sn, Pb, Bi

Lower oxidation states become more stable going down a group because the energy needed to remove additional electrons can't be recovered by forming additional bonds. This is because bond strength decreases as the atoms become larger.

18.80 Bauxite, Al_2O_3

$Al_2O_3(s)$ + impurities(s) $\xrightarrow{OH^-}$ $AlO_2^-(aq)$ + impurities(s)

$AlO_2^- + H_3O^+ \longrightarrow Al(OH)_3(s)$

$2Al(OH)_3 \xrightarrow{heat} Al_2O_3 + 3H_2O$

18.81 Structural metal, kitchen utensils, automobiles, aircraft, beverage cans, aluminum foil

18.82 The Al_2O_3 on its surface protects the metal beneath. Forming an amalgam with the Al surface prevents Al_2O_3 from adhering and causes rapid corrosion.

18.83 $2Al + 6H^+ \longrightarrow 2Al^{3+} + 3H_2(g)$

$2Al + 2OH^- + 2H_2O \longrightarrow 2AlO_2^- + 3H_2(g)$

18.84 γ-Al_2O_3 is quite reactive; α-Al_2O_3 is quite inert. Gems composed of Al_2O_3 are ruby, sapphire, topaz, amethyst.

18.85 $Fe_2O_3(s) + 2Al(s) \longrightarrow Al_2O_3(\ell) + 2Fe(\ell)$ + heat

18.86 See figure in the Section on Chemical Properties and Compounds of Aluminum.

18.87 Hydrolysis: $Al(H_2O)_6^{3+} + H_2O \rightleftharpoons [Al(H_2O)_5OH]^{2+} + H_3O^+$

18.88 $Al(H_2O)_6^{3+} + OH^- \longrightarrow Al(H_2O)_5OH^{2+} + H_2O$

$Al(H_2O)_5OH^{2+} + OH^- \longrightarrow Al(H_2O)_4(OH)_2^+ + H_2O$

$Al(H_2O)_4(OH)_2^+ + OH^- \longrightarrow Al(H_2O)_3(OH)_3(s) + H_2O$

$Al(H_2O)_3(OH)_3(s) + OH^- \longrightarrow Al(H_2O)_2(OH)_4^- + H_2O$

18.89 AlO_2^- and $Al(H_2O)_2(OH)_4^-$

18.90 When solutions of $Al_2(SO_4)_3$ are made basic, hydrated aluminum hydroxide precipitates. As it settles, it carries fine sediment and bacteria with it.

18.91 A double salt of general formula $M^+M^{3+}(SO_4)_2 \cdot 12H_2O$. Example is $NaAl(SO_4)_2 \cdot 12H_2O$. This is the alum in baking powders. It evolves CO_2 from $NaHCO_3$ because the aluminum ion hydrolyzes, releasing H_3O^+ which reacts with the $NaHCO_3$.

18.92 $Al_2O_3 + 2OH^- \longrightarrow 2AlO_2^- + H_2O$

18.93 Tin: $SnO_2 + C \longrightarrow Sn + CO_2$

Lead: $2PbS + 3O_2 \longrightarrow 2PbO + 2SO_2$

$2PbO + C \longrightarrow 2Pb + CO_2$

Bismuth: $2Bi_2S_3 + 9O_2 \longrightarrow 2Bi_2O_3 + 6SO_2$

$2Bi_2O_3 + 3C \longrightarrow 4Bi + 3CO_2$

18.94 Iron is more easily oxidized than tin. A galvanic cell is established in which iron is the anode.

18.95 Allotropes are different forms of the same element. Tin exhibits allotropism.

18.96 It expands slightly when its liquid freezes. Woods metal is an alloy of 50% Bi, 25% Pb, 12.5% Sn, and 12.5% Cd. It has a low melting point (70°C) and is used in fuses and in triggering mechanisms for automatic sprinkler systems.

18.97 $Sn + 4HNO_3 \longrightarrow SnO_2 + 4NO_2 + 2H_2O$

$3Pb + 8HNO_3 \longrightarrow 3Pb(NO_3)_2 + 2NO + 4H_2O$

$Sn + 2Cl_2 \longrightarrow SnCl_4$

$Pb + Cl_2 \longrightarrow PbCl_2$

In each case, tin gives the 4+ state; lead gives the 2+ state.

18.98 Bi^{5+} is such a powerful oxidizing agent it would oxidize Cl^- to Cl_2.

18.99 $Sn + 2OH^- + 2H_2O \longrightarrow Sn(OH)_4^{2-} + H_2(g)$

$Pb + 2OH^- + 2H_2O \longrightarrow Pb(OH)_4^- + H_2(g)$

18.100 PbO (litharge); used in pottery glazes and making lead crystal.

Pb_3O_4 (red lead); used in corrosion-inhibiting paint.

PbO_2; cathode material in the lead storage battery.

18.101 Reaction of Pb^{2+} with airborn H_2S gives black PbS.

18.102 Cosmetics and pharmaceuticals. Bismuthyl ion is BiO^+.

19 THE CHEMISTRY OF SELECTED NONMETALS, PART I: HYDROGEN, CARBON, OXYGEN, AND NITROGEN

19.1 Dihydrogen

19.2 Hydrogen

19.3 The Earth's gravity wasn't strong enough to hold on to the hydrogen.

19.4 It reacts so readily with oxygen.

19.5 Advantage: less dense than He, so it has greater lifting power.

Disadvantage: hydrogen burns but helium doesn't.

19.6 Because there are no electrons below hydrogen's valence shell. It is in Group IA because of its valence shell configuration.

19.7 ${}^{1}_{1}H$, protium; ${}^{2}_{1}H$, deuterium; ${}^{3}_{1}H$, tritium. Tritium is radioactive and is dangerous because it can replace ordinary hydrogen in molecules in the body.

19.8 Advantages: it is clean burning and plentiful.

Disadvantages: difficult to store and must first be extracted from water.

19.9 (a) $CH_4 + H_2O \longrightarrow CO + 3H_2$

$CO + H_2O \longrightarrow CO_2 + H_2$

(b) $C + H_2O \longrightarrow CO + H_2$

19.10 $2CO + O_2 \longrightarrow 2CO_2$

$2H_2 + O_2 \longrightarrow 2H_2O$

19.11 Hydrogen is a byproduct in the preparation of caustic soda.

19.12 Preparation of ammonia. $3H_2 + N_2 \longrightarrow 2NH_3$

19.13 $Zn + H_2SO_4 \longrightarrow ZnSO_4 + H_2$ See Figure 19.1.

19.14 $CO + 2H_2 \xrightarrow[\text{pressure heat}]{\text{catalyst}} CH_3OH$

Provides a route from coal to a liquid fuel.

19.15 $H{-}C{\equiv}C{-}H + 2H_2 \longrightarrow CH_3{-}CH_3$

Hydrogenation of vegatable oils gives solid fats.

19.16 Hydrides. NaH is sodium hydride.

$2Na(s) + H_2(g) \longrightarrow 2NaH(s)$

$NaH + H_2O \longrightarrow NaOH + H_2(g)$

19.17 One. It has only one valence electron and needs only one more to fill its valence shell.

19.18 (a) nonlinear (b) trigonal pyramidal (c) tetrahedral

19.19 Acid-base

H^-	+	H_2O	$\longrightarrow$	H_2	+	OH^-
base		acid		acid		base

Redox

H^- is oxidized to give H_2, H^+ in H_2O is reduced.

19.20 Linking together of atoms of the same element to form chains. Carbon catenates most. Tendency to catenate decreases going down a group.

19.21 Some have positive ΔG°_f. Those that can be made by direct combination are:

CH_4, NH_3, H_2O, H_2S, HF, HCl, HBr.

19.22 X^{n-} becomes stronger from right to left in a period (e.g., C^{4-} is a stronger base than F^-), and from bottom to top in a group (e.g., O^{2-} is a stronger base than S^{2-}).

19.23 Hydrocarbons and those compounds derived from hydrocarbons by replacing H with other atoms.

19.24 Heating coal in the absence of air.

19.25 In diamond, C is sp^3 hybridized and gives a 3-dimensional interlocking network of bonds. In graphite, C is sp^2 hybridized and arranged in planar sheets with a delocalized π-electron cloud covering upper and lower surfaces. Sheets are stacked one on another and slide over each other easily.

19.26 As a lubricant and in electrodes.

19.27 Carbon formed by heating wood in the absence of air. Its large surface area per unit mass allows it to adsorb large numbers of molecules.

19.28 Burning CH_4 in a limited supply of O_2.

$$CH_4 + O_2 \longrightarrow C + 2H_2O$$

Used as a pigment and in making automobile tires.

19.29 :C≡O:, :Ö=C=Ö:

19.30 $HCHO_2(\ell) \xrightarrow{H_2SO_4} H_2O(\ell) + CO(g)$

19.31 $Fe_2O_3(s) + 3CO(g) \xrightarrow{heat} 2Fe(s) + 3CO_2(g)$

19.32 Compound formed between a metal and CO. $Ni(CO)_4$.

19.33 Commercially: from limestone.

$CaCO_3 \xrightarrow{heat} CaO + CO_2$

Laboratory:

$CaCO_3(s) + 2H^+(aq) \longrightarrow Ca^{2+}(aq) + CO_2(g) + H_2O$

19.34 Making Na_2CO_3, refrigeration, beverage carbonation.

19.35 By photosynthesis, to make cellulose (polymer of glucose).

19.36 $CaCO_3(s) + H_2CO_3(aq) \rightleftharpoons Ca(HCO_3)_2(aq)$

19.37 As H_2O evaporates, H_2CO_3 decomposes as shown by the equation given in the answer to Question 19.36 when proceeding from right to left.

19.38 Water containing Ca^{2+}, Mg^{2+}, Fe^{3+}. Addition of washing soda, $Na_2CO_3{\cdot}10H_2O$ or heating it, if it contians HCO_3^-.

19.39 Wash with dilute acid, which will dissolve $CaCO_3$.

19.40 SiC. Si replaces half of C atoms in the diamond structure.

$SiO_2(s) + 3C(s) \longrightarrow 2CO(g) + SiC(s)$

19.41 $Al_4C_3 + 12H_2O \longrightarrow 4Al(OH)_3 + 3CH_4(g)$

19.42 $CaC_2(s) + 2H_2O \longrightarrow Ca(OH)_2(s) + C_2H_2(g)$

19.43 Carbon atoms are located between atoms of host lattice. Tungsten carbide, WC.

19.44 $NH_3 + CH_4 \longrightarrow HCN + 3H_2$ HCN deactivates critical enzymes and binds irreversibly to iron in hemoglobin in the blood.

19.45 $:\ddot{S}=C=\ddot{S}:$; CS_2 is very flammable.

19.46 The atmosphere.

19.47 Dihydrogen, dioxygen, dinitrogen.

19.48 Catalytic decomposition of $KClO_3$

$$2KClO_3 \xrightarrow[\text{heat}]{MnO_2} 2KCl + 3O_2(g)$$

19.49 Manufacture of steel.

19.50 $O{=}O{-}O \longleftrightarrow O{-}O{=}O$ (resonance structures) Made by electric discharge through O_2.

O_3 doesn't form poisonous compounds with impurities in the water, but it does kill bacteria.

19.51 $O_2 \xrightarrow{h\nu} 2O$ then $O_2 + O \longrightarrow O_3$

Ozone protects the earth by absorbing harmful UV radiation.

Removal of O_3 from the ozone layer by nitrogen oxide pollutants:

($NO + O_3 \longrightarrow NO_2 + O_2$ then $NO_2 + O \longrightarrow O_2 + NO$)

and by Freons: ($CFCl_3 \xrightarrow{h\nu} CFCl_2 + Cl$, $Cl + O_3 \longrightarrow ClO + O_2$, and

$ClO + O \longrightarrow Cl + O_2$)

19.52 $O^{2-} + H_2O \longrightarrow 2OH^-$

19.53 Removal of Fe_2O_3 (rust) by reaction with acid.

19.54 $Al_2O_3 + 6H^+ \longrightarrow 2Al^{3+} + 3H_2O$

$Al_2O_3 + 2OH^- \longrightarrow 2AlO_2^- + H_2O$

19.55 From elemental carbon: $C + O_2 \longrightarrow CO_2$

From lower oxides: $2CO + O_2 \longrightarrow 2CO_2$

From hydride: $CH_4 + 2O_2 \longrightarrow CO_2 + 2H_2O$

19.56 Its $\Delta G°_f$ is positive, so $K_c \ll 1$ for its formation.

19.57 $4NH_3 + 5O_2 \longrightarrow 4NO + 6H_2O$

19.58 (a) $Cu + 2NO_3^- + 4H^+ \longrightarrow Cu^{2+} + 2NO_2 + 2H_2O$ (concentrated)

(b) $3Cu + 2NO_3^- + 8H^+ \longrightarrow 3Cu^{2+} + 2NO + 4H_2O$ (dilute)

19.59 (a) $2Na + O_2 \longrightarrow Na_2O_2$ (b) $K + O_2 \longrightarrow KO_2$

19.60 $H{-}\ddot{\underset{\cdot\cdot}{O}}{-}\ddot{\underset{\cdot\cdot}{O}}{-}H$, see Figure 19.6.

19.61 $2H_2O_2(\ell) \longrightarrow O_2\,(g) + 2H_2O(\ell)$

19.62 Because of its very strong triple bond.

19.63 Making ammonia; as an unreactive gaseous blanket during the manufacture of chemicals; as a refrigerant (liquid N_2).

19.64 Bacteria that remove N_2 from the air and make nitrogen compounds with it.

19.65 Warming a solution containing NH_4^+ and NO_2^-.

19.66 Lithium

19.67 It hydrolyzes to give NH_3.

$Mg_3N_2 + 6H_2O \longrightarrow 3Mg(OH)_2 + 2NH_3$

19.68 It forms hydrogen bonds with water.

19.69 NH_3

19.70 $2NH_4Cl + CaO \longrightarrow 2NH_3 + H_2O + CaCl_2$

It can't be collected by displacement of water because it is too soluble in water.

19.71 Warm it with base, which causes NH_3 to be evolved. The NH_3 can be detected by its odor or its basic effect on moist blue litmus paper.

19.72 $4NH_3 + 5O_2 \longrightarrow 4NO + 6H_2O$

$2NO + O_2 \longrightarrow 2NO_2$

$3NO_2 + H_2O \longrightarrow 2H^+ + 2NO_3^- + NO$

19.73 Photodecomposition gives NO_2.

$4HNO_3 \xrightarrow{hv} 4NO_2 + O_2 + 2H_2O$

19.74 $NaNO_3 + H_2SO_4 \xrightarrow{heat} NaHSO_4 + HNO_3$

19.75 Manufacture of fertilizers, explosives, and as a meat preservative.

19.76 NH_4^+

19.77 H^+ is not a strong enough oxidizing agent to dissolve Ag or Cu. Nitric acid contains NO_3^- as an oxidizing agent, which is able to oxidize Ag and Cu.

19.78 One part HNO_3 and three parts HCl, by volume. Chloride ion acts as a complex ion-forming agent to help dissolve the noble metals.

19.79 (a) NH_3 (b) NH_2OH (c) N_2O (d) N_2O_3 (e) N_2O_5

19.80 $N_2 + 3H_2 \xrightarrow[\text{catalyst}]{\text{iron}} 2NH_3$

Temp; 400-500°C. Pressure; several hundred atmospheres. These conditions chosen to produce maximum amount of NH_3 in shortest time.

19.81 KNH_2. In water, NH_2^- hydrolyzes immediately to give NH_3 because NH_2^- is a very strong base.

19.82 A reaction in which the same chemical undergoes both oxidation and reduction.

19.83 They prolonged WWI by allowing Germany to make munitions without having to import nitrates from Chile.

19.84 H–N̈–N̈–H , see Figure 19.8
(each N also bonded to an H below: H H)

19.85 $2NH_3 + NaOCl \longrightarrow N_2H_4 + NaCl + H_2O$

Used in rockets because combustion of hydrazine is very exothermic.

19.86 H–N̈–Ö–H (N also bonded to H below; O with two lone pairs) Basicities increase: $NH_2OH < N_2H_4 < NH_3$.

19.87 They can react to form N_2H_4, which is very poisonous.

19.88 $NH_4NO_3(\ell) \xrightarrow{\text{heat}} N_2O(g) + 2H_2O(g)$

:N̈═N═Ö: <—>:N≡N–Ö: (O with three lone pairs)

19.89 The $\Delta G°_f$ of N_2O, NO, NO_2 are all positive. Their decompositions, therefore, have negative $\Delta G°$, so they should proceed far toward completion. Stabilities of the oxides result because their rate of decomposition is slow.

19.90 Bond order: $NO^- < NO < NO^+$

$$O_2^{2-} < O_2^- < O_2 < O_2^+$$

Bond length: $NO^- > NO > NO^+$

$$O_2^{2-} > O_2^- > O_2 > O_2^+$$

Bond energy: $NO^- < NO < NO^+$

$$O_2^{2-} < O_2^- < O_2 < O_2^+$$

19.91 N, O O ; O O N–N O O

$2NO_2 \rightleftharpoons N_2O_4$

19.92 O O N–N O

$NO + NO_2 \xrightarrow{\text{cool}} N_2O_3$

N_2O_3 is anhydride of HNO_2.

19.93 $3HNO_2 \longrightarrow HNO_3 + H_2O + 2NO$

19.94 [Lewis structures of NO_2 and $[NO_2]^-$]

NO_2 should have the larger O--N--O bond angle because the single electron on the nitrogen in NO_2 doesn't offer as much resistance to increasing the O--N--O bond angle as does the pair of electrons on N in NO_2^-.

19.95 (a) $H^+ + 5HNO_2 + 2MnO_4^- \longrightarrow 5NO_3^- + 2Mn^{2+} + 3H_2O$

(b) $2H^+ + 2HNO_2 + 2I^- \longrightarrow I_2 + 2NO + 2H_2O$

19.96 $NaNO_3 + C \xrightarrow{heat} NaNO_2 + CO$

$NaNO_2$ retards growth of harmful bacteria and retains color of the meat. $NaNO_2$ may also cause cancer if HNO_2 produced in the stomach forms nitrosoamines with proteins, but the risk of food poisoning without the use of $NaNO_2$ may outweigh the risk of cancer if $NaNO_2$ is present in the meat.

19.97 [Lewis structure of $O_2N{-}O{-}NO_2$] (vapor); $NO_2^+NO_3^-$ in solid

19.98 Dehydration of HNO_3.

19.99 $N_2O_5 + H_2O \longrightarrow 2HNO_3$

19.100 **(a)** $\Delta H = 8 \text{ mol } CO_2(g)\ (-394 \text{ kJ mol}^{-1}) + 9 \text{ mol } H_2O(g)\ (-242 \text{ kJ mol}^{-1})$ -

$[1 \text{ mol } C_8H_{18}(\ell)\ (-255.1 \text{ kJ mol}^{-1}) - 0]$ = **-5075 kJ**

(b) $\Delta H = 8 \text{ mol } CO_2(g)\ (-394 \text{ kJ mol}^{-1}) + 9 \text{ mol } H_2O(g)\ (-242 \text{ kJ mol}^{-1})$ +

$0 - [1 \text{ mol } C_8H_{18}(\ell)\ (-255.1 \text{ kJ mol}^{-1}) + 25 \text{ mol } N_2O(g)\ (81.5 \text{ kJ mol}^{-1})]$

= **-7112 kJ**

19.101 $N_2 + O_2 \rightleftharpoons 2NO$

$2NO + O_2 \longrightarrow 2NO_2$

$NO_2 \xrightarrow{hv} NO + O$

$O + O_2 \longrightarrow O_3$

O_3 + hydrocarbons —> PAN

19.102 NO_2, PAN is

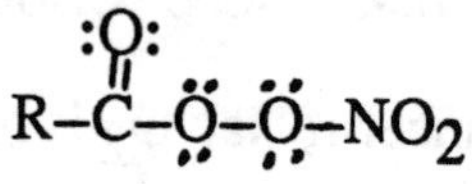

$$R-\overset{\overset{\displaystyle :\ddot{O}:}{\|}}{C}-\ddot{\underset{\cdot\cdot}{O}}-\ddot{\underset{\cdot\cdot}{O}}-NO_2$$

20 THE CHEMISTRY OF SELECTED NONMETALS, PART II: PHOSPHORUS, SULFUR, THE HALOGENS, THE NOBLE GASES, AND SILICON

20.1 $Ca_3(PO_4)_2$

20.2 In DNA, phospholipids (cell membranes), energy storage.

20.3 $1s^2 2s^2 2p^6 3s^2 3p^3$

20.4 Tetrahedral. The P–P–P bonds are strained and quite weak.

20.5 $2Ca_3(PO_4)_2 + 6SiO_2 + 10C \longrightarrow 6CaSiO_3 + 10CO + P_4$

20.6 A furnace in which the contents are heated by passing an electric current through them.

20.7 **Red phosphorus** - believed to consist of P_4 tetrahedral joined to each other.
Black phosphorous - layers of phosphorus atoms in which atoms in a given layer are covalently bonded to each other. Binding between layers is weak.
Both of these forms are less reactive than white phosphorous.

20.8 **(a)** $P_4 + 5O_2 \longrightarrow P_4O_{10}$ **(b)** $P_4 + 3O_2 \longrightarrow P_4O_6$

20.9 **(a)** See Figure 20.2 **(b)** See Figure 20.3

20.10 **(a)** $P_4O_{10} + 6H_2O \longrightarrow 4H_3PO_4$ **(b)** $P_4O_6 + 6H_2O \longrightarrow 4H_3PO_3$

20.11 A substance that removes H_2O from a gas mixture. P_4O_{10} reacts with water to give H_3PO_4, thus giving a moisture-free gas.

20.12 $Ca_3(PO_4)_2 + 3H_2SO_4 + 6H_2O \longrightarrow 3CaSO_4{\cdot}2H_2O + 2H_3PO_4$

20.13 Concentrated H_3PO_4.

20.14 Combustion of phosphorus to P_4O_{10} then reaction of the P_4O_{10} with H_2O.

20.15 Fertilizers, food additives, and detergents.

20.16

$Mg(H_2PO_4)_2$	magnesium dihydrogen phosphate
$MgHPO_4$	magnesium hydrogen phosphate
$Mg_3(PO_4)_2$	magnesium phosphate

20.17 H_3PO_4

20.18 $H_2PO_4^-$ and HPO_4^{2-}. $H_2PO_4^-$ neutralizes strong base, HPO_4^{2-} neutralizes strong acid.

20.19 Water softener, cleaning agent. Hydrolysis of PO_4^{3-} makes the solution basic.

20.20

```
       :Ö:                 :Ö:
        |                   |
   H–Ö–P–Ö–H           H–Ö–P–Ö–H
        |                   |
       :O:                  H
        |
        H
```

20.21 A mixture of calcium sulfate and calcium dihydrogen phosphate.

$Ca_3(PO_4)_2 + 2H_2SO_4 + 4H_2O \longrightarrow 2CaSO_4{\cdot}2H_2O + Ca(H_2PO_4)_2$

20.22 $Ca_3(PO_4)_2$ is insoluble, so little phosphate enters solution to be available for absorption by plants.

20.23 (a) sodium hydrogen phosphate **(b)** sodium dihydrogen phosphate

20.24 $12Na + P_4 \rightarrow 4Na_3P$

$Na_3P + 3H_2O \rightarrow 3NaOH + PH_3$

20.25

$$H{-}\ddot{O}{-}P(=\ddot{O})(\ddot{O}H){-}\ddot{O}H + H{-}\ddot{O}{-}P(=\ddot{O})(\ddot{O}H){-}\ddot{O}H \rightarrow HO{-}P(=\ddot{O})(\ddot{O}H){-}\ddot{O}{-}P(=\ddot{O})(\ddot{O}H){-}\ddot{O}H + H_2O$$

20.26 A PO_4 tetrahedron.

20.27 $(PO_3^-)_n$ is the metaphosphate ion. Formed by condensation of $H_2PO_4^-$.

$$\cdots HO{-}P(O^-)(O){-}OH \quad HO{-}P(O^-)(O){-}OH \quad HO{-}P(O^-)(O){-}OH \cdots \text{ etc.} \quad (-H_2O,\ -H_2O)$$

20.28 See the structure near the end of the section on Polymeric Phosphoric Acids and Their Ions. It is used in solid detergents.

20.29 3 mol NaH_2PO_4 to 2 mol Na_2HPO_4 (the HPO_4^{2-} units terminate the ends of the chains).

20.30 They promote algae blooms which deplete the oxygen from the lake when the algae die and decompose. This kills fish and other aquatic life.

20.31 Phosphorous acid. $Mg(H_2PO_3)_2$ and $MgHPO_3$ (H_3PO_3 is a diprotic acid).

20.32 H_3PO_4 is a poor oxidizing agent. H_3PO_3 is a moderately good reducing agent.

20.33 See Figure 20.4 PCl_5 exists as $PCl_4^+PCl_6^-$ in the solid. In PCl_3, phosphorous uses sp^3 hybrids; in PCl_5 it uses dsp^3 hybrids.

20.34 $1s^22s^22p^63s^23p^4$

20.35 Elemental sulfur. It means "stone that burns."

20.36 As deposits of elemental sulfur, in sulfates, in sulfides.

20.37 Rhombic sulfur and monoclinic sulfur. They have different packing of S_8 rings in their crystals. When heated, solid sulfur melts to give an amber liquid containing S_8 rings. The rings break and join with S_x chains as the liquid darkens and thickens. The S_x chains break into smaller fragments at still higher temperatures.

20.38 A form of sulfur produced when hot sulfur containing long S_x chains is suddenly cooled.

20.39 Superheated water is pumped into the sulfur deposit where it melts the sulfur. This is then foamed to the surface with compressed air.

20.40 SO_2

20.41 $S + O_2 \longrightarrow SO_2$

$2SO_2 + O_2 \xrightarrow{\text{catalyst}} 2SO_3$

$SO_3 + H_2SO_4 \longrightarrow H_2S_2O_7$

$H_2S_2O_7 + H_2O \longrightarrow 2H_2SO_4$

20.42 The reaction of SO_2 with O_2 is slow.

20.43 By reaction of a sulfite (e.g., Na_2SO_3) or bisulfite (e.g., $NaHSO_3$) with an acid.

20.44 (a) $SO_2 + H_2O \rightleftharpoons H_2SO_3$ (b) $SO_3 + H_2O \longrightarrow H_2SO_4$

20.45 Rain falling through air that is polluted with SO_2 and SO_3 becomes acidic because SO_2 and SO_3 react with water to form H_2SO_3 and H_2SO_4. It causes structural damage to buildings, causes corrosion of metals, and kills fish and plants.

20.46 H_2SO_4 is a stronger acid than H_2SO_3. The two lone oxygens on S in H_2SO_4 cause a greater polarization of the O–H bonds than does the single lone oxygen attached to S in H_2SO_3.

20.47 Production of fertilizers, refining petroleum, lead storage batteries, manufacture of other chemicals, steel industry.

20.48 :Ö=S̈–Ö: <—> :Ö–S̈=Ö: , nonlinear

:O:=S(–:Ö:)(–:Ö:) <—> :Ö:–S(=:O:)(–:Ö:) <—> :Ö:–S(–:Ö:)(=:O:) , planar triangular

20.49 Add conc. H_2SO_4 to the water.

20.50 The first step in the dissociation is complete; the second step proceeds about 10% to completion. A solution having 1 mol H_2SO_4 contains more than 1 mol H_3O^+.

20.51 $C_6H_{12}O_6 \xrightarrow{H_2SO_4} 6C + 6H_2O$

20.52 (a) sodium sulfite (b) sodium hydrogen sulfate

20.53

```
       :Ö:   :Ö:
        |     |
  HÖ—S—Ö—S—ÖH
        |     |
       :Ö:   :Ö:
```

20.54 [:N≡C–S̤̈:]⁻

20.55 $CH_3CSNH_2 + 2H_2O \longrightarrow CH_3CO_2^- + NH_4^+ + H_2S$

20.56 H_2S is poisonous.

20.57

```
⌈   :Ö:   ⌉2-
|    |    |
| :S̤̈—S—Ö̤: |
|    |    |
⌊   :O̤:   ⌋
```

; $S(s) + SO_3^{2-}(aq) \longrightarrow S_2O_3^{2-}(aq)$

20.58 It forms a complex ion with Ag^+ and helps dissolve and remove unexposed silver halide from the film.

20.59 (a) $S_2O_3^{2-} + 4Cl_2 + 5H_2O \longrightarrow 8Cl^- + 2SO_4^{2-} + 10H^+$

(b) $2S_2O_3^{2-} + I_2 \longrightarrow S_4O_6^{2-} + 2I^-$

20.60 (a) I_2 and SO_2 (b) Cu^{2+} and SO_2 (c) S or H_2S and Zn^{2+}

(d) Zn^{2+} and H_2 (e) no reaction

20.61 F, $1s^22s^22p^5$; Cl, $1s^22s^22p^63s^23p^5$; Br, $1s^22s^22p^63s^23p^63d^{10}4s^24p^5$; I, $1s^22s^22p^63s^23p^63d^{10}4s^24p^64d^{10}5s^25p^5$

20.62 The name halogen comes from the Greek "halos" meaning salt. The name reflects the state in which the halogens are found in nature.

20.63 In the combined state in compounds, normally as halide ions.

20.64 Fluorine: CaF_2, Na_3AlF_6, $Ca_5(PO_4)_3F$

Chlorine: NaCl in sea water and mineral deposits.

Bromine: Sea water and brine wells.

Iodine: Seaweed and as an impurity in saltpeter imported from Chile.

20.65 Electrolysis of HF dissolved in molten KF.

20.66 Lab: $MnO_2(s) + 4HCl(aq) \longrightarrow MnCl_2(aq) + Cl_2(g) + 2H_2O$

Commercially: Electrolysis of molten NaCl or brine.

Uses: Treating drinking water, making solvents, manufacture of pesticides.

20.67 F_2: Pale yellow gas with b.p. of -188°C

Cl_2: Pale green gas, b.p. =-34.6°C

Br_2: Dark red liquid, b.p. = 58.8°C

I_2: Dark, metallic-looking solid, m.p. = 113.5°C

20.68 (a) $Cl_2 + 2KI \longrightarrow I_2 + 2KCl$ (b) $F_2 + 2KBr \longrightarrow Br_2 + 2KF$

(c) $I_2 + NaCl \longrightarrow$ N.R. (d) $Br_2 + 2NaI \longrightarrow I_2 + 2NaBr$

20.69 The F–F bond is quite weak.

20.70 Recovered commercially from sea water by the reaction,

$2Br^-(aq) + Cl_2(aq) \longrightarrow Br_2(aq) + 2Cl^-(aq)$

Blowing air through the water removes the volatile Br_2. Uses are in making $Pb(C_2H_5)_4$ and AgBr. In the lab, Br_2 can be made by the reaction,

$MnO_2 + 2Br^- + 4H^+ \longrightarrow Mn^{2+} + Br_2 + 2H_2O$

20.71 Recovered from seaweed and from $NaIO_3$, which is an impurity in Chile saltpeter.

20.72 F_2 combines instantly and explosively with H_2 to form HF. Cl_2 combines with H_2 explosively if the mixture is heated or exposed to UV light. Reactions of H_2 with Br_2 and I_2 are less vigorous.

20.73 $CaF_2 + H_2SO_4 \longrightarrow CaSO_4 + 2HF(g)$

20.74 $NaCl + H_2SO_4 \longrightarrow HCl(g) + NaHSO_4$

HCl is used to remove rust from steel and in the manufacture of other chemicals.

20.75 $NaBr + H_3PO_4 \xrightarrow{heat} HBr + NaH_2PO_4$

$NaI + H_3PO_4 \xrightarrow{heat} HI + NaH_2PO_4$

20.76 Volatile SiF_4 is formed. $SiO_2(s) + 4HF(aq) \longrightarrow SiF_4(g) + 2H_2O(\ell)$

20.77 HF > HCl < HBr < HI. HF is hydrogen bonded into staggered chains.

20.78 Because HF can cause very severe skin burns.

20.79 (a) hypobromous acid (b) sodium hypochlorite (c) potassium bromate (d) magnesium perchlorate (e) periodic acid (f) bromic acid (g) sodium iodate (h) potassium chlorite

20.80 The same substance undergoes both oxidation and reduction; a portion of it is oxidized while the rest is reduced.

20.81 (a) $Cl_2 + H_2O \rightleftharpoons H^+ + Cl^- + HOCl$

(b) $Cl_2 + 2OH^- \longrightarrow OCl^- + Cl^- + H_2O$

20.82 $CaCl(OCl) + 2H^+ \longrightarrow Ca^{2+} + H_2O + Cl_2$

20.83 OCl^- is stable, OBr^- reacts moderately fast, OI^- reacts very rapidly. Stability of OCl^- is related to slow rate of reaction rather than to thermodynamic stability.

20.84 $4KClO_3 \xrightarrow{heat} 3KClO_4 + KCl$

$2KClO_3 \xrightarrow{MnO_2} 2KCl + 3O_2$

20.85 $Ca(OCl)_2$

20.86 (a) nonlinear (b) trigonal bipyramidal (c) octahedral (d) trigonal pyramidal (e) T-shaped (f) distorted tetrahedral (g) square pyramidal (h) tetrahedral

20.87 Seven fluorine atoms cannot fit around the smaller chlorine atoms.

20.88 Oxygen is too small to accommodate four fluorine atoms and in OF_4 there would be more than an octet of electrons in the valence shell of oxygen, which is not permitted.

20.89 $GeCl_4 + 2H_2O \longrightarrow GeO_2 + 4HCl$

20.90 Si has vacant d orbitals that can be used by attacking H_2O molecules, but C does not.

20.91 NH_3 is a good Lewis base; NF_3 is a poor Lewis base because the highly electronegative fluorine atoms make the nitrogen a poor electron pair donor.

20.92 Noble gas atoms trapped in cagelike sites in a crystal lattice.

20.93 XeF_4, square planar; XeF_2, linear.

20.94 They had believed that the completed octet was chemically inert.

20.95 $SiO_2(s) + 2C(s) \xrightarrow{heat} Si(s) + 2CO(g)$

20.96 A thin section of a bar of the substance to be refined is melted and the molten zone is gradually moved from one end of the bar to the other. The impurities collect in the molten zone.

20.97 Because Si does not form stable π-bonds to other Si atoms.

20.98 Because Si does not form stable π-bonds to oxygen or any other atoms.

20.99

```
 [      ..      ] 4-
 [     :O:      ]
 [      |       ]
 [ ..       ..  ]
 [:O – Si – O:  ]
 [ ..       ..  ]
 [      |       ]
 [     :O:      ]
 [      ..      ]
```

20.100 See the Lewis structure in the section on "Compounds With Silicon Oxygen Bonds."

20.101 $[Si_6O_{18}]^{12-}$ (cyclic ring of six SiO_4 tetrahedra, each Si bonded to two bridging O and two terminal O)

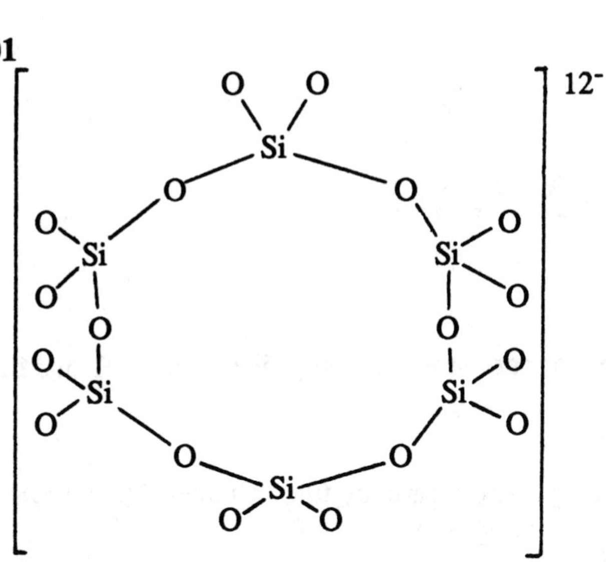

Found in beryl, $Be_3Al_2(Si_6O_{18})$

20.102 See Figure 20.19 Repeating unit is $Si_4O_{11}{}^{6-}$.

20.103 See Figure 20.18

20.104 Planar sheet silicates - examples are soapstone and talc.

20.105 SiO_2. There are left- and right-handed helices of SiO_4 tetrahedra possible, which gives rise to "left-" and "right-handed" crystals that are mirror images of each other.

20.106 –Si–O–Si–O–S–O– chain.

20.107

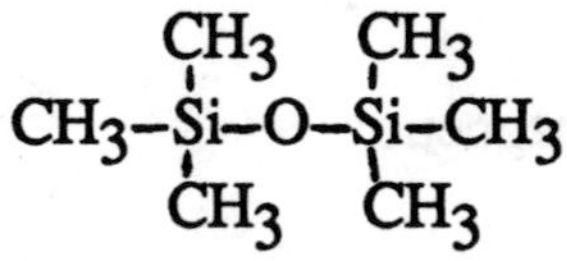

$$\begin{array}{ccccc} & CH_3 & & CH_3 & \\ & | & & | & \\ CH_3- & Si & -O- & Si & -CH_3 \\ & | & & | & \\ & CH_3 & & CH_3 & \end{array}$$

20.108

$$\left(\begin{array}{c} CH_3 \\ | \\ -Si-O- \\ | \\ CH_3 \end{array}\right)_x$$

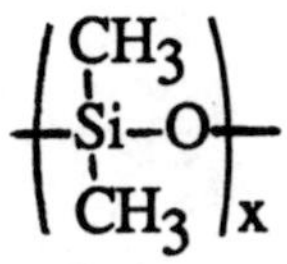

Also known as silicone

21 THE TRANSITION METALS

21.1 A transition element is one that possesses a partially filled d subshell and fits between Groups IIA and IIIA.

21.2 The inner transition elements possess a partially filled f sublevel that is two below the outermost energy level.

21.3 Compounds of elements in the A and B groups have similar composition, structure, and oxidation states.

21.4 None of these nine elements have counterparts among the representative elements

21.5 Fe, Co, Ni

21.6 This question will be answered differently by different students.

21.7 Four general properties of the transition elements are:

(1) They exhibit multiple oxidation states.

(2) Many transition metal compounds are paramagnetic.

(3) Many compounds are colored.

(4) They tend to form complex ions.

21.8 SO_4^{2-} and $S_2O_7^{2-}$

21.9 $KMnO_4$

21.10 See Table 21.2

21.11 Many have a pair of electrons in the outer S orbital. These are the first electrons to be lost.

21.12 They have a partially filled d subshell below the outer shell.

21.13 Going from left to right in a period, the lower oxidation states become relatively more stable. Going from top to bottom in a B-group, the higher oxidation states become relatively more stable.

21.14 CrO_4^{2-}

21.15 Ni^{3+}

21.16 Cr^{2+}

21.17 Cu^{3+}

21.18 The lanthanide contraction is the gradual decrease in size that occurs across the lanthanide series. It occurs because the f subshell lying 2 shells below the outer shell is being filled while the charge of the nucleus is increasing.

21.19 The differences in electron configuration occur in a subshell that is two shells below the outer shell.

21.20

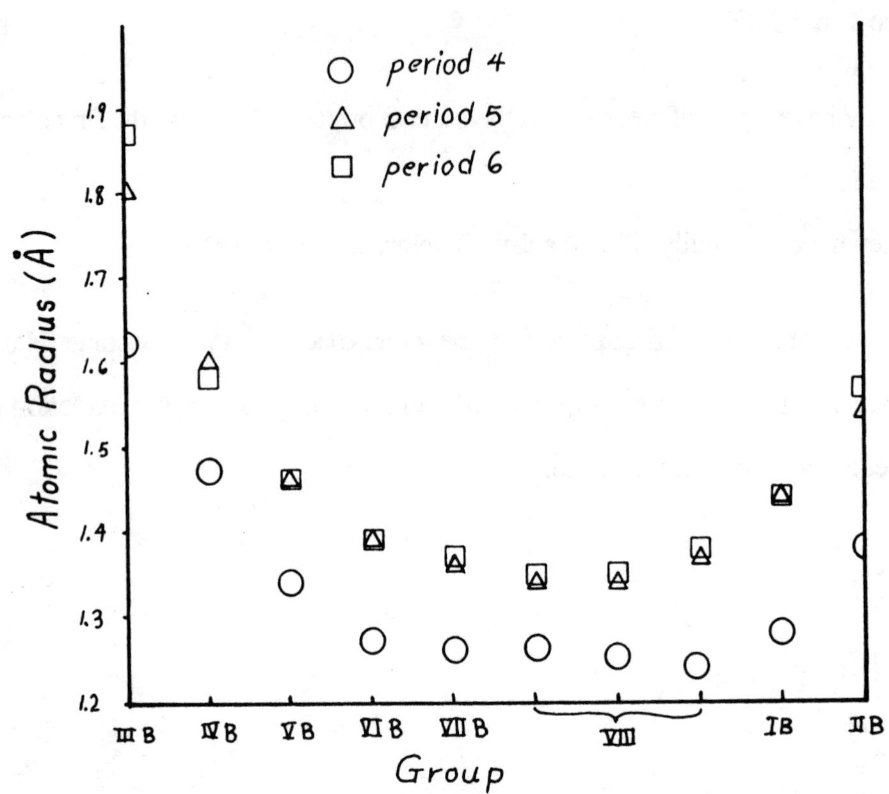

The atomic radii of the transition elements of periods 5 and 6 are nearly identical from Group IVB onward. In general, atoms with large numbers of unpaired electrons have small atomic radii.

21.21 They have the same electron structure in their outer shells and because of the lanthanide contraction, Hf is very nearly the same size as Zr. Thus, their chemical properties are very similar.

21.22 Since their atomic radii are equal (139 pm, Table 21.5), one would conclude that the densities of W and Mo would be in the same ratio as their atomic masses: $(10.2\ \text{g/cm}^3)(183.85/95.94) = 19.5\ \text{g/cm}^3$ vs. the experimental value of $19.3\ \text{g/cm}^3$.

21.23 The effects of increased nuclear charge by the addition of protons and increased shielding by the added electrons nearly off-set each other in the transition elements.

21.24 Fe, Co and Ni

21.25 Paramagnetic substances are weakly drawn into a magnetic field,whereas, ferromagnetic substances are strongly drawn into a magnetic field. Both properties are a result of unpaired electrons. A ferromagnetic substance can become permanently magnetized by placing it in a strong magnetic field so that the domains become aligned with the field. The domains remain aligned even after removal of the external field.

21.26 When a substance that possesses ferromagnetism is melted, it becomes simply paramagnetic because the domains become randomly oriented by thermal motion.

21.27 Sc, Y, La $\quad 2M + 6H_2O \longrightarrow 2M(OH)_3 + 3H_2$

21.28 $CrO_2(OH)_2$ contains two lone oxygens. Because of their high electronegativity, electron density is drained from the O–H bonds, making it easy for the hydrogen to be removed as H^+. This is not the case, however, for $Cr(OH)_3$.

21.29 Oxides of metals in high oxidation states are anhydrides of oxoacids that have one or more lone oxygens and are therefore acidic.

21.30 Because of low toxicity and because it doesn't darken in the presence of H_2S. Titanium is considerably less dense than steel and does not lose its strength at high temperature.

21.31 The energy for removal of 4 electrons is so high that Ti^{+4} ion does not have a real existence.

21.32 $TiCl_4 + 2H_2O \longrightarrow TiO_2 + 4HCl$

21.33 Because it is lustrous and resistant to corrosion. Oxidation states are 2+, 3+, and 6+.

21.34 Stainless steel is an alloy of chromium, nickel, and iron. It is very resistant to corrosion. It usually is not ferromagnetic.

21.35 $Cr(H_2O)_6{}^{3+}$ is a weak acid. $Cr(H_2O)_6{}^{3+} + 3OH^- \quad Cr(H_2O)_3(OH)_3 + 3H_3O^+$

21.36 $Cr(H_2O)_3(OH)_3 + H_3O^+ \longrightarrow Cr(H_2O)_4(OH)_2{}^+ + H_2O$

$Cr(H_2O)_3(OH)_3 + OH^- \longrightarrow Cr(H_2O)_2(OH)_4{}^- + H_2O$

21.37

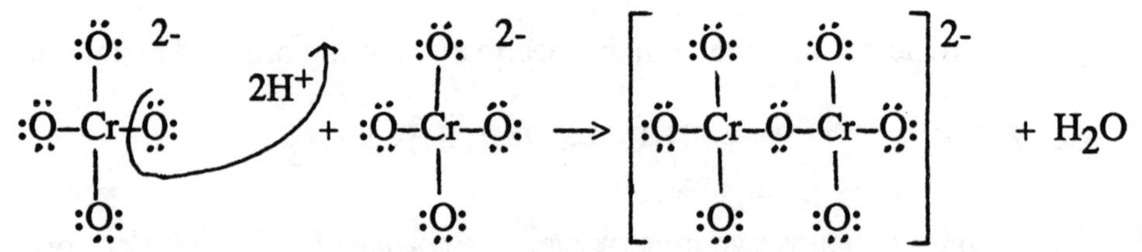

```
   :Ö: 2-                    :Ö: 2-          ┌  :Ö:    :Ö:   ┐2-
    |         2H+             |              │   |      |    │
:Ö—Cr—Ö:   (curved arrow)  + :Ö—Cr—Ö:   —>   │:Ö—Cr—Ö—Cr—Ö:  │      + H2O
    |                         |              │   |      |    │
   :Ö:                       :Ö:             └  :Ö:    :Ö:   ┘
```

21.38 2+, 4+, 6+, 7+; the 2+ is the most stable oxidation state.

21.39 It is deeply colored and its reduction product in acid solution, Mn^{2+}, is nearly colorless. In neutral or basic solution, the reduction product is brown, insoluble MnO_2.

21.40 $2HCl + Mn \longrightarrow MnCl_2 + H_2$

21.41 $3MnO_4{}^{2-} + 4H^+ \longrightarrow 2MnO_4{}^- + MnO_2 + 2H_2O$

21.42 It is abundant and easily extracted from its ores.

21.43 FeO, Fe_2O_3, Fe_3O_4. Only Fe_3O_4 is magnetic.

21.44 $Fe \longrightarrow Fe^{2+} + 2e^-$

$2e^- + 1/2O_2 + H_2O \longrightarrow 2OH^-$

$Fe^{2+} + 2OH^- \longrightarrow Fe(OH)_2$

$4Fe(OH)_2 + O_2 + 2H_2O \longrightarrow 4Fe(OH)_3$

21.45 $2H^+(aq) + Fe(s) \longrightarrow Fe^{2+}(aq) + H_2(g)$

21.46 It is useful in high-temperature alloys that are employed in tools for cutting and machining other metals at high speed. +2 and +3

21.47 It is resistant to corrosion and its alloys are resistant to impact.

21.48 Because of the ion, $Ni(H_2O)_6{}^{2+}$, which is green. NiO_2 is used as the cathode in nickel-cadmium batteries.

21.49 Their reactivity decreases from Cu to Ag to Au, and their occurrence in nature as the free metal increases from Cu to Ag to Au.

21.50 Copper - electrical wire Silver - photography

Gold - plating of low voltage electrical contacts

21.51 Principal oxidation states: copper, +1 and +2; silver, +1; gold, +1 and +3.

21.52 H^+ is not a strong enough oxidizing agent. Copper and silver react with HNO_3.

$3Cu + 8HNO_3 \longrightarrow 3Cu(NO_3)_2 + 2NO + 4H_2O$

$(3Cu + 8H^+ + 2NO_3{}^- \longrightarrow 3Cu^{2+} + 2NO + 4H_2O)$

$3Ag + 4HNO_3 \longrightarrow 3AgNO_3 + NO + 2H_2O$

$(3Ag + 4H^+ + NO_3{}^- \longrightarrow 3Ag^+ + NO + 2H_2O)$

21.53 $Au + 6H^+ + 3NO_3^- + 4Cl^- \longrightarrow AuCl_4^- + 3H_2O + 3NO_2$

21.54 AgCl, AgBr, AgI

21.55 Add HCl to the solution suspected to contain Ag^+. If a precipitate forms, separate it from the solution and dissolve it with aqueous ammonia. Then acidify the ammonia solution. A white precipitate of AgCl confirms the presence of Ag^+ in the original solution.

$Ag^+ + Cl^- \longrightarrow AgCl(s)$

$AgCl(s) + 2NH_3 \longrightarrow Ag(NH_3)_2^+ + Cl^-$

$Ag(NH_3)_2^+ + Cl^- + 2H^+ \longrightarrow AgCl(s) + 2NH_4^+$

21.56 The deep blue $Cu(NH_3)_4^{2+}$ ion is formed.

21.57 $Zn(s) + H_2SO_4(aq) \longrightarrow ZnSO_4(aq) + H_2$

$Cd(s) + H_2SO_4(aq) \longrightarrow CdSO_4(aq) + H_2$

$Hg(\ell) + H_2SO_4(aq) \longrightarrow$ no reaction

21.58 The protection of a metal from corrosion by connecting it electrically to a metal that is more easily oxidized and which will be preferentially oxidized.

21.59 Covering a metal with a coating of zinc. It protects steel by providing a barrier to oxygen and moisture and by cathodic protection.

21.60 Cadmium is used when a basic environment is anticipated because zinc is attacked by base but cadmium is not. Cadmium is not used more often because it is less abundant than zinc and because its salts are very toxic.

21.61 Brass and bronze.

21.62 Paint pigment, sun screen, fast-setting dental cements.

21.63 $HgCl_2$ is a weak electrolyte. $HgCl_2 + H_2O \rightleftharpoons Hg(OH)Cl + H^+ + Cl^-$

21.64 Add HCl, which will cause Hg_2Cl_2 to precipitate. Treatment of Hg_2Cl_2 with aqueous NH_3 gives a black precipitate because of disproportionation.

21.65 **(a)** cobalt **(b)** nickel

21.66 $K_{sp} = [Hg^+]\,[Cl^-] = 2.2 \times 10^{-18}, 4.4 \times 10^{-18}, 1.1 \times 10^{-17}$, and 2.2×10^{-17}

Not Constant

$K_{sp} = [Hg_2^{2+}]\,[Cl^-]^2 = 1.1 \times 10^{-18}, 1.1 \times 10^{-18}, 1.1 \times 10^{-18}$, and 1.1×10^{-18}

Constant Value **correct formula = Hg_2^{2+}**

21.67 Ligands tend to be Lewis bases that have an unshared pair of electrons which can be shared with a metal cation. Ligands attached to the metal are considered to be in a first coordination sphere. Compounds of the transition elements in which the metal cation is attached to one or more ions or molecules are called coordination compounds. Ligands which have one atom that can bond to a metal cation are called monodentate ligands. Ligands which have more than one donor atom that can bond to a metal cation are called polydentate ligands. A chelate is formed by a polydentate ligand that can hold the metal cation in its "claws." The coordination number refers to the total number of ligand atoms that are bound to a given metal ion in a complex.

21.68 See Table 21.7

21.69 (a) en stands for ethylenediamine

(b) EDTA stands for ethylenediaminetetraacetate

21.70 Removal of silver salts from photographic film, water softening, as a catalyst and to alleviate metal poisoning, and to retard food spoilage.

21.71 EDTA is an antidote in lead poisoning and a water softener in shampoos. It also ties up metal ions that catalyze oxidation of food products and increases the storage life of whole blood.

21.72 (a) hexaamminenickel(II) ion

(b) triamminetrichlorochromium(III)

(c) hexanitrocobaltate(III) ion

(d) trioxalatomanganate(III) ion

(e) tetraoxomanganganate(VII) ion

21.73 (a) diiodoargentate(I) ion

(b) pentaamminechlorochromium(III) ion

(c) diamminetetraaquacobalt(II) chloride

(d) diaquabis(ethylenediamine)cobalt(III) sulfate

(e) tetraamminedichlorochromium(III) chloride

21.74 (a) $[Fe(H_2O)_4(CN)_2]^+$ (b) $[Ni(NH_3)_4(C_2O_4)]$

(c) $K_3[Mn(CN)_6]$ (d) $[CuCl_4]^{2-}$ (e) $[CrO_4]^{2-}$

21.75 (a) $[AuCl_4]^-$ (b) $[Fe(en)_2(NO)_2]_2SO_4$ (c) $[Co(NH_3)_4CO_3]NO_3$

(d) $[Fe(EDTA)]^{2-}$ (e) $[Ag(S_2O_3)_2]^{3-}$

21.76 See Figure 21.9

21.77 

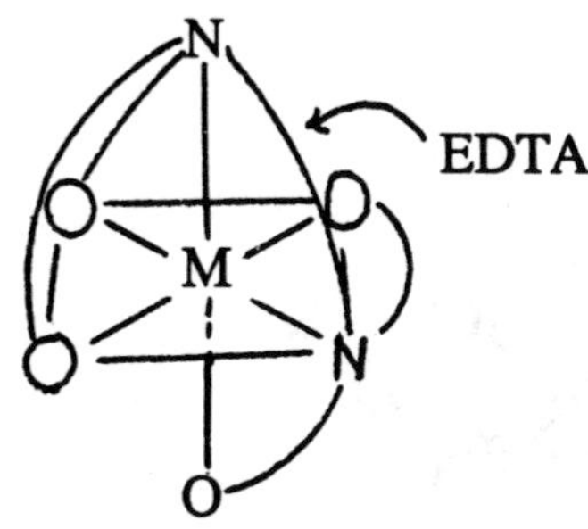

21.78 NTA can coordinate to four sites in an octahedral complex in much the same manner as EDTA.

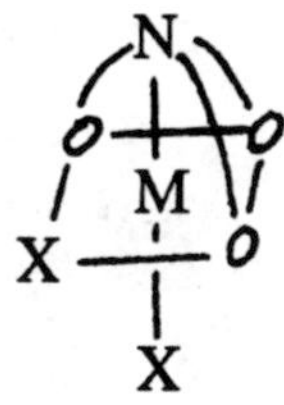

The remaining two sites, X can be occupied by other ligands or by H_2O molecules.

The NTA would increase the solubility of metal salts by shifting equilibria such as: $MX_n(s) + NTA \rightleftharpoons M(NTA)\,(aq) + X(aq)$ to the right.

21.79 Isomers are two different compounds that have the same molecular formula but differ in the way their atoms are arranged. Stereoisomers result when a given molecule or ion can exist in more than one structural form in which the same atoms are bound to one another but find themselves oriented differently in space.

21.80 Isomers of $[Co(NH_3)_2Cl_4]^-$

trans　　　　　　cis

Isomers of $[Co(NH_3)_3Cl_3]$

21.81 One isomer cannot be superimposable on its mirror image.

21.82 They or their solutions rotate the plane of polarized light which passes them.

21.83 Isomers of $[Cr(en)_2Cl_2]^+$

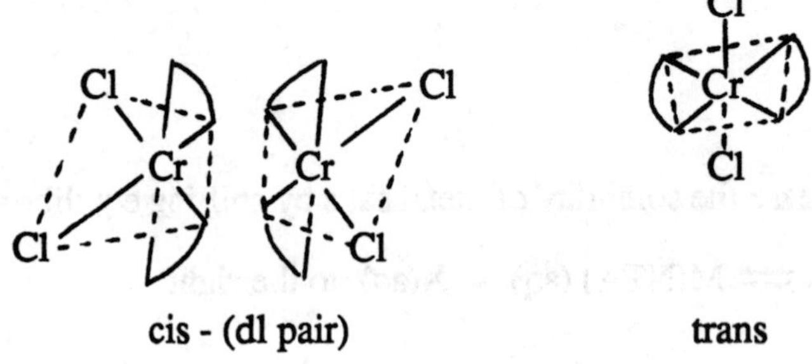

cis - (dl pair)　　　　　　trans

21.84

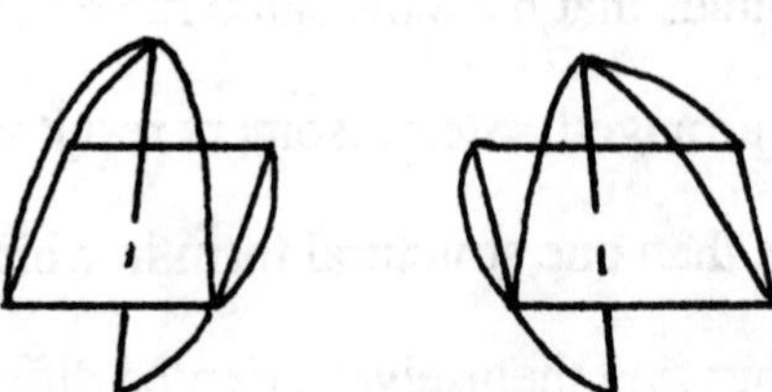

21.85 Enantiomers of a complex are two nonidentical mirror image isomers; e.g. $[Co(en)_3]^{3+}$, Figure 21.14. A racemic compound contains an equal mixture of two enantiomers.

21.86 In an inner orbital complex of first series of transition elements the 3d orbitals are being used in hybridization and in an outer orbital complex the 4d orbitals are being used.

21.87

	3d	4s	4p	4d
(a) inner	↑ ↑ __ xx xx	xx	xx xx xx	__ __ __ __ __
(b) outer	↑↓ ↑↓ ↑↓ ↑ ↑	xx	xx xx xx	xx xx __ __ __
(c) outer	↑ ↑ ↑ ↑ ↑	xx	xx xx xx	xx xx __ __ __
(d) inner	↑↓ ↑↓ ↑↓ xx xx	xx	xx xx xx	__ __ __ __ __
(e) inner	↑ ↑ ↑ xx xx	xx	xx xx xx	__ __ __ __ __

An inner orbital with three unpaired electrons.

21.88 paramagnetic with one unpaired electron

21.89 (a) four (outer orbital, high spin)

(b) two (inner orbital, low spin)

21.90 See Figure 21.20

21.91

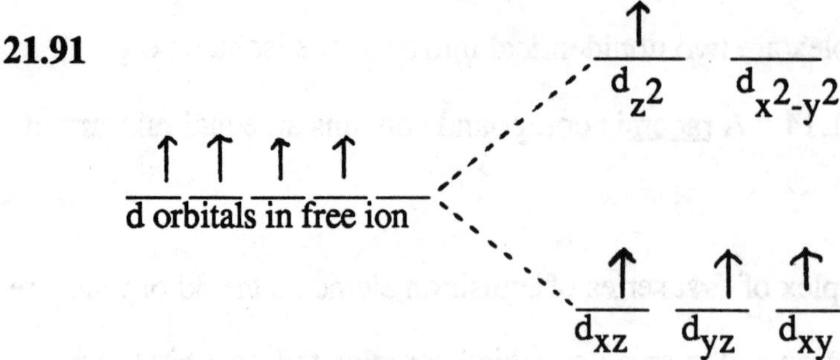

21.92 A portion of visible light is absorbed in promoting electrons from the t_{2g} level to the e_g level in octahedral complexes. The observed color of the complex is due to the wavelengths that are <u>not</u> absorbed.

21.93 If $\Delta < P$, a paramagnetic complex will be formed; when $\Delta > P$, a diamagnetic complex will form.

21.94 A high-spin complex is one that possesses the maximum number of possible unpaired electrons. A low-spin complex possesses electrons paired in low energy orbitals. Inner orbital complexes would be low-spin and outer orbital complexes would be high-spin.

21.95 (a) See Figure 21.27 (b) See Figure 21.29

21.96

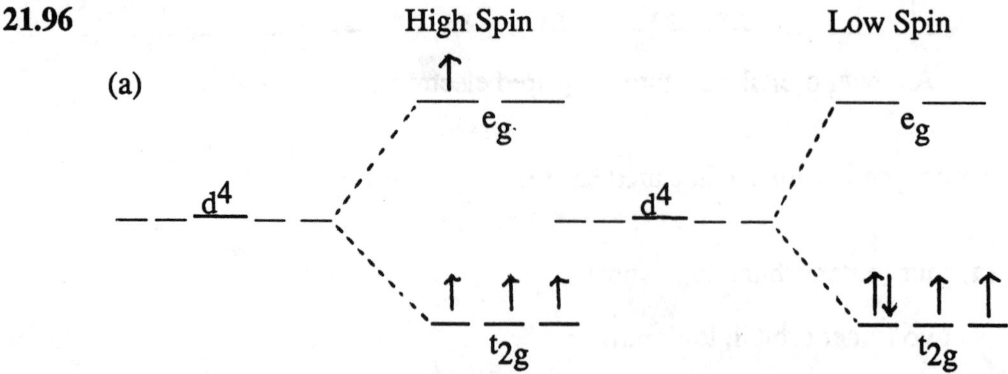

(21.96 continued)

(b)

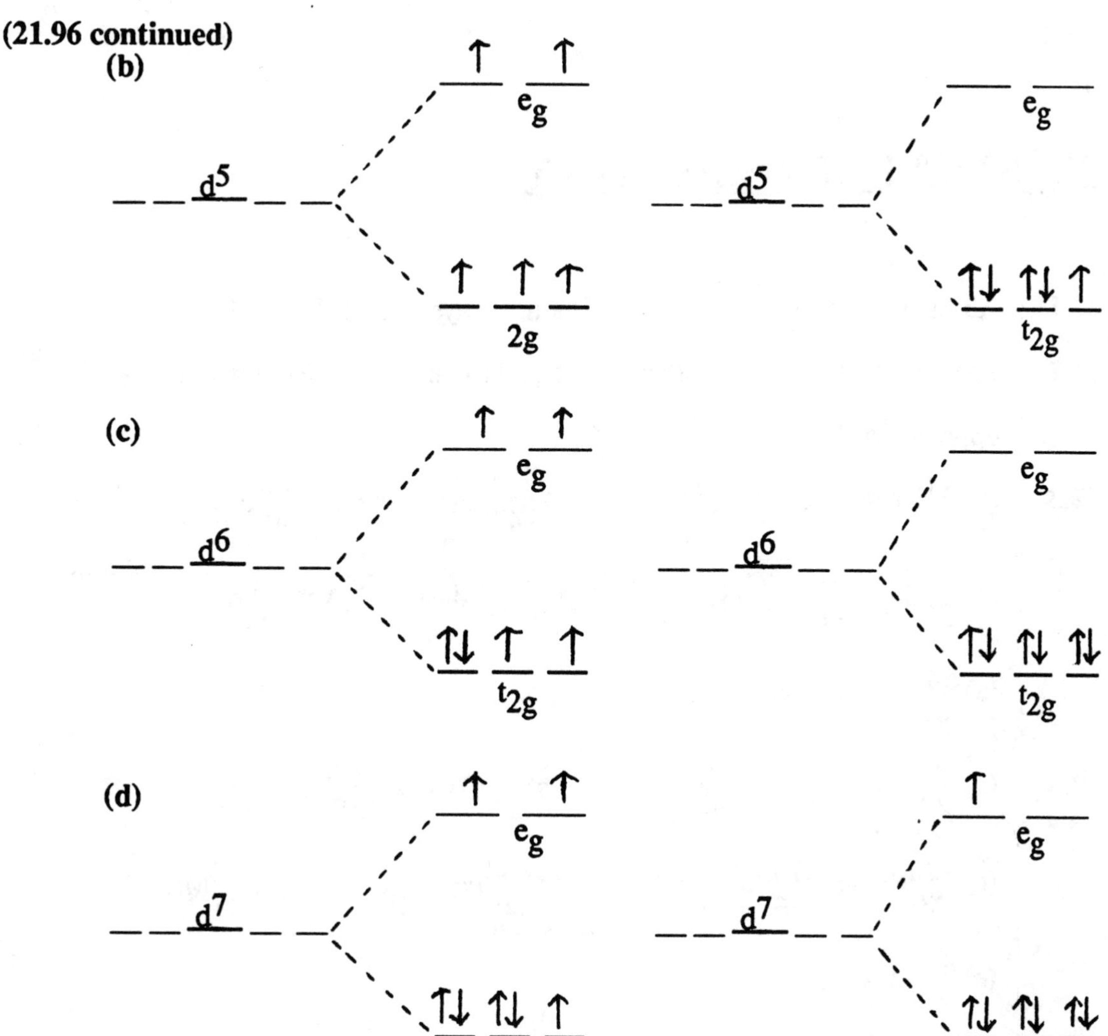

22 NUCLEAR CHEMISTRY

22.1 Alpha particles, beta particles and gamma rays. See Table 22.1

22.2 They are both particles with a mass equal to that of the electron, but they are opposite in charge.

22.3 (a) ${}^{81}_{36}\text{Kr} + {}^{0}_{-1}\text{e} \rightarrow {}^{81}_{35}\text{Br}$ (b) ${}^{104}_{47}\text{Ag} \rightarrow {}^{0}_{1}\text{e} + {}^{104}_{46}\text{Pd}$

(c) ${}^{73}_{31}\text{Ga} \rightarrow {}^{0}_{-1}\text{e} + {}^{73}_{32}\text{Ge}$ (d) ${}^{104}_{48}\text{Cd} \rightarrow {}^{104}_{47}\text{Ag} + {}^{0}_{1}\text{e}$

(e) ${}^{54}_{25}\text{Mn} + {}^{0}_{-1}\text{e} \rightarrow {}^{54}_{24}\text{Cr}$

22.4 (a) ${}^{47}_{20}\text{Ca} \rightarrow {}^{47}_{21}\text{Sc} + {}^{0}_{-1}\text{e}$ (b) ${}^{55}_{27}\text{Co} \rightarrow {}^{55}_{26}\text{Fe} + {}^{0}_{1}\text{e}$

(c) ${}^{220}_{86}\text{Rn} \rightarrow {}^{216}_{84}\text{Po} + {}^{4}_{2}\text{He}$ (d) ${}^{54}_{26}\text{Fe} + {}^{1}_{0}\text{n} \rightarrow {}^{1}_{1}\text{H} + {}^{54}_{25}\text{Mn}$

(e) ${}^{46}_{20}\text{Ca} + {}^{1}_{0}\text{n} \rightarrow {}^{47}_{20}\text{Ca}$

22.5 (a) ${}^{135}_{53}\text{I} \rightarrow {}^{135}_{54}\text{Xe} + {}^{0}_{-1}\text{e}$ (b) ${}^{245}_{97}\text{Bk} \rightarrow {}^{4}_{2}\text{He} + {}^{241}_{95}\text{Am}$

(c) ${}^{238}_{92}\text{U} + {}^{12}_{6}\text{C} \rightarrow {}^{246}_{98}\text{Cf} + 4\,{}^{1}_{0}\text{n}$ (d) ${}^{96}_{42}\text{Mo} + {}^{2}_{1}\text{H} \rightarrow {}^{1}_{0}\text{n} + {}^{97}_{43}\text{Tc}$

(e) ${}^{20}_{8}\text{O} \rightarrow {}^{20}_{9}\text{F} + {}^{0}_{-1}\text{e}$

22.6 (a) $^{35}_{17}Cl + ^{1}_{0}n \rightarrow ^{35}_{16}S + ^{1}_{1}H$ (b) $^{40}_{19}K \rightarrow ^{0}_{-1}e + ^{40}_{20}Ca$

(c) $^{98}_{42}Mo + ^{1}_{0}n \rightarrow ^{0}_{-1}e + ^{99}_{43}Tc$ (d) $^{229}_{90}Th \rightarrow ^{4}_{2}He + ^{225}_{88}Ra$

(e) $^{184}_{80}Hg \rightarrow ^{184}_{79}Au + ^{0}_{1}e$

22.7 (a) $^{11}_{5}B \rightarrow ^{4}_{2}He + ^{7}_{3}Li$ (b) $^{98}_{38}Sr \rightarrow ^{0}_{-1}e + ^{98}_{39}Y$

(c) $^{107}_{47}Ag + ^{1}_{0}n \rightarrow ^{108}_{47}Ag$ (d) $^{88}_{35}Br \rightarrow ^{1}_{0}n + ^{87}_{35}Br$

(e) $^{116}_{51}Sb + ^{0}_{-1}e \rightarrow ^{116}_{50}Sn$ (f) $^{70}_{33}As \rightarrow ^{0}_{1}e + ^{70}_{32}Ge$

(g) $^{41}_{19}K \rightarrow ^{1}_{1}H + ^{40}_{18}Ar$

22.8 A radioactive decay series is a series of nuclear changes in which one isotope decays to another and that to another, and so on. The ^{238}U series stops at ^{206}Pb because ^{206}Pb is the first non-radioactive isotope formed.

22.9 In a radioactive decay, the isotope that decays is called the parent isotope and the isotope that is formed is referred to as the daughter isotope.

22.10 41

22.11 $\ln \frac{[A]_o}{[A]} = kt$ (Equation 22.1) $[A]_t = 1/2\,[A]_o$ @ $t_{1/2}$

$$\ln \frac{[A]_o}{1/2[A]_o} = kt_{1/2}$$

$\ln(2) = kt_{1/2}$ or $t_{1/2} = \frac{\ln(2)}{k}$ $t_{1/2} = \frac{0.693}{k}$ **(Equation 22.2)**

22.12 **(a)** $k = \dfrac{0.693}{t_{1/2}}$ $kt_{1/2} = 0.693$; therefore, $kt = 0.693$ x no. of half-life periods

$\ln (^{60}Co)_o / (^{60}Co)_a = 1 \times 0.693 = \ln \dfrac{1.00\ g\ ^{60}Co}{(^{60}Co)_a} = 0.693$

$\dfrac{1.00\ g\ ^{60}Co}{(^{60}Co)_a} = 2.00$ Therefore, $(^{60}Co)_a = \underline{0.500\ g}$

(b) $\ln (^{60}Co)_o / (^{60}Co)_b = \ln (1.0 / X) = 3 \times 0.693 = 2.079$

$\ln(1.00 / X) = 2.079$

$1.00 / X = 7.996$

$X = 0.125$ $(^{60}Co)_b = \underline{0.125\ g}$

(c) $\ln [(^{60}Co)_o / (^{60}Co)_c] = 5 \times 0.693$

$\ln(1.00 / X) = 3.465$

$1.00 / X = 31.98$ $X = 0.0313$

$X = 0.0313$ g $(^{60}Co)_c = \underline{0.0313\ g}$

(An alternative method is shown below.)

When "n" is the number of half-life periods, the fraction of the original sample which remains = $1/2^n$.

(a) 1.00 g x $(1/2)^1$ = 0.500 g **(b) 1.00 g x $(1/2)^3$ = 0.125 g**

(c) 1.00 g x $(1/2)^5$ = 0.0313 g

22.13 (See Problem 22.12)

(a) $\ln \dfrac{8.00\text{ g}}{X_a} = \dfrac{240}{120}(\text{no. of half-life periods}) \times 0.693 = 1.386$

$X_a = 2.00$ g

(b) (4 half-life periods) $X_b = 0.500$ g (c) (8 half-lives) $X_c = 0.0313$ g

22.14 $t_{1/2} = \dfrac{0.693}{k} = \dfrac{0.693}{4.23 \times 10^{-3}\text{ days}^{-1}} = \underline{164\text{ days}}$

22.15 $t_{1/2} = \dfrac{0.693}{k} = \dfrac{0.693}{2.30 \times 10^{-6}\text{ year}^{-1}} = \underline{3.01 \times 10^{5}\text{ yr}}$

22.16 $k = \dfrac{0.693}{27.72\text{ days}} \times \dfrac{1.00\text{ day}}{24 \times 60 \times 60\text{ s}} = \underline{2.89 \times 10^{-7}\text{s}^{-1}}$

22.17 $k = \dfrac{0.693}{t_{1/2}} = \dfrac{0.693}{470\text{ days}} = \underline{0.00147\text{ day}^{-1}}$

22.18

$k = \dfrac{1}{t} \times \ln \dfrac{[A]_0}{[A]_t}$

$k = \dfrac{1}{96.0\text{ hr}} \times \ln \dfrac{4720}{2560}$

$\underline{k = 6.37 \times 10^{-3}\text{ hr}^{-1}}$

ln (cpm) vs. time in hours

slope = (8.46 - 7.85) /(96.0)

= 6.35 x 10^{-3} hr^{-1} = k

$t_{1/2} = 0.693 / k =$ **109 hr**

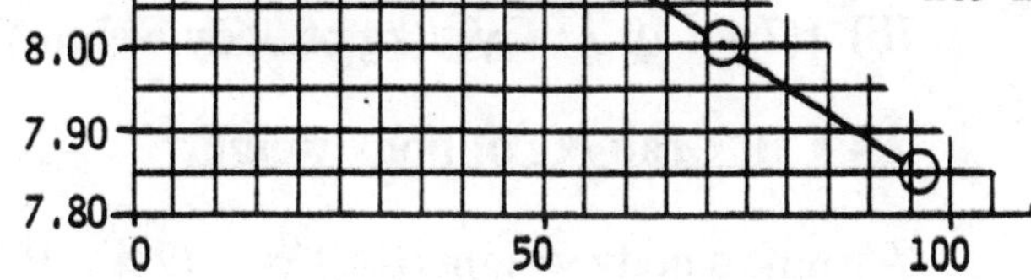

22.19 See Figures 22.4 and 22.5 and the first part of the section on "Measurement of Radioactivity".

22.20 **(a)** Becquerel = 1 disintegration /s = 1 Bk

(b) Curie = 3.7×10^{10} disintegrations /s = 3.7×10^{10} Bk = 1 Ci

(c) Specific activity = disintegrations per second per gram = Bk /g

(d) Gray = joules of energy absorbed per kilogram of absorbing material = J/ kg = Gy

(e) Rad = 10^{-5} J absorbed per gram = 10^{-5} J /g = rad

22.21 The rem takes into consideration the amount of damage the various forms of radiation can cause to animal tissue. Rad does not differentiate between types of radiation.

22.22 **(a)** 1.24 Ci x 3.7×10^{10} Bk /Ci = 4.6×10^{10} Bk

(b) 1.24 Ci x 3.7×10^{10} Bk /Ci x (1/150 g) = 3.1×10^{8} Bk /g (specific activity)

22.23 **(a)** (140 Bk /g) x 1.0 mg x (1.00 g /1,000 mg) x (1.00 dis s^{-1} /Bk) x 10 min x (60 s /min) x (1.80 MeV /dis) x (1.60 x 10^{-13} J /MeV) x [1 /(kg body weight)] x (1 Gy /J kg^{-1}) = Gy

Answer = **<u>2.4×10^{-11} Gy /kg of body weight</u>** If we assume the average body weight is 60 kg, then the answer is **<u>1.4×10^{-9} Gy</u>**

(b) [(2.4 x 10^{-11} Gy) /(kg of body weight)] x (100 rad /Gy) =

<u>2.4×10^{-9} rad /kg of body weight</u>

Assume a body weight of 60 kg: (2.4 x 10^{-9} rad /kg) (60 kg) =

<u>1.4×10^{-7} rad</u>

22.24 **(a)** β **(b)** γ

22.25 mol ^{40}Ar formed = mol ^{40}K decayed = 1.15×10^{-5} mol

$$K = \frac{0.693}{t_{1/2}} = \frac{0.693}{1.3 \times 10^9 \text{ yr}} = 5.3 \times 10^{-10} \text{ yr}^{-1} \qquad t = \frac{2.303}{k} \times \log\frac{[A]_0}{[A]_t}$$

$[A]_0 = (2.07 \times 10^{-5} + 1.15 \times 10^{-5})$ mol ^{40}K $\qquad [A]_t = 2.07 \times 10^{-5}$ mol ^{40}K

$$t = \frac{2.303}{5.3 \times 10^{-10} \text{ yr}^{-1}} \times \log\frac{3.22 \times 10^{-5}}{2.07 \times 10^{-5}} = \underline{8.3 \times 10^8 \text{ yr}}$$

22.26 Since three half-life periods would reduce the ^{14}C to one eighth the initial value, the age of the wood equals 3 x 5770 yr (17,300)

22.27 ON + O*NO bond breaking at 1

ONO*NO (bond ① and bond ②)

ONO + *NO bond breaking at 2

22.28 Approximately half of the CH_3HgI should contain the labeled Hg. Two molecules of CH_3HgI could form $(CH_3)_2Hg$ plus HgI_2 when the reaction proceeds in the reverse direction. When the $(CH_3)_2Hg$ reacts in the forward direction, it can combine with either labeled or unlabeled HgI_2 producing labeled CH_3*HgI.

22.29 One possible experiment would be to make the complex and allow the racemization to occur in a medium containing labeled $C_2O_4^{2-}$. If the racemization occurs by the dissociation of a $C_2O_4^{2-}$, the complex should pick up some labeled $C_2O_4^{2-}$.

22.30 $?\text{mL (cool.)} = 10\ \text{mL}\ CH_3OH \times \frac{0.792\ \text{g}\ CH_3OH}{1\ \text{mL}\ CH_3OH} \times \frac{580\ \text{cpm}}{1\ \text{g}\ CH_3OH} \times$

$\frac{1\ \text{mL (cool.)}}{0.884\text{g (cool.)}} \times \frac{1\ \text{g (cool.)}}{29\ \text{cpm}} = \underline{\textbf{180 mL (cool.)}}$ (2 sig. fig.)

22.31 $?\text{mol Cr} = 165\ \text{cpm} \times \frac{1\ \text{g}\ K_2Cr_2O_7}{843\ \text{cpm}} \times \frac{2\ \text{mol Cr}}{294\ \text{g}\ K_2Cr_2O_7} = 1.33 \times 10^{-3}\ \text{mol Cr}$

$?\text{mol}\ C_2O_4^{2-} = 83\ \text{cpm} \times \frac{1\ \text{g}\ H_2C_2O_4}{345\ \text{cpm}} \times \frac{1\ \text{mol}\ C_2O_4^{2-}}{90.0\ \text{g}\ H_2C_2O_4}$

$= 2.67 \times 10^{-3}\ \text{mol}\ C_2O_4^{2-}$

Therefore, there are two oxalate ions bound to each Cr(VI) in the complex ion.

22.32 As the number of protons in the nucleus increases there must be more and more neutrons present to help overcome the strong repulsive forces between the protons. Also, there seems to be an upper limit to the number of protons that can exist in a stable nucleus, that number being reached with bismuth. Nuclides above the band of stability must either lose neutrons or gain protons in order to achieve stability.

22.33 Elements higher than 83 must lose both neutrons and protons to achieve a stable n /p ratio. The only way this is possible is by α-emission or fission.

22.34 Nuclei that contain certain specific numbers of protons and neutrons possess a degree of extra stability. For protons these magic numbers are 2, 8, 20, 28, 50 and 82; for neutrons, 2, 8, 20, 28, 50, 82 and 126. The magic numbers for orbital electrons are 2, 8, 18, 36, and 54 (the number of electrons in closed electron shells).

22.35 e = even, o = odd, * = magic number

$$^{4}_{2}He > ^{58}_{28}Ni > ^{39}_{20}Ca > ^{71}_{32}Ge > ^{10}_{5}B$$

(p,n) (e*,e*) (e*,e) (e*,o) (e,o) (o,o)

22.36 e = even, o = odd, * = magic number

$$^{192}_{77}Ir < ^{13}_{6}C < ^{3}_{2}He < ^{116}_{50}Sn < ^{40}_{20}Ca$$

(p,n)(o,o) (e,o) (e*,o) (e*,e) (e*,e*)

22.37 Radiation emitted in quantum packets can be used to explain nuclear shells just as Bohr did in explaining his atomic theory. If protons move from shell to shell in the nucleus, each transition would result in an emission of energy.

22.38 Both Tc and Pm have an odd number of protons.

22.39 A nuclear transformation is a nuclear reaction in which a bombarding particle is absorbed and causes the absorbing nucleus to change into a nucleus of another element.

22.40 The cyclotron produces particles of very high velocities by the use of oscillating voltage to accelerate the particles and a magnetic field to help guide the particles.

22.41 Transuranium elements are elements 93 to 105 (elements with atomic numbers greater than that of uranium).

22.42 (a) ${}^{27}_{13}Al + {}^{4}_{2}He \rightarrow {}^{1}_{0}n + {}^{30}_{15}P$ (b) ${}^{209}_{83}Bi + {}^{2}_{1}H \rightarrow {}^{1}_{0}n + {}^{210}_{84}Po$

(c) ${}^{15}_{7}N + {}^{1}_{1}H \rightarrow {}^{4}_{2}He + {}^{12}_{6}C$ (d) ${}^{12}_{6}C + {}^{1}_{1}H \rightarrow {}^{13}_{7}N + \gamma$

(e) ${}^{14}_{7}N + {}^{4}_{2}He \rightarrow {}^{1}_{1}H + {}^{17}_{8}O$

22.43 (a) ${}^{242}_{96}Cm + {}^{4}_{2}He \rightarrow {}^{245}_{98}Cf + {}^{1}_{0}n$ (b) ${}^{108}_{48}Cd + {}^{1}_{0}n \rightarrow {}^{109}_{48}Cd + \gamma$

(c) ${}^{14}_{7}N + {}^{1}_{0}n \rightarrow {}^{14}_{6}C + {}^{1}_{1}H$ (d) ${}^{27}_{13}Al + {}^{2}_{1}H \rightarrow {}^{25}_{12}Mg + {}^{4}_{2}He$

(e) ${}^{249}_{98}Cf + {}^{18}_{8}O \rightarrow {}^{263}_{106}Xe + 4\,{}^{1}_{0}n$

22.44 Element 114 would fall under lead in Group IVA. It, therefore, would be a soft metal with a relatively low melting point. Its most stable oxidation state would be 2+ and would form such compounds as MO and MCl_2. A likely spot to discover this element would be wherever lead ores are found.

22.45 (a) Na_2X (b) H_2X (c) XO_2 (d) Since Po is a metalloid, 116 would probably have metallic properties.

22.46 298 and 310

22.47 The bombarding nuclei have to contain a very large n /p ratio to place the products on the island of stability (Figure 22.7). Light nuclei, however, contain n /p ratios of nearly 1.

22.48 (a) ununpentium

(b) unbiseptium

22.49 (a) 148 (b) 125 (c) 103

22.50 Mass defect is the difference between the actual mass of a nucleus and the sum of the masses of its individual protons, neutrons and electrons.

22.51 ^{56}Fe = 26 p x 1.007277 amu /p + 30 n x 1.008665 amu /n + 26 e x 5.4859 x 10^{-4} amu /e = 56.463415 amu Since the actual atomic mass = 55.9349 amu, the mass defect = 0.5285 amu. What is the binding energy per nucleon?

$$?\text{MeV} = \frac{0.5285 \text{ amu}}{56 \text{ nucleon}} \times \frac{931 \text{ MeV}}{1 \text{ amu}} = \underline{8.79 \text{ MeV /nucleon}}$$

Since this is the largest value of binding energy per nucleon (the highest point on the curve in Figure 22.10), neither fission nor fusion of iron 56 can yield energy.

22.52 $\Delta m = 2 \times 2.014102 - 4.002603 = 0.025601$ $E = \Delta m \times c^2$

$E = (0.025601 \text{ amu}) (2.9979 \times 10^8 \text{ m s}^{-1})^2 \times 6.022 \times 10^{23} \text{ mol}^{-1} \times 1 \text{ kg} /6.022 \times 10^{26} \text{ amu} \times 1 \text{ kJ} /10^3 \text{ kg m}^2 \text{ s}^{-2} = \underline{2.3009 \times 10^9 \text{ kJ mol}^{-1}}$

(This answer was not limited to 4 sig. fig. because the Avogadro number was expressed to only four since the 6.022 cancelled exactly in numerator and denominator.)

22.53 $E = mc^2$ $E = 2 \times 9.1096 \times 10^{-31} \text{ kg } (2.9979 \times 10^8 \text{ m s}^{-1})^2 =$

$\underline{1.6374 \times 10^{-13} \text{ J}}$ $(\underline{1 \text{ kg m}^2 \text{ s}^{-2} = 1 \text{ J}})$

22.54 Δm^7Li = (3 x 1.007277 + 4 x 1.008665 + 3 x 0.0005486) - (7.01600) = 0.042137 amu $E = \Delta mc^2$ = 0.042137 g x mol^{-1} x (2.9979 x 10^8 m $s^{-1})^2$ x $\frac{1kg}{10^3 g}$ = 3.7870 x 10^{12} J mol^{-1}

<u>^7Li 3.7870 x 10^9 kJ mol^{-1}, 39.250 MeV</u>

for: <u>^{19}F 1.4261 x 10^{10} kJ mol^{-1}, 147.73 MeV</u>

<u>^{14}N 1.0098 x 10^{10} kJ mol^{-1}, 104.61 MeV</u>

22.55 Fission is the splitting of an atom into approximately equal parts. The fission of ^{235}U releases energy and neutrons that can cause other atoms of ^{235}U to undergo fission. The result could be a nuclear explosion.

22.56 In nuclear reactors the rate of fission is controlled by use of control rods which absorb neutrons and, thus, prohibit the chain reaction from occuring.

22.57 Fusion reactions are nuclear reactions in which two isotopes are brought together to form a heavier one. Fusion reactions release greater amounts of energy than do fission reactions.

22.58 Because fusion reactions have very high energies of activation, a very high temperature is required. A fusion reactor is difficult to construct since there is not an acceptable means of achieving the very high temperatures..

22.59 A plasma is a reacting mass of ions. A plasma is difficult to contain because it is very reactive and at a very high temperature.

22.60 Fusion reactions might be better sources of energy in the future since they (1) produce much more energy than do fission reactions and (2) they produce products that usually are not radioactive while most fission reactions produce radioactive products.

22.61 **(a)** **2.3009×10^9 kJ mol^{-1}** (seeProblem 22.52)

(b) $2 \times 12.00000 - 23.98504 = 0.01496$;

therefore, **$E = 1.345 \times 10^9$ kJ mol^{-1}**

Reaction (a) produces more energy per mole of product. On the basis of energy produced per gram of reactants, **reaction (a) wins by a larger margin, slightly more than 10:1.**

Since carbon 12 is used as the basis of the atomic mass scale, the mass of this isotope is exactly 12.

22.62 $C_8H_{18}(\ell) + 25/2\ O_2(g) \longrightarrow 8CO_2(g) + 9H_2O(\ell)$

$$8\ \Delta H_f(CO_2(g)) + 9\ \Delta H_f(H_2O(\ell)) - \Delta H_f(C_8H_{18}(\ell)) = \Delta H_{comb.}(C_8H_{18}(\ell))$$

$$8(-394\ \text{kJ/mol}) + 9(-286\ \text{kJ/mol}) - (208.4\ \text{kJ/mol}) = -5520\ \text{kJ}$$

$$(C_8H_{18}(\ell)) = 1\ \text{mol}\ {}^4\text{He} \times \frac{2.3009 \times 10^9\ \text{kJ}}{1\ \text{mol}\ {}^4\text{He}} \times \frac{1\ \text{mol}\ C_8H_{18}}{5520\ \text{kJ}} \times$$

$$\frac{114\ \text{g}\ C_8H_{18}}{1\ \text{mol}\ C_8H_{18}} \times \frac{1\ \text{L}\ C_8H_{18}}{703\ \text{g}\ C_8H_{18}} \times \frac{1\ \text{gal}\ C_8H_{18}}{3.79\ \text{L}\ C_8H_{18}} =$$

1.78×10^4 gal $C_8H_{18}(\ell)$

23 ORGANIC CHEMISTRY

23.1 Unsaturated hydrocarbons contain one or more double and/or triple bonds between the carbons. Saturated compounds contain only single bonds.

23.2 As the chain length increases, the London forces become stronger because each molecule is attracted to others at more points along the chain.

23.3 (a) $C_{30}H_{62}$ (b) $C_{27}H_{54}$ (c) $C_{33}H_{64}$

23.4 (a) $C_{17}H_{36}$ (b) $C_{17}H_{34}$ (c) $C_{17}H_{32}$ (d) $C_{17}H_{30}$ (e) $C_{17}H_{28}$

23.5 A series where one member differs from the next by the same repeating cluster of atoms.

23.6 This compound is one of the 13 isomers of hexene. These are shown in the answer to Question 23.10.

23.7 An asymmetric carbon atom must be present for optical isomerism.

```
     H               H
     |               |
 Br--C--I         I--C--Br
     |               |
     Cl              Cl
```

23.8

```
CH3–CH2          CH3
       \        /
        C══C
       /        \
      H          H
           cis
```

```
CH3–CH2           H
       \         /
        C══C
       /        \
      H          CH3
          trans
```

23.9 Asterisk indicates asymmetric carbon atom.

```
  H H H H H H H
  | | | | | | |
H–C–C–C–C–C–C–C–H
  | | | | | | |
  H H H H H H H
```

n-heptane

```
  H H H H H H
  | | | | | |
H–C–C–C–C–C–C–H
  | | | | | |
  H H H H | H
          |
        H–C–H
          |
          H
```

2-methylhexane

```
  H H H H   H H
  | | | |   | |
H–C–C–C–C*–C–C–H
  | | | |   | |
  H H H |   H H
        |
      H–C–H
        |
        H
```

3-methylhexane

```
  H H H H H
  | | | | |
H–C–C–C–C–C–H
  | | | | |
  H | H | H
    |   |
H–C–H H–C–H
  |     |
  H     H
```

2,4-dimethylpentane

(23.9 continued)

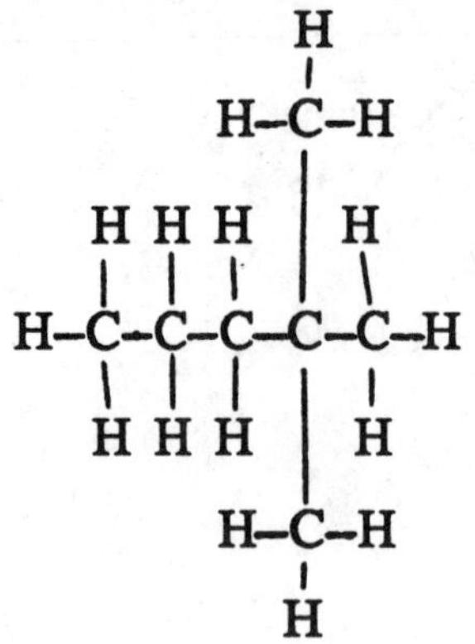

```
                 H
                 |
               H-C-H
                 |
     H  H  H     |   H
     |  |  |     |   |
   H-C--C--C-----C---C-H
     |  |  |     |   |
     H  H  H     |   H
                 |
               H-C-H
                 |
                 H
```

2,2-dimethylpentane

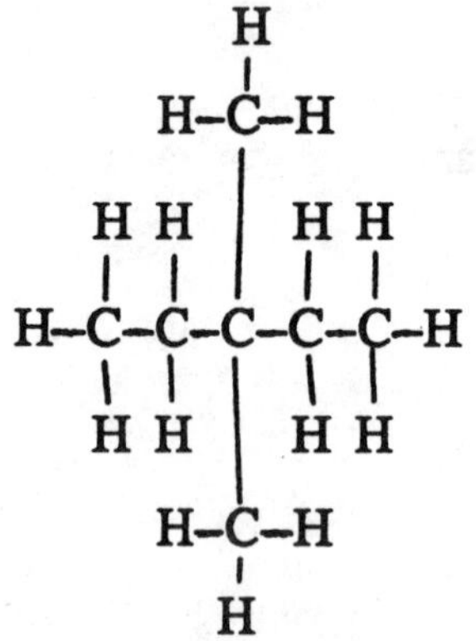

```
              H
              |
            H-C-H
              |
     H  H     |     H  H
     |  |     |     |  |
   H-C--C-----C-----C--C-H
     |  |     |     |  |
     H  H     |     H  H
              |
            H-C-H
              |
              H
```

3,3-dimethylpentane

```
                   H
                   |
                 H-C-H
                   |
     H  H  H       |   H
     |  |  |       |   |
   H-C--C--C*------C---C-H
     |  |  |       |   |
     H  H  |       H   H
           |
         H-C-H
           |
           H
```

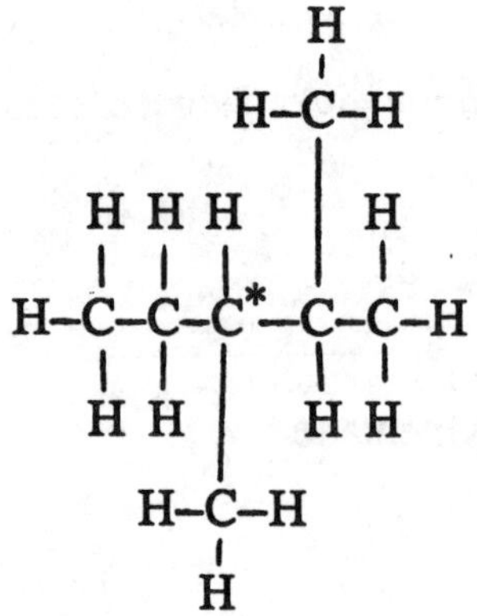

2,3-dimethylpentane

(23.9 continued)

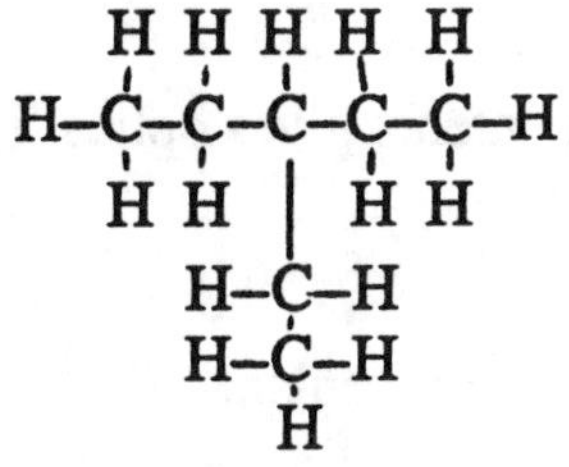

```
    H H H H  H
H–C–C–C–C–C–H
    H H  |  H H
       H–C–H
       H–C–H
          H
```

3-ethylpentane

```
                     H
                     |
  H     H      H–C–H  H
H–C——C———C——C–H
  H  H–C–H  H–C–H  H
          |            |
          H            H
```

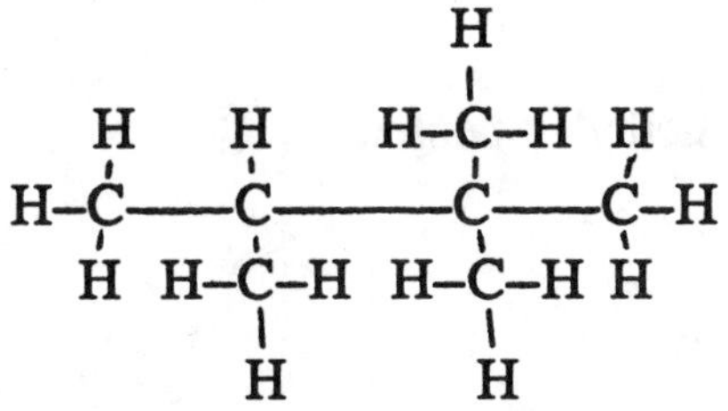

2,2,3-trimethylbutane

23.10 There are 13 isomers:

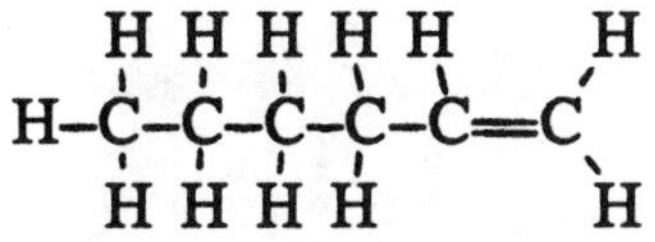

```
    H H H H H      H
H–C–C–C–C–C=C
    H H H H         H
```

1-hexene

```
    H H H H   H H
H–C–C–C–C=C–C–H
    H H H          H
```

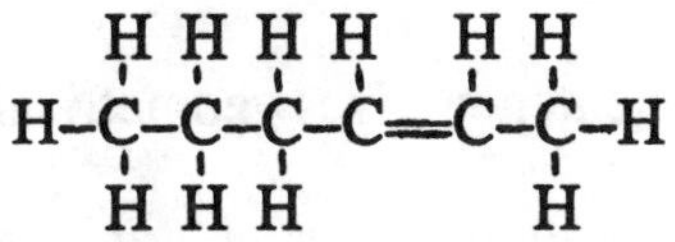

2-hexene; gives geometrical isomer

```
    H H          H H
H–C–C–C=C–C–C–H
    H H H   H H H
```

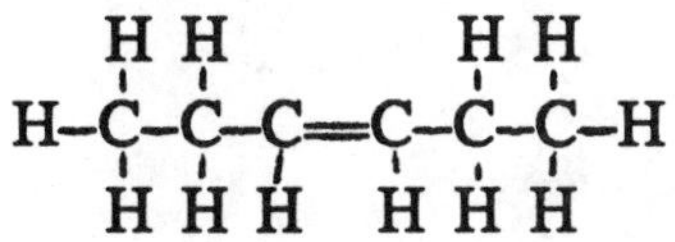

3-hexene; gives geometrical isomer

```
    H H H          H
    |  |  |          /
H–C–C–C–C=C
    |  |  |  |       \
    H H H  |        H
               |
          H–C–H
              H
```

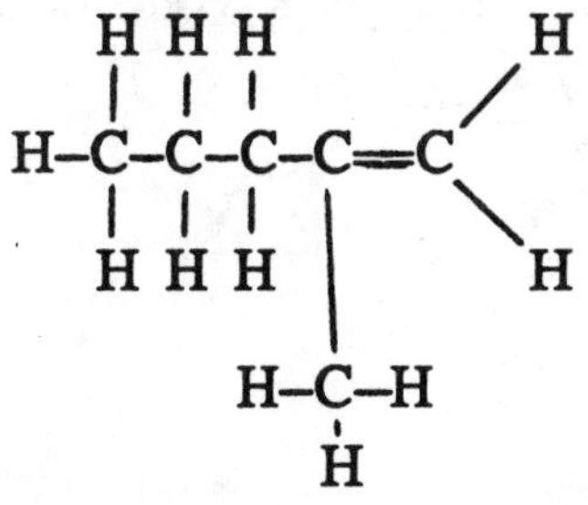

2-methyl-1-pentene

(23.10 continued)

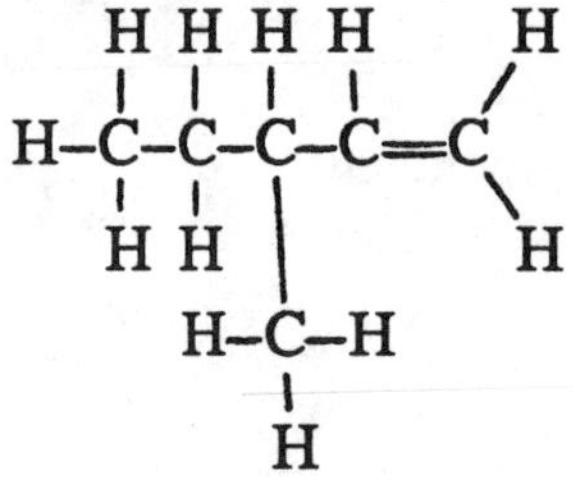

```
H H H H     H
| | | |    /
H-C-C-C-C=C
| |   |    \
H H   |     H
    H-C-H
      |
      H
```

3-methyl-1-pentene; gives optical isomers

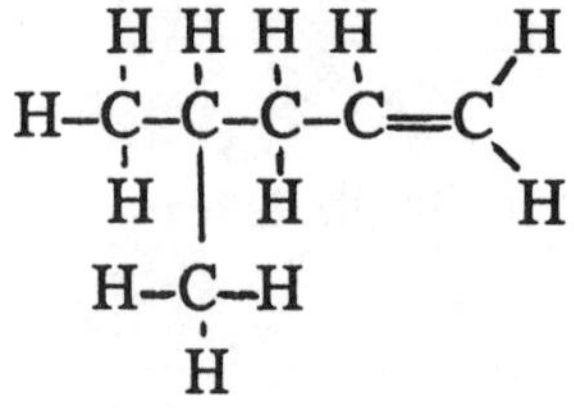

```
H H H H     H
| | | |    /
H-C-C-C-C=C
|   |      \
H | H       H
H-C-H
  |
  H
```

4-methyl-1-pentene

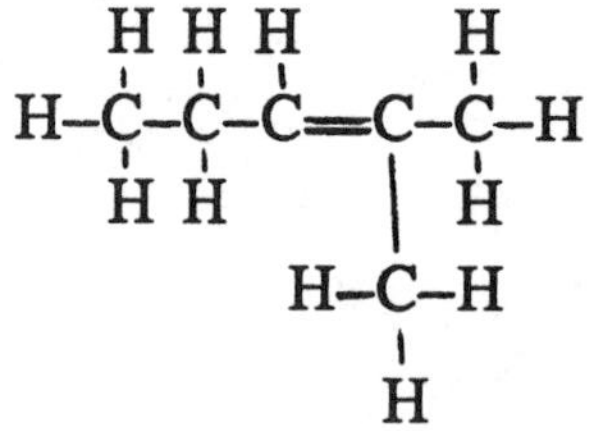

```
H H H     H
| | |     |
H-C-C-C=C-C-H
| |     | |
H H     | H
      H-C-H
        |
        H
```

2-methyl-2-pentene

```
H H     H H
| |     | |
H-C-C-C=C-C-H
| |   |   |
H H   |   H
    H-C-H
      |
      H
```

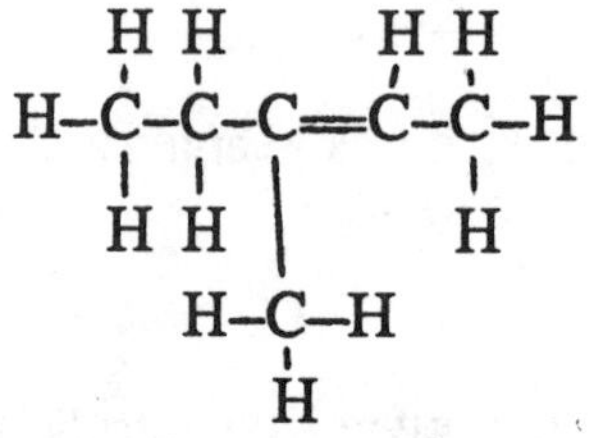

3-methyl-2-pentene; gives geometrical isomers

```
H H     H H
| |     | |
H-C-C-C=C-C-H
|   | |     |
H   | H     H
H-C-H
  |
  H
```

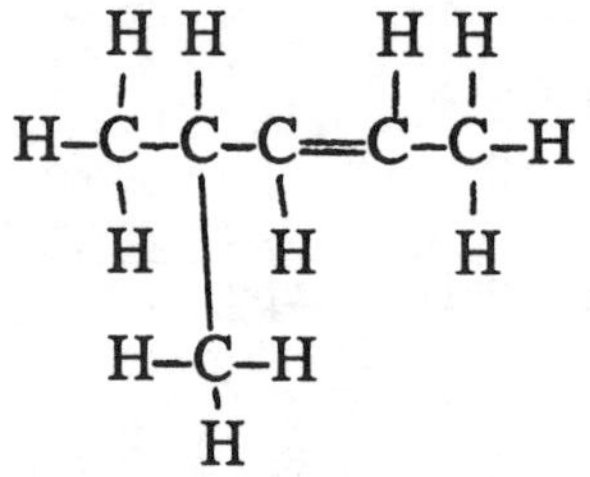

4-methyl-2-pentene; gives geometrical isomers

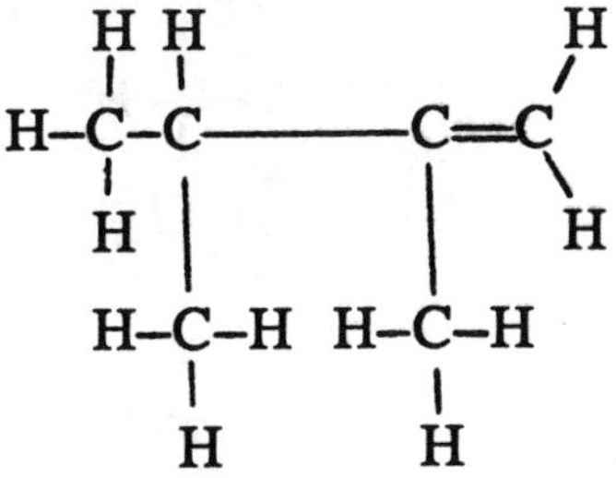

```
H H                    H
| |                   /
H-C-C--------------C=C
  |  |             |  \
  H  |             |   H
     |             |
 H-C-H         H-C-H
   |             |
   H             H
```

2,3-dimethyl-1-butene

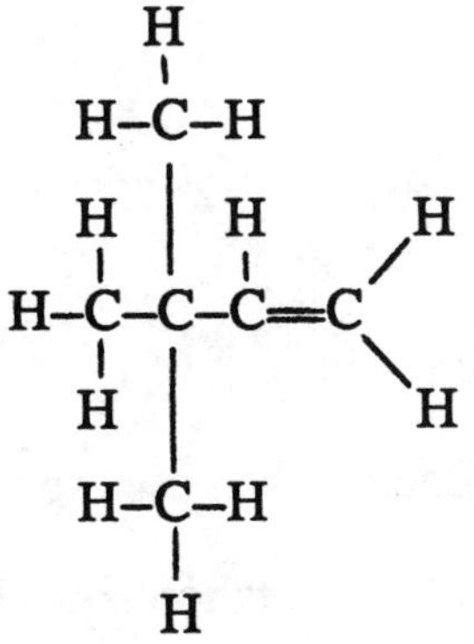

```
       H
       |
     H-C-H
       |
   H   |   H     H
   |   |   |    /
 H-C---C---C==C
   |   |        \
   H   |         H
       |
     H-C-H
       |
       H
```

3,3-dimethyl-1-butene

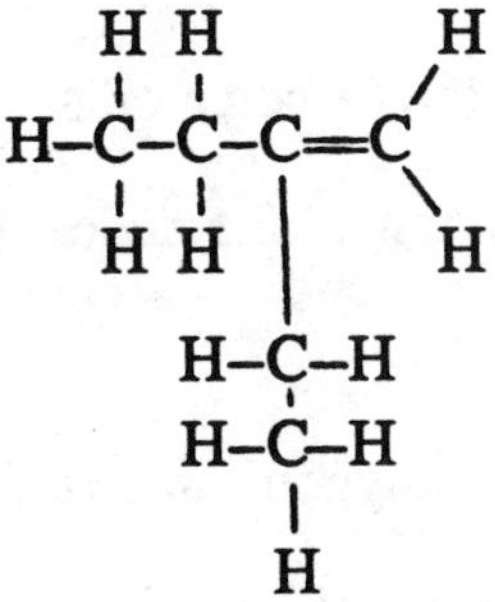

```
   H H        H
   | |       /
 H-C-C-C==C
   | | |     \
   H H |      H
       |
     H-C-H
     H-C-H
       |
       H
```

2-ethyl-1-butene

```
   H                 H
   |                 |
 H-C-C=============C-C-H
   | |             | |
   H |             | H
     |             |
 H-C-H         H-C-H
   |             |
   H             H
```

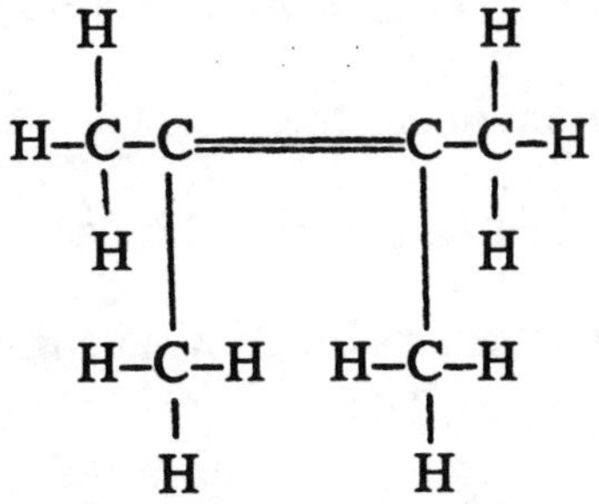

2,3-dimethyl-2-butene

23.11

```
Cl          H          H          H          H          H
  \         |           \         |           \         |
   C==C--C--H            C==C--C--H            C==C--C--H
  /    |  |             /    |  |             /    |  |
Cl     H  H           Cl     Cl H           Cl     H  Cl


H        H          H     H  Cl         Cl     Cl        H     Cl
 \       |           \    |  |            \   /            \   /
  C==C--C--H          C==C--C--H            C                C
  |    |  |           |       |            / \              / \     Cl
  |    |  |           |       |           /   \            /   \   /
H      Cl Cl          H       Cl      H2C-----CH2      H2C-----C
                                                                \
                                                                 H
```

23.12 Tetrahedral

23.13 Because of the double bond between the carbons. Each carbon uses sp^2 hybrid orbitals which gives a planar configuration and there is no rotation about the double bond.

23.14 The chain in butane arises from sp^3 hybridization on the carbon atoms. The hybridization is different in two of the carbons in 2-butyne. The middle two carbons are sp hybridized.

23.15 60°, 90°, 108°, 120° {The internal angles in a regular polygon can be calculated from the formula, [180 -(360 /n)], where n is the number of sides.}

23.16 In the boat form two hydrogen atoms point at each other across the top of the "boat", leading to some repulsion. This is absent in the chair form.

23.17 The molar solubility will decrease because of their large size and because of the decrease in polar character. The molecules become less like H_2O and more like hydrocarbons.

23.18 (a) Sigma bonds by overlap of sp^2 hybrid orbitals and pi bond by overlap of unhybridized p orbitals (b) Sigma bonds by overlap of sp hybrid orbitals and 2 pi bonds by overlap of unhybridized p orbitals

23.19 Because of the existence of geometric isomers of 2-butene, there is restricted rotation about the C═C double bond but not about C–C single bonds.

23.20 Because the bond angles are much less than those found in other sp^3 hybrid carbon compounds causing bond strain.

23.21 The bond strain is too great. In cyclopentene the bond angles are 108° vs 120° for sp^2 hybrid orbitals and for cyclopentyne the angles are 108° vs 180° for sp hybrid orbitals.

23.22 The bonding in benzene and graphite are nearly identical. Each carbon is sp^2 hybridized which accounts for C–C and C–H bonds; and, in addition, each has a pure p orbital and electron. These electrons become delocalized in the π orbital around the ring in benzene or across a planar sheet in graphite.

23.23 (a) 2,4-dimethylhexane (b) 3,5-dimethylheptane
(c) 5-ethyl-3-methyloctane (d) 5-methyl-3-heptene
(e) 2,4-dimethylhexane

23.24 (a) 4-ethyl-3,5-dimethyl-2,4-heptadiene (b) 5-methyl-3-heptyne
(c) 2,3,3,4,4-pentamethylhexane (d) 4-methyl-2-pentyne
(e) 3,4-dimethyl-3,5-octadiene

23.25 (a) cyclohexane (b) 3-chloro-1-methylbenzene (or 3-chlorotoluene)
(c) butanone (d) 1-amino-2-methylpropane

23.26 (a) $CH_3–CH(CH_3)–CH_2–CH_2–CH_3$

$$\begin{array}{l} CH_3-\underset{\displaystyle CH_3}{\underset{|}{C}H}-CH_2-CH_2-CH_3 \end{array}$$

(b) $CH_3–CH(CH_3)–CH(CH_3)–CH_3$

$$CH_3-\underset{\displaystyle CH_3}{\underset{|}{C}H}-\underset{\displaystyle CH_3}{\underset{|}{C}H}-CH_3$$

(c) $CH_3–C(CH_3){=}C(CH_3)–CH_3$

$$CH_3-\underset{\displaystyle CH_3}{\underset{|}{C}}=\underset{\displaystyle CH_3}{\underset{|}{C}}-CH_3$$

(d) $CH_2{=}CH–CH{=}CH–CH{=}CH–CH_2–CH_3$

(e)

$$CH{\equiv}C-\overset{\displaystyle CH_3}{\overset{|}{\underset{\displaystyle CH_3}{\underset{|}{C}}}}-\underset{\displaystyle CH_3}{\underset{|}{C}H}-CH_3$$

23.27 3,3,4,4,5-pentamethylheptane

23.28 (a)

$$\begin{array}{ccc} Cl & & Cl \\ & \diagdown\;\;\;\diagup & \\ & C{=}C & \\ & \diagup\;\;\;\diagdown & \\ CH_3 & & H \end{array}$$

(b)

$$\overset{\displaystyle CH_3}{\overset{|}{}}$$
$$CH_3-\overset{\displaystyle CH_3}{\overset{|}{C}H}-CH_2-CH_2-CH_3$$

(c)

$$CH_3-\overset{\displaystyle OH}{\overset{|}{C}H}-CH_3$$

(d) Benzene ring with ring carbons labelled: C–Cl (top), C–H, C–Cl, C–H (bottom), H–C, H–C

$$C_6H_4Cl_2$$

23.29 (a)

$$CH_3-CH_2-\underset{\displaystyle CH_3}{\underset{|}{C}}=CH_2$$

(b)

$$CH_3-\overset{\displaystyle OH}{\overset{|}{\underset{\displaystyle CH_3}{\underset{|}{C}}}}-\underset{\displaystyle CH_3}{\underset{|}{C}H}-CH_3$$

(c)

$$CH_3-\overset{\displaystyle Br}{\overset{|}{C}H}-CH_2-C_6H_5$$

(d)

$$CH_3-\overset{\displaystyle O}{\overset{\|}{C}}-\underset{\displaystyle CH_3}{\underset{|}{C}H}-CH_2-CH_3$$

(e) Benzene ring with substituents Br (top), Cl, Cl, Br, Br, Cl (bottom)

$$C_6Br_3Cl_3$$

23.30 Gases (fuels) for cooling and heating, gasoline, kerosene, lubricating oils and paraffin for candles.

23.31 A carcinogen is a cancer-causing agent. Benzopyrene and graphite are similar because they consist of planes of fused hexagonal rings. Incomplete combustion tends to produce carbon (graphite). Benzopyrene is, in a sense, a "fragment" of graphite.

23.32 Dry cleaning solvents, refrigerants, aerosol propellants, insecticides.

23.33 Student answers will vary greatly for this question.

23.34 Esters

23.35 Amines

23.36 A functional group is an atom or group of atoms that bestow some characteristic property to a molecule so that any molecule with the same grouping will react chemically in a similar fashion.

(a) $CH_3-\overset{\overset{\large O}{||}}{C}-H$ (b) $CH_3-\overset{\overset{\large O}{||}}{C}-CH_3$ (c) $CH_3-\overset{\overset{\large O}{||}}{C}-OH$ (d) CH_3-NH_2

(e) CH_3-CH_2-OH (f) $CH_3-\overset{\overset{\large O}{||}}{C}-O-CH_2-CH_3$ (g) CH_3-O-CH_3

23.37 C═O, OH and ether.

23.38 (a) $CH_3\underset{\underset{O}{||}}{C}OCH(CH_3)_2$ (b) $CH_3-\underset{\underset{O}{||}}{C}-O-CH_2CH_2CH_2CH_2CH_3$

(c) $C_6H_5-\underset{\underset{O}{||}}{C}OCH_3$ (d) $H\underset{\underset{O}{||}}{C}-OCH_3$

23.39 $(CH_3CH_2)_2NH + H_2O \rightleftharpoons (CH_3CH_2)_2NH_2^+ + OH^-$

23.40 Alkenes and alkynes tend to undergo addition reactions whereas alkanes tend to undergo substitution reactions.

23.41 (a) $CH_3CH_2CH{=}CH_2 + HI \longrightarrow CH_3CH_2CHICH_3$

1-butene → 2-iodobutane

(b)

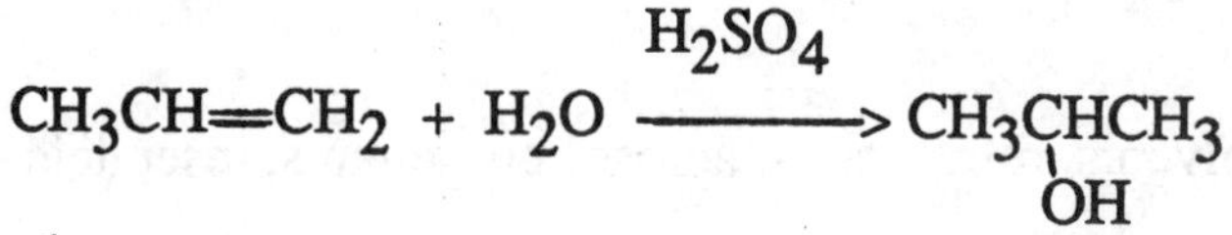

$$CH_3CH{=}CH_2 + H_2O \xrightarrow{H_2SO_4} CH_3\underset{\displaystyle OH}{\underset{|}{C}}HCH_3$$

1-propene → 2-propanol

(c)

$$CH_3CH_2CH{=}C(CH_3)_2 + H_2O \xrightarrow{H_2SO_4} CH_3CH_2CH_2{-}\overset{\displaystyle CH_3}{\overset{|}{\underset{\displaystyle CH_3}{\underset{|}{C}}}}{-}OH$$

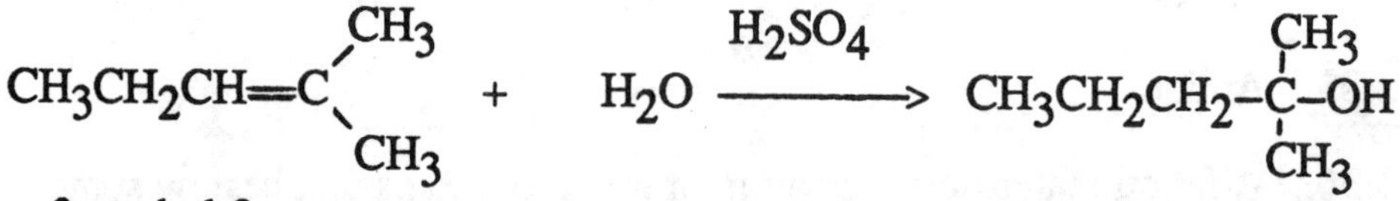

2-methyl-2-pentene → 2-methyl-2-pentanol

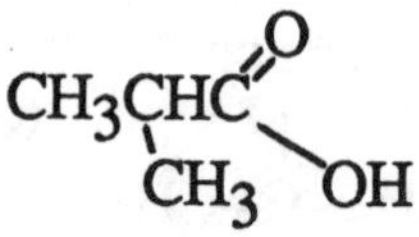

23.42 (a) $CH_3{-}C(=O)OH$ (b) $CH_3CH(CH_3)C(=O)OH$ (c) $CH_3\overset{O}{\overset{\|}{C}}CH_3$

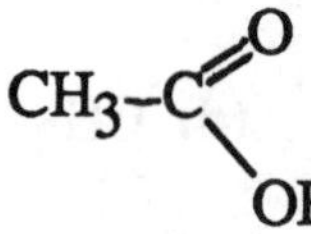

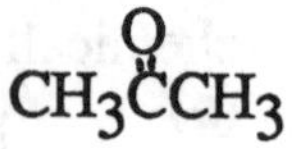

(d) $CH_3CH_2C(=O)OH$ (e) N.R. (f) N.R. (g) N.R.

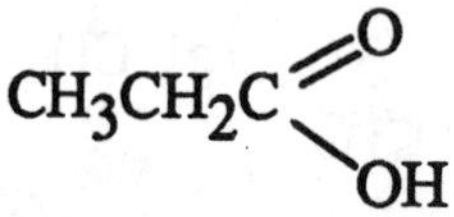

23.43 (a) mild oxidation; 2-propanol would give acetone; 2-methly-2-propanol won't be oxidized

(b) oxidation: 1-butanol —> butyric acid; 2-butanol —> ketone

(c) addition of Br_2 to butene; no reaction with butane

(d) mild oxidation: ethanal —> acetic acid; 2-propanone —> N.R.

23.44 **(a)**

$$CH_3CH_2-\overset{\overset{O}{\|}}{C}-OCH_3 + NaOH \xrightarrow{H_2O} CH_3OH + NaO-\overset{\overset{O}{\|}}{C}-CH_2CH_3$$

(b)

$$CH_3CH_2O\text{-}\overset{\overset{O}{\|}}{C}CH_2CH_2\overset{\overset{O}{\|}}{C}\text{-}OCH_2CH_3 + NaOH \xrightarrow{H_2O} 2CH_3CH_2OH +$$

$$NaO\overset{\overset{O}{\|}}{C}CH_2CH_2\overset{\overset{O}{\|}}{C}ONa$$

23.45 **(a)**

$$H_2C{=}CH_2 + Cl_2 \longrightarrow H-\underset{\underset{Cl}{|}}{\overset{\overset{H}{|}}{C}}-\underset{\underset{Cl}{|}}{\overset{\overset{H}{|}}{C}}-H$$

(b)

$$CH_3CH_2CH_2OH \xrightarrow[H^+]{Cr_2O_7^{2-}} CH_3CH_2COOH$$

(c) $CH_3CH_2CH_2Cl + KOH \xrightarrow{\text{alcohol}} CH_3CH{=}CH_2 + KCl$

$$H_2O + CH_3-CH{=}CH_2 \xrightarrow{H^+} CH_3-\underset{\underset{OH}{|}}{C}-CH_3$$

(d)

$$CH_3CHO \xrightarrow[H^+]{Cr_2O_7^{2-}} CH_3COOH$$

$$CH_3CH_2OH + CH_3COOH \longrightarrow CH_3COOC_2H_5$$

(e) $CH_3CH_2CH_2CH_2Br + KOH \xrightarrow{\text{alcohol}} CH_3CH_2CH{=}CH_2 + KBr$

$$CH_3CH_2CH{=}CH_2 + H_2O \xrightarrow{H^+} CH_3CH_2\underset{\underset{OH}{|}}{CH}-CH_3$$

$$CH_3CH_2\underset{\underset{OH}{|}}{C}HCH_3 \xrightarrow{\text{oxid}} CH_3-CH_2-\underset{\underset{O}{\|}}{C}-CH_3$$

23.46 (a) $CH_3COOCH_2CH_3$ (b) CH_3CH_2COOH

(c) $CH_3CH_2\underset{\underset{O}{\|}}{C}CH_3$ (d) $CH_3CH_2CH{=}CH_2$ is an acceptable student answer. Or, $(CH_3CH_2CH_2CH_2)_2O$

23.47 $CH_3CH_2CH_2O\underset{\underset{O}{\|}}{C}CH_3 + NaOH \xrightarrow{H_2O} CH_3CH_2CH_2OH + NaO\underset{\underset{O}{\|}}{C}CH_3$

The NaOH drives this reaction by neutralizing the acid as soon as it forms.

23.48 When an aldehyde is reduced with hydrogen, a primary alcohol is produced.

When a ketone is reduced in this fashion, a secondary alcohol is produced.

23.49 $\left(\begin{array}{cc} H & H \\ | & | \\ -C- & C- \\ | & | \\ H & C_6H_5 \end{array}\right)_x$

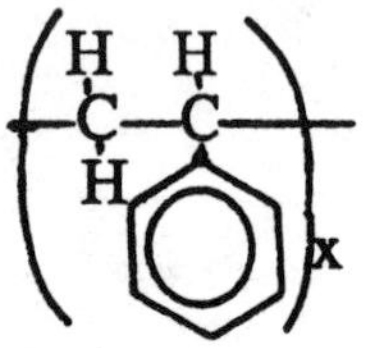

23.50 In addition polymers, monomer units are simply joined together. In condensation polymers this joining together of monomers is done at the expense of a small molecule that is eliminated.

23.51 $\left(CH_2-\underset{Cl}{\overset{Cl}{C}}-CH_2\underset{Cl}{CH}\right)_x CH_2-\underset{Cl}{\overset{Cl}{C}}-CH_2\underset{Cl}{CH}-$

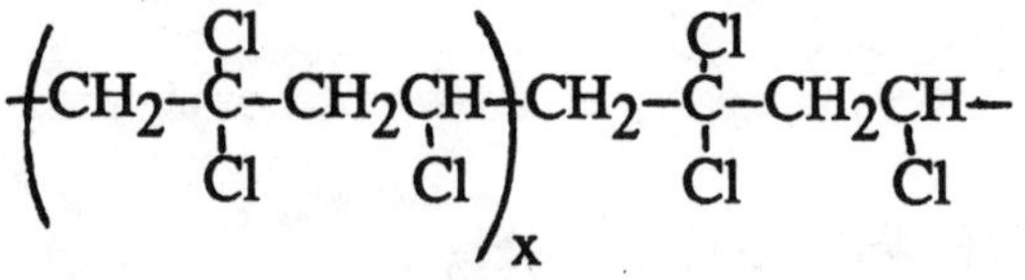

23.52 $\left(O-\underset{\underset{O}{\|}}{C}-CH_2-\underset{\underset{O}{\|}}{C}-O-CH_2-CH_2\right)_x$

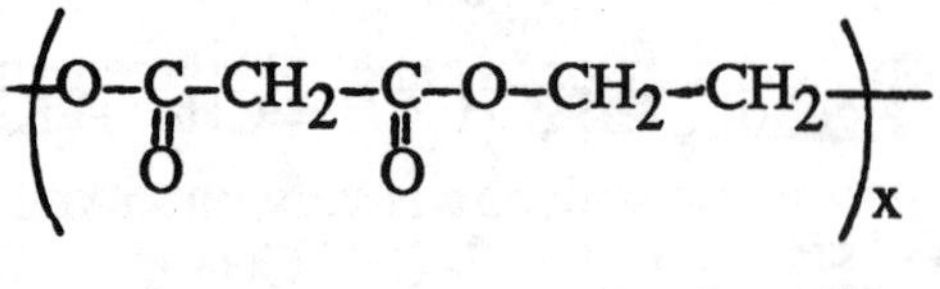

23.53 The acid promotes hydrolysis of the nylon.

23.54 Cross-linking is the forming of bonds between adjacent polymer molecules. The greater the degree of cross-linking, the stronger will be the material.

24 BIOCHEMISTRY

24.1 An α-amino acid is a bifunctional organic molecule that contains both a carboxyl and an amine group, with the amine group attached to the carbon adjacent to the carboxyl group. A peptide with its peptide bond would be

$$H_2N-\overset{\overset{\large H}{|}}{\underset{\underset{\large R}{|}}{C}}-\overset{\overset{\large O}{\|}}{C}-\underset{\underset{\large H}{|}}{N}-\overset{\overset{\large H}{|}}{\underset{\underset{\large R}{|}}{C}}-COOH$$

A polypeptide would be

$$-\underset{\underset{\large H}{|}}{N}-\overset{\overset{\large H}{|}}{\underset{\underset{\large R}{|}}{C}}-\overset{\overset{\large O}{\|}}{C}-\underset{\underset{\large H}{|}}{N}-\overset{\overset{\large H}{|}}{\underset{\underset{\large R'}{|}}{C}}-\overset{\overset{\large O}{\|}}{C}-\underset{\underset{\large H}{|}}{N}-\overset{\overset{\large H}{|}}{\underset{\underset{\large R''}{|}}{C}}-\overset{\overset{\large O}{\|}}{C}-\underset{\underset{\large H}{|}}{N}-\overset{\overset{\large H}{|}}{\underset{\underset{\large R'''}{|}}{C}}-\overset{\overset{\large O}{\|}}{C}-$$

24.2 A zwitterion contains one end that is positively charged and one end that is negatively charged. In amino acids the hydrogen on the carboxyl group leaves and attaches itself to the amino group.

24.3 This should not be surprising. In proteins only one isomer of a given amino acid is generally found. This means that isomeric structure is very important in determining physiological activity.

24.4 Glycine is not optically active because it does not have an asymmetric carbon atom.

24.5 The reaction is an acid-base type. The lye can break the peptide bonds by hydrolysis to produce smaller units.

24.6 The <u>primary structure</u> of a protein is the amino acid sequence that exists in the polypeptide. The twisting and turning of the polypeptide chain is its <u>secondary structure</u>. A <u>tertiary structure</u> is the folded chains of the coiled polypeptide. The way in which these folded chains orient themselves with respect to others gives rise to a <u>quaternary structure</u> in substances like hemoglobin.

24.7 They can act as enzymes and catalyze biochemical reactions, or transport substances through an organism. Proteins are the major constituent of such things as muscles, hair, nails, skin and tendons.

24.8 In many proteins the polypeptide chains coil themselves in an α-helix structure (Figure 24.3). Hydrogen bonding between the oxygen in a carbonyl group and the hydrogen attached to a nitrogen that lies in an adjacent loop holds the structure in place.

24.9 In polar solvents the nonpolar R groups are forced toward the center of the folded polypeptide chain and the chain tends to fold in such a way that non-polar groups do not contact the solvent. Ionic attractions occur between a negatively charged deprotonated carboxyl group and a positively charged protonated amine group.

24.10 The quaternary structure is determined by the way in which the folded proteins orient themselves with respect to one another. Proteins that contain more than one independent polypeptide chain exhibit quaternary structure.

24.11 Hemoglobin carries oxygen in the blood stream whereas myoglobin stores oxygen in muscle tissue. Both contain heme groups.

24.12 The basic square planar structure found in heme is an example of a porphyrin. Two other biologically important porphyrin structures are contained in chlorophyll and vitamin B_{12} coenzyme.

24.13 Enzymes catalyze very specific biochemical reactions to give very nearly 100% product and no by-products. A buildup of by-products would occur if reactions took place without enzymes and this would create a waste disposal problem for the organism.

24.14 An enzyme binds to a reactant molecule, called the substrate. A slight alteration in the shape of the enzyme causes a strain in certain key bonds in the substrate, making them more susceptible to attack. Enzyme inhibition occurs when a substance other than the enzyme substrate becomes bound to the active site of an enzyme, thereby inhibiting its catalytic activity. Sulfa drugs rely on competitive inhibition for their effectiveness. The sulfa drug occupies the active site of an enzyme preventing the production of a critical coenzyme.

24.15 See Section on "Enzyme Inhibition." Organophosphate insecticides function by attacking the central nervous system of the insect.

24.16 Monosaccharides are simple sugars; i.e., they are the simple units that come together to form the more complex polysaccharides. (a) ribose (b) glucose

24.17 8

24.18 In starch the polysaccharide chains coil in a helical structure with the polar OH groups pointing outward. Cellulose forms linear chains that interact with each other by hydrogen bonding.

24.19

```
   CHO             CHO            CHO           CHO
 H-C-OH         HO-C-H        HO-C-H        H-C-OH
 H-C-OH          H-C-OH       HO-C-H       HO-C-H
 H-C-OH          H-C-OH        H-C-OH      HO-C-H
   CH2OH           CH2OH         CH2OH         CH2OH

   CHO             CHO            CHO
 H-C-OH          H-C-OH       HO-C-H
 H-C-OH         HO-C-H        HO-C-H
HO-C-H           H-C-OH       HO-C-H
   CH2OH           CH2OH         CH2OH
```

24.20 Glucose and fructose

24.21 Carbohydrates are a source of energy, a source of carbon and a structural element in cells and tissues.

24.22 Lipids are water insoluble substances (e.g., fats and oils) that can be extracted from other cell components by nonpolar organic solvents. Lipids mainly serve as storage of energy-rich fuel for use in metabolism, as components of cell membranes, and as steroids.

24.23 Fatty acids are long unbranched hydrocarbon chains terminated at one end with a carboxyl group.

```
  H   O
H-C-O-C-C17H35
  |   O
H-C-O-C-C17H35        tristearin
  |   O
H-C-O-C-C17H35
  H
```

Saturated triglycerides tend to be solids and unsaturated ones tend to be liquids.

24.24

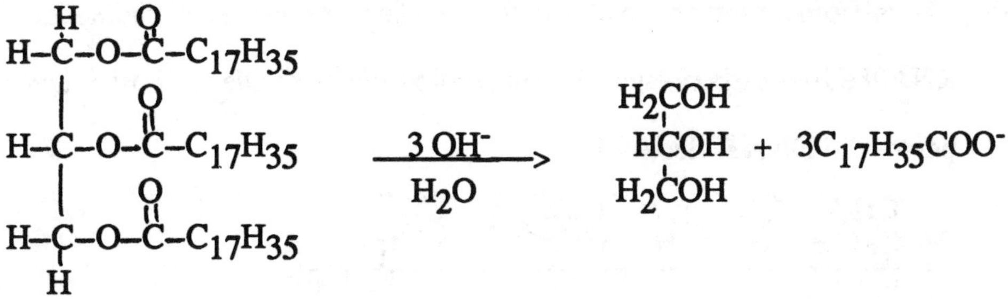

$$\begin{array}{l} \quad\;\; \text{H} \quad\;\; \text{O} \\ \text{H–C–O–}\overset{\|}{\text{C}}\text{–}C_{17}H_{35} \\ \quad\;\; | \qquad\; \text{O} \\ \text{H–C–O–}\overset{\|}{\text{C}}\text{–}C_{17}H_{35} \\ \quad\;\; | \qquad\; \text{O} \\ \text{H–C–O–}\overset{\|}{\text{C}}\text{–}C_{17}H_{35} \\ \quad\;\; \text{H} \end{array} \xrightarrow[H_2O]{3\,OH^-} \begin{array}{c} H_2COH \\ HCOH \\ H_2COH \end{array} + 3C_{17}H_{35}COO^-$$

24.25

$$\begin{array}{l} \quad\;\; \text{H} \quad\;\; \text{O} \\ \text{H–C–O–}\overset{\|}{\text{C}}(CH_2)_7CH{=}CH(CH_2)_7CH_3 \\ \quad\;\; | \qquad\; \text{O} \\ \text{H–C–O–}\overset{\|}{\text{C}}(CH_2)_7CH{=}CH(CH_2)_7CH_3 \\ \quad\;\; | \qquad\; \text{O} \\ \text{H–C–O–}\overset{\|}{\text{C}}(CH_2)_7CH{=}CH(CH_2)_7CH_3 \\ \quad\;\; \text{H} \end{array}$$

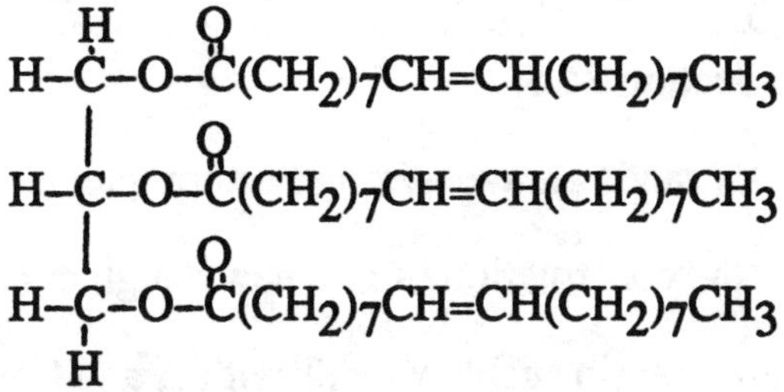

The reaction of triolein with H_2 would saturate the molecule, making tristearin which is a solid.

24.26 A soap is an anion that forms when a fat is saponified. In water these anions group themselves into small globules called micelles. The polar head dissolves in water and the nonpolar tail dissolves the grease.

24.27 In phospholipids only two fatty acid molecules are esterfied to glycerol. The third position is esterfied to a phosphoric acid group which in turn is esterified to another alcohol.

23.28 Phospholipids in membranes appear to be arranged on a bilayer in which the nonpolar tails face each other, exposing the polar heads to the aqueous environment on either side of the membrane.

23.29 Steroids possess the fused ring structure shown in Section 24.4.

24.30 The monomer units that make up the nucleic acids are called nucleotides. In RNA the five-carbon sugar that makes up the nucleotide is ribose whereas the pentose in DNA is deoxyribose.

24.31 T G A G C T A G T A C

24.32 Hydrogen bonding is responsible for holding together the two DNA strands. The base pairing is illustrated in Section 24.5.

24.33 During cell division the two DNA strands unravel giving two complementary chains that serve as templates for the construction of two new daughter chains. The unraveled strand then begins to pair in such a way (T with A and C with G) that the two new strands are identical to the old one.

24.34 The genetic code is the set of base sequences that allow the tRNA to construct a protein with the correct amino acid sequence. Each amino acid in a polypeptide is specified by one or more sets of three bases. tRNA deciphers the code and brings amino acids to their proper positions along the mRNA. The mRNA carries the genetic code from the DNA template within the nucleus to the ribosomes outside.

24.35 CGU–UUA–AAA–GGU–UGU. (There are other base sequences that could be chosen from Table 24.3.)

24.36 U U A G C A U C C G A C A U C

24.37 Ser–Ile–Leu–Ser–Asn

24.38 G C T C C T G A T T A T A T T G G T

24.39 Leu–Ala–Ser–Asp–Ile

24.40 UAG — CAU — CCG — ACA — UC

Terminate — His — Pro — Thr — Terminate

24.41 Diseases arising from an altering of the base sequence in a DNA molecule. It is not always fatal to the cell.

24.42 The high energy X rays or γ rays can, by breaking bonds, cause reactions that would not occur otherwise. This can disrupt the base sequence in a DNA molecule and cause mutations.